PEARSON   ALWAYS LEARNING

General Education Mathematics

Custom Edition for Moraine Valley Community College

Taken from:
Mathematics All Around, Fourth Edition
by Thomas L. Pirnot

A Survey of Mathematics with Applications, Ninth Edition
by Allen R. Angel, Christine D. Abbott, Dennis C. Runde

Cover Art: Courtesy of Optical and Geometrical Patterns and Designs by Spyros Horemis,
Dover Publications, Inc.

Taken from:

Mathematics All Around, Fourth Edition
by Thomas L. Pirnot
Copyright © 2010, 2007, 2004, 2001 by Pearson Education
Published by Addison-Wesley
Boston, MA 02134

A Survey of Mathematics with Applications, Ninth Edition
by Allen R. Angel, Christine D. Abbott, Dennis C. Runde
Copyright © 2013, 2009, 2005, 2001 by Pearson Education

All rights reserved. No part of this book may be reproduced, in any form or by any means, without permission
in writing from the publisher.

This special edition published in cooperation with Pearson Learning Solutions.

All trademarks, service marks, registered trademarks, and registered service marks are the property of their
respective owners and are used herein for identification purposes only.

Pearson Learning Solutions, 501 Boylston Street, Suite 900, Boston, MA 02116
A Pearson Education Company
www.pearsoned.com

Printed in the United States of America

 9 10 V092 16 15

000200010271661492

CM

ISBN 10:1-256-79411-2
ISBN 13:978-1-256-79411-0

Contents

Taken from: *Mathematics All Around,* Fourth Edition by Thomas L. Pirnot

9 Consumer Mathematics

The Mathematics of Everyday Life   395

9.1   Percent Change and Taxes   396
9.2   Interest   404
9.3   Consumer Loans   414
9.4   Annuities   422
9.5   Amortization   430
9.6   Looking Deeper: Annual Percentage Rate   439
        Chapter Summary   445
        Chapter Review Exercises   447
        Chapter Test   448

10 Geometry

Ancient and Modern Mathematics Embrace   450

10.1   Lines, Angles, and Circles   451
10.2   Polygons   460
10.3   Perimeter and Area   470
10.4   Volume and Surface Area   482
10.5   The Metric System and Dimensional Analysis   490
        Chapter Summary   523
        Chapter Review Exercises   525
        Chapter Test   527

Taken from: *A Survey of Mathematics with Applications,* Ninth Edition by Allen R. Angel, Christine D. Abbott, Dennis C. Runde

13 Statistics   773

13.1   Sampling Techniques   774
13.2   The Misuses of Statistics   779
13.3   Frequency Distributions and Statistical Graphs   783
13.4   Measures of Central Tendency   796
13.5   Measures of Dispersion   807
13.6   The Normal Curve   816

Taken from: *Mathematics All Around,* Fourth Edition by Thomas L. Pirnot

14   **Probability**
What Are the Chances?   658

14.1   The Basics of Probability Theory   659
14.2   Complements and Unions of Events   673
14.3   Conditional Probability and Intersections of Events   681
14.4   Expected Value   695
        Chapter Summary   710
        Chapter Review Exercises   711
        Chapter Test   712

Appendix A   776

Answers to Exercises   784

ANSWERS   A-1

To The Student: How To Succeed At Mathematics

I would like to suggest to you some things that you can do before, during, and after class to become a more successful mathematics student.

Prepare ahead.

Although it takes discipline to do so, you will get much more out of your mathematics class if you are able to read the material (even briefly) before it is covered in class. Reading ahead will make lectures more meaningful and questions might occur to you that you would not think to ask had you not read the section in advance. You should use the Key Points that are highlighted in the margins at the beginning of each subsection to get an overview of the topics covered before trying to read the section more carefully.

Read slowly and carefully.

Also remember that reading a math book is very different from reading a textbook in other subjects, such as history, sociology, or music. Because mathematical language is very compressed, a few symbols or words usually contain a lot of information. By paying careful attention to the exact meaning of the definitions and notation being used, you will increase your understanding of mathematics. As you read your book, always try to be actively involved with the material. After reading an example, cover the solution and then try to rework the example yourself. If you cannot work all of the way through, restudy the example to see what points you are missing and try again.

Try to understand the big picture.

I cannot emphasize strongly enough that mathematics is much more than a list of facts, formulas, and equations to be memorized. The more that you can see the big picture of how the material is developed, the better your overall understanding of mathematics will be. If your instructor makes comments in class about the reasons for doing a particular example, or how one topic relates to another, be sure to get those comments in your notes.

Remember how to remember.

Although it is important to remember the basic material for a test, you will find that memorizing without understanding is not very useful. Throughout this text, we will use many diagrams, analogies, and examples to help you understand mathematical terminology, formulas, equations, and solution methods. If you work at understanding the intuitive meaning behind mathematical concepts, those ideas will become more permanent in your memory. We call this process "Remembering How to Remember," and you will find this method of studying an effective way to retain information and hone your math skills.

Do homework intelligently.

When doing exercises, first work on those labeled Looking Back that begin each exercise set. These exercises closely follow the order of the topics presented in the section and will reinforce your understanding of the overall plan of the section.

Students sometimes tell me that although they understand the lectures and do the homework, they still are not successful on exams. I believe that this occurs because they are too book-dependent; that is, they can only do a certain type of problem when they know where it is placed in the book. I have helped many such students improve their grade dramatically by encouraging them to make 3×5 flash cards. To make these cards, choose typical problems from each section. Put a question on one side of a card and its solution on the back. Then when studying, shuffle these cards and give yourself a test so that the questions are coming randomly. This is a great help in finding out whether you can do problems on your own or can only do them when you are looking at a particular section of the text.

Study with a friend.

It is a great study aid if you can team up with other members in your class to study before quizzes and exams. Other students in your class are hearing the same lectures and will understand your instructor's point of view on the material. You can quiz each other by using the flash cards and the Looking Back exercises. I have seen many students' grades improve once they started working in study groups.

I sincerely hope that you enjoy reading this book as much as I have enjoyed writing it. Good luck in your mathematical studies!

Consumer Mathematics

The Mathematics of Everyday Life

9

As I was rewriting this chapter, there was a swirl of excitement going on in the world of personal finance. Credit card debt was at a record high and major lenders such as Citibank, American Express, and Capital One were setting aside billions of dollars to cover a flood of defaults by those who were unable to pay off their cards. In addition to credit card debt, foreclosures were increasing at an alarming rate and millions of families were in danger of losing their homes. On top of that, many students graduating from college were facing a future with overwhelming student loan payments.

If you research student loans, credit card regulations, mortgages, and various other forms of personal finance on the Internet, you would be amazed at the financial dangers that can befall an unwary consumer.

On the other hand, by understanding and applying the financial principles that you will learn in this chapter, you can avoid the financial pitfalls mentioned above and use your knowledge of the mathematics of how money works to your advantage.

9.1 Percent Change and Taxes

Objectives

1. Understand how to calculate with percent.
2. Use percents to represent change.
3. Apply the percent equation to solve applied problems.
4. Use percent in calculating income taxes.

Throughout this chapter, we will be discussing various aspects of your future financial life—student loans, credit card borrowing, investments, and mortgages. To understand these ideas and also much of the other information that you encounter daily, you must be comfortable with the notion of percent.

✎ **KEY POINT**

Percent means "per hundred."

Percent

The word *percent* is derived from the Latin "per centum," which means "per hundred." Therefore, 17% means "seventeen per hundred." We can write 17% as $\frac{17}{100}$ or in decimal form as 0.17. In this chapter, we will usually write percents in decimal form.

EXAMPLE 1 *Writing Percents as Decimals*

a) Write each of the following percents in decimal form:

36%   19.32%

b) Write each of the following decimals as percents:

0.29   0.354

SOLUTION:

a) Think of 36% as the decimal thirty-six hundredths, or 0.36, as we show in Figure 9.1(a). To write 19.32%, recall the problem-solving advice from Section 1.1 that it is often helpful to solve a simpler problem instead. If we had asked you to write 19% as a decimal, you would write it as 0.19. Now, once you have positioned the 1 and the 9 properly in the decimal, write the 3 and the 2 immediately to their right, as we show in Figure 9.1(b). Thus, 19.32% is equal to 0.1932.

Quiz Yourself ❶ *

a) Write 17.45% as a decimal.
b) Write 0.05% as a decimal.
c) Write 2.45 as a percent.
d) Write 0.025 as a percent.

┌─At first, ignore 32.
19. 32   percent
19. 32   hundredths
.19 32   (decimal form of 19 hundredths)
.19 32
└─ hundredths

36   percent
36   hundredths
.36   (decimal form of 36 hundredths)
└─ hundredths

(a)   (b)

FIGURE 9.1 The key to converting percents to decimals is what you write in the hundredths place.

b) To translate decimals to percents, we first examine what numbers are in the tenths and hundredths place. To rewrite 0.29, we see that we have 29 hundredths, so 0.29 equals 29%. To rewrite 0.354, recognize that 0.35 would be 35%, so 0.354 is 35.4%.

Now try Exercises 5 to 20. ❈

PROBLEM SOLVING
The Analogies Principle

You may have been told that when converting a percent to a decimal, you move the decimal point two places to the left and that in converting a decimal to a percent, you move the decimal point two places to the right. It is all right to use such memory devices, provided that you understand where they come from.

Always remember that percent means hundredths. If you understand how to rewrite 0.29 as 29%, then you also know how to rewrite 1.29 as a percent. Similarly, if you know that 19% equals 0.19, then you also know how to rewrite 19.32% as a decimal.

If you want, you can use the following rules:

To convert from a percent to a decimal, drop the percent sign and divide by 100.

To convert from a decimal to a percent, multiply by 100 and add a percent sign.

We often have to convert a fraction to a percent. Example 2 shows how to do this.

EXAMPLE 2   *Converting a Fraction to a Percent*

Write $\frac{3}{8}$ as a percent.

SOLUTION: Because we already know how to rewrite a decimal as a percent, we first convert $\frac{3}{8}$ to a decimal and then rewrite the decimal as a percent.

If we divide the denominator into the numerator, we get $\frac{3}{8} = 0.375$. Next, we see that 0.375 is equal to 37.5%. Thus, $\frac{3}{8} = 37.5$ percent.

Now try Exercises 21 to 28. ✳

Percent of Change

Example 3 shows how you can use the simple notion of percent to compare changes in data over long periods of time.

EXAMPLE 3   *Changes in Defense Spending as a Percent of the Federal Budget over Time*

According to the Office of Management and Budget, in 1970 the U.S. government spent $82 billion for defense at a time when the federal budget was $196 billion. Thirty-seven years later, in 2007, spending for defense was $495 billion and the budget was $2,472 billion. What percent of the federal budget was spent for defense in 1970? In 2007?

SOLUTION: In 1970, $82 billion out of $196 billion was spent for defense. We can write this as the fraction $\frac{82}{196} \approx 0.418 = 41.8\%$. In 2007, this fraction was $\frac{495}{2,472} \approx 0.2002 \approx 20\%$.

Thus, you see, as a percentage of the federal budget, defense spending was considerably less in 2007 than it was in 1970. ✳

The media often uses percentages to explain the change in some quantity. For example, you may hear that, on a particularly bleak day on Wall Street, the stock market is down 1.2%. Or on a good day, the evening news tells us that consumer confidence in the economy is up 13.5% over last month. To make such statements, we have to understand several quantities.

The percent of change is always in relationship to a previous, or **base amount**. We then compare a **new amount** with the base amount as follows:

$$\text{percent of change} = \frac{\text{new amount} - \text{base amount}}{\text{base amount}}. \, *$$

We illustrate this idea in Example 4.

EXAMPLE 4   *Finding the Percent of a Tuition Increase*

This year the tuition at Good Old State was $7,965, and for next year, the board of trustees has decided to raise the tuition to $8,435. What is the percent of increase in tuition?

SOLUTION: In this example, the base amount is $7,965 and the new amount is $8,435. To find the percent of tuition increase, we calculate

$$\text{percent of change} = \frac{\text{new amount} - \text{base amount}}{\text{base amount}}$$

$$= \frac{8,435 - 7,965}{7,965} = \frac{470}{7,965} \approx 0.059 = 5.9\%.$$

Thus, the tuition will increase almost 6% from this year to the next. ✸ **2**

Quiz Yourself **2**

The population of Florida increased from 12.9 million in 1990 to 16 million in 2000. What was the percent of increase of Florida's population over these 10 years?

Merchants often use percents to describe the deals that they are giving to the public when they have a sale. The increase that a merchant adds to his base price is called **markup**.

EXAMPLE 5   *Investigating a Sale Price on a New Car*

Monte's Autorama is having an end-of-year clearance in which the TV ads proclaim that all cars are sold at 5% markup over the dealer's cost. Monte has a new Exfinity for sale for $18,970. On the Internet, you find out that this particular model has a dealer cost of $17,500. Is Monte being honest in his advertising?

SOLUTION: To find the percent markup on this particular Exfinity, you can calculate the percent of markup, which is the same as the percent of change in the base price (dealer's cost) of the car.

We calculate as in Example 4:

$$\text{percent of markup} = \frac{\overset{\text{new amount}}{\overbrace{\text{selling price}}} - \overset{\text{base amount}}{\overbrace{\text{dealer cost}}}}{\underset{\text{base amount}}{\underbrace{\text{dealer cost}}}}$$

$$= \frac{18,970 - 17,500}{17,500} = \frac{1,470}{17,500} = 0.084 = 8.4\%.$$

Thus, Monte is not being quite truthful here because his markup on this model is 8.4%, which is well above the amount he stated in his TV ads.

Now try Exercises 57 and 58. ✸

KEY POINT

Many percent problems are based on the same equation.

The Percent Equation

We will conclude this section with several examples of percent problems; however, it is important for you to recognize that these problems are all variations of the same equation. In each case, we will be taking some *percent* of a *base* quantity and setting it equal to an *amount*. We can write this as the equation

$$\text{percent} \times \text{base} = \text{amount}.$$

We will call this equation, *the percent equation.*

---

*If the new amount is less than the base amount, then the percent of change will be negative.

You saw this pattern in Example 5, where the percent was 8.4% = 0.084, the base (dealer's price) was $17,500, and the amount (markup) was $1,470. Notice that 0.084 × 17,500 = 1,470. In the remaining examples, we will give you two of the three quantities, percent, base, and amount, and ask you to find the third.

EXAMPLE 6   *Using the Percent Equation*

a) What is 35% of 140?

b) 63 is 18% of what number?

c) 288 is what percent of 640?

SOLUTION: We will illustrate the percent equation graphically to solve each problem.

a) The base is 140 and the percent is 35% = 0.35.

$$\text{percent} \times \text{base} = \text{amount}$$
$$\quad\;\; 0.35 \qquad 140$$

So the amount is 0.35 × 140 = 49.

b) Using the percent equation again, we get

$$\text{percent} \times \text{base} = \text{amount}.$$
$$\quad\;\; 0.18 \qquad\quad 63$$

Therefore, we have 0.18 × base = 63, or, dividing both sides of this equation by 0.18, we get

$$\text{base} = \frac{63}{0.18} = 350.$$

c) Here the base is 640 and the amount is 288.

$$\text{percent} \times \text{base} = \text{amount}.$$
$$\qquad\qquad 640 \qquad 288$$

Thus, we have percent × 640 = 288. Dividing both sides of this equation by 640, we get

$$\text{percent} = \frac{288}{640} = 0.45 = 45\%.$$

Now try Exercises 29 to 38. ❋ **3**

Quiz Yourself **3**

a) What is 15% of 60?

b) 18 is 24% of what number?

c) 96 is what percent of 320?

EXAMPLE 7   *Calculating Sports Statistics*

In the 2006–2007 season, the Detroit Pistons, of the National Basketball Association, had a record of 53 wins and 29 losses. What percent of their games did they win?

SOLUTION: Again, you can use the percent equation to solve this problem; however, you have to be careful. The base is not 53, but rather the total number of games played, which is 53 + 29 = 82. The amount is the number of victories, 53. So we have

$$\text{percent} \times \text{base} = \text{amount}.$$
$$\qquad\qquad 82 \qquad\; 53$$

Dividing both sides of the equation—percent × 82 = 53—by 82 gives us

$$\text{percent} = \frac{53}{82} \approx 0.646 = 64.6\%. ❋$$

✳ ✳ ✳ HIGHLIGHT

Between the Numbers—Pay Careful Attention to What They *Don't* Tell You

When negotiating, people often want you to focus on their numbers and distract you from noticing other information that might be useful in making your decision. For example, consider the following situation that occurred several years ago when our faculty union was negotiating with the Commonwealth of Pennsylvania for a new contract.

The state negotiator recommended that we "back-load" the contract over 3 years by accepting raises of 0%, 2%, and 3% over 3 years instead of raises of 3%, 2%, and 0%. He stated that at the end of three years, the percentage of increase would be the same in either case, because

$1 \cdot (1.02)(1.03) = (1.03)(1.02) \cdot 1 = 1.0506$, giving a 5.06% increase. If we focus just on the percent of increase by the third year, the negotiator was telling the truth. So you might ask, "What's the difference?"

In the spirit of the Three-Way Principle, let's look at what effect both types of raises will have on a salary of $100 in Table 9.1.

With front-loading, we earn $13.12 − $7.06 = $6.06 more money on our initial $100 than with back-loading. Over three years, a person earning $50,000 (which is 500 times as large as $100) would earn 500($6.06) = $3,030 more with front-loading versus back-loading.

	Back-Loading	**Front-Loading**
Original Amount	$100	$100
Amount in 1st year	$100 + 0% ($100) = $100	$100 + 3% (100) = $103
Amount in 2nd year	$100 + 2% (100) = $102	$103 + 2% (103) = $105.06
Amount in 3rd year	$102 + 3% (102) = $105.06	$105.06 + 0% (105.06) = $105.06
	In 3 years, we gain 2 + 5.06 = $7.06 more than if we had no raise at all.	In 3 years, we gain 3 + 5.06 + 5.06 = $13.12 more than if we had no raise at all.

TABLE 9.1 Comparing back-loading versus front-loading.

EXAMPLE 8 *Increase in Student Loan Debt*

According to the American Association of State Colleges and Universities, in 2006 the average borrower who graduated from a public college owed $17,250 from student loans. This amount was up 115.625% from 1996. Find the average amount of student loan debt that graduates from these schools owed in 1996.

SOLUTION: In this case, the base is unknown. In deciding what percent to use in the percent equation, you have to be careful. The 115.625% is only the increase. The amount $17,250 represents 100% of the debt owed in 1996 plus the 115.625% increase. Therefore, the percent that we will use in the percent equation is

$$100\% + 115.625\% = 215.625\% = 2.15625.$$

Substituting in the percent equation, we get

$$\overset{\text{percent}}{2.15625} \times \overset{\text{amount}}{\text{base} = 17{,}250}.$$

Dividing both sides of this equation by 2.15625, gives us

$$\text{base} = \frac{17{,}250}{2.15625} = 8{,}000.$$

So, the average student loan debt in 1996 was $8,000. ✳

Taxes

Calculating various kinds of taxes relies heavily on using percents properly.

EXAMPLE 9   *Calculating Your Income Tax*

Table 9.2 is taken from the instructions for filling out Form 1040 to compute the federal income tax for a person whose marriage status is single.

	If your taxable income is Over—	But not Over—	The tax is	Of the amount Over—
Line 1	$0	7,550	. . . . 10%	0$
Line 2	7,550	30,650	$755.00 + 15%	7,550
Line 3	30,650	74,200	$4,220.00 + 25%	30,650
Line 4	74,200	154,800	$15,107.50 + 28%	74,200
Line 5	154,800	336,550	$37,675.50 + 33%	154,800
Line 6	336,550	. . . .	$97,653.00 + 38%	336,550

TABLE 9.2 Federal income taxes due for a single person.

a) If Jaye is unmarried and has a taxable income* of $41,458, what is the amount of federal income tax she owes?

b) How did the IRS arrive at the $4,220 amount in column 3 of line 3?

SOLUTION:

a) In calculating this tax, you first must identify the line of the table that is relevant to Jaye's situation. Because her income is above $30,650 and below $74,200, we will use line 3 (highlighted) from Table 9.2.

     So Jaye must pay $4,220 + 25% of the amount of taxable income over $30,650. Therefore, her tax is

$$\underset{25\%}{} 4{,}220 + (0.25)\underset{\substack{\text{amount over}\\ \$30{,}650}}{(41{,}458 - 30{,}650)} = 4{,}220 + (0.25)(10{,}808) = 4{,}220 + 2{,}702 = \$6{,}922.$$

b) The table is treating Jaye's income as being divided into two parts. Up to $30,650, she is being taxed according to the instructions on line 2 of the table. The tax on $30,650 would be $755 + 15% of the amount of taxable income over $7,550. So her tax is

$$755 + (0.15)(30{,}650 - 7{,}550) = 755 + (0.15)(23{,}100) = 755 + 3{,}465 = \$4{,}220.$$

Now try Exercises 67 to 70. ❋ ④

Quiz Yourself ④

Use Table 9.2 to calculate Aliyah's federal income tax that is due if her taxable income last year was $85,500.

---

*It is too complicated to get into detail here, but in essence, after you have totaled your wages, tips, interest earned, etc., you then reduce this total by making various kinds of adjustments such as exemptions, deductions for charitable contributions, work-related expenses, and other deductions to calculate what is called your *taxable income*.

Exercises 9.1

Looking Back*

These exercises follow the general outline of the topics presented in this section and will give you a good overview of the material that you have just studied.

1. In Example 1, what was the key in writing 19.32% as a decimal?

2. In converting a fraction to a percent as we did in Example 2, what did we do first?

3. How did we find the percent of markup in Example 5?

4. Why is it not a good idea to make conversions between decimals and percents by thinking only about moving the decimal point one way or the other?

Sharpening Your Skills

Convert each of the following percents to decimals.

5. 78%   **6.** 65%   **7.** 8%   **8.** 3%

9. 27.35%   **10.** 83.75%   **11.** 0.35%   **12.** 0.08%

Write each of the following decimals as percents.

13. 0.43   **14.** 0.95   **15.** 0.365   **16.** 0.875

17. 1.45   **18.** 2.25   **19.** 0.002   **20.** 0.0035

Convert each of the following fractions to percents.

21. $\frac{3}{4}$ **22.** $\frac{7}{8}$ **23.** $\frac{5}{16}$ **24.** $\frac{9}{25}$

25. $\frac{5}{2}$ **26.** $\frac{11}{8}$ **27.** $\frac{4}{250}$ **28.** $\frac{3}{500}$

29. 12 is what percent of 80?   **30.** What is 24% of 125?

31. 77 is 22% of what number?

32. 33.6 is what percent of 96?

33. What is 12.25% of 160?

34. 47.74 is 38.5% of what number?

35. 8.4 is what percent of 48?   **36.** What is 23% of 140?

37. 29.76 is 23.25% of what number?

38. 149.5 is what percent of 130?

Applying What You've Learned

39. **Cookie sales.** In a recent year, the top-selling cookie in America was Nabisco's Chips Ahoy with sales of $294.6 million. The total cookie sales for that year were $3,124 million. What percent of the total cookie sales was due to Chips Ahoy? (*Source:* Information Resources, Inc.)

40. **Pizza sales.** In a recent year, DiGiorno sold $478.3 million worth of frozen pizzas. If total frozen pizza sales were $2,844.8 million, what percent of frozen pizza sales was due to DiGiorno? (*Source:* Information Resources, Inc.)

41. **Price of new homes.** According to the U.S. Bureau of the Census, from 2005 to 2006, the average price of a new home in the Northeast increased by 7.88% to $428,000. What was the average price of a new home in the Northeast in 2005? Round your answer to the nearest thousand.

42. **Music stations.** The number of country music stations decreased by 6.6% from 2004 to 2006. If there were 2,045 country music stations in 2006, how many were there in 2004? (*Source:* M Street Corporation.)

According to USA Today, the number of visitors (in millions) to the top five Web sites in 2006 is given in the following graph. Use this information to solve Exercises 43–46.

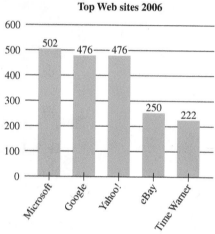

Top Web sites 2006

43. **Comparing Web site visitors.** What percent of the total visitors to these five sites visited Microsoft?

44. **Comparing Web site visitors.** What percent of the visitors to these sites was due to Google and eBay combined?

45. **Comparing Web site visitors.** What percent greater was the number of visitors to Yahoo! than Time Warner?

46. **Comparing Web site visitors.** What percent smaller was the number of visitors to Time Warner than eBay?

The graph below shows the sales (in thousands) of the five top-selling cars in 2006. Use this information to solve Exercises 47–50. (Source: The New York Times 2007 Almanac.)

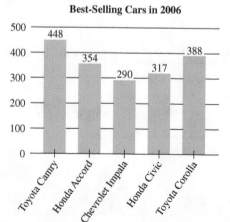

Best-Selling Cars in 2006

---

*Before doing these exercises, you may find it useful to review the note How to Succeed at Mathematics on page xix.

47. **Comparing car sales.** What percent of the sales of these five cars was due to the Toyota Camry?

48. **Comparing car sales.** What percent of the sales of these five cars was due to Hondas?

49. **Comparing car sales.** What percent greater was sales of the Camry than the Civic?

50. **Comparing car sales.** What percent smaller was the sales of the Impala than the Honda models?

51. **Autographs.** According to *The Useless Information Society,* only 6% of Beatles' autographs in circulation are estimated to be real. If there are 81 authentic autographs of the Beatles in circulation, then how many nonauthentic autographs are there in circulation?

52. **Happy Meal sales.** In the fourth quarter of 2007, McDonald's profits from Happy Meals were $508 million. If that accounted for 40% of the profits, how much profit came from selling other items?

53. **Population.** According to the U.S. Bureau of the Census, from 2000 to 2007 the population of the United States grew from 281 million to 301.6 million. What was the percent of increase?

54. **Population.** From 2000 to 2007 California's population grew from 33.9 million to 36.6 million. What was the percent of increase?

55. **Music downloads.** The Recording Industry Association of America found that downloaded album sales increased by 103.3% from 2005 to 2006. If there were 13.6 million albums downloaded in 2005, how many were downloaded in 2006?

56. **Music video sales.** The Recording Industry Association of America found that music video sales decreased by 31.7% from 2005 to 2006. If there were 33.8 million videos sold in 2005, how many were sold in 2006?

57. **Dealer markup on a car.**
   a. If a dealer buys a car from the manufacturer for $14,875 and then sells it for $16,065, what is his markup?
   b. In doing this problem, Angela got an incorrect answer of 7.4%. What mistake did she make?

58. **Dealer markup on a computer.**
   a. A computer retailer buys a multimedia computer for $1,850 and then sells it for $2,081. What is her markup on the computer?
   b. In doing this problem, Deepak got an incorrect answer of 11.1%. What mistake did Deepak make?

59. **Salary increase.** Marcy is working in a 2-year probationary period as a paralegal. She currently earns $28,000 a year and after her probationary period, her salary will increase by 35%. What will her yearly salary be at that time?

60. **Salary decrease.** Jed works for Metal Fabricators, Inc., which just lost a large contract and has asked employees to take a 12% pay cut. If Jed now makes $34,500 per year, what will his yearly pay be after the pay cut?

61. **Buying a grill.** Kirby is buying a new gas barbecue grill that has been reduced for an end-of-summer sale by 15% to $578. What was the original price of the grill?

62. **Increasing workload.** Gisela is an insurance claims adjuster. Last quarter she settled 124 claims and this quarter she settled 155 claims. What is the percent increase in the claims that she settled this quarter over last quarter?

63. **Markup on a boat.** Carlos is a boat dealer who bought a sailboat for $11,400 and then sold it for $12,711. What percent was his markup on the boat?

64. **Markup on an appliance.** Anna, who owns a small appliance store, bought a food processor for $524 and then sold it for $589.50. What percent was her markup on the food processor?

65. **Change in the stock market.** Due to a slump in the economy, Omarosa's mutual fund has dropped by 12% from last quarter to this quarter. If her fund is now worth $11,264, how much was her fund worth last quarter?

66. **Gas mileage.** Renaldo bought a new Honda Civic hybrid that gets 26.3% more miles per gallon than he got with his old Civic. If his new car gets 48 miles per gallon, what was the gas mileage on his old car?

For Exercises 67–70, use Table 9.2 in Example 9 to calculate the federal income tax due for the given taxable income.

67. $148,000
68. $28,750
69. $47,800
70. $440,000

Communicating Mathematics

Assume that you are studying with a friend for a quiz on percents. Your friend insists on blindly memorizing which way to "move the decimal point" in doing percent problems. Explain how you would help your friend understand how to do the conversions in Exercises 71–74 without relying solely on memorization.

71. You are converting 28.35% to a decimal.
72. You are converting 1.285 to a percent.
73. You are converting 0.0375 to a percent.
74. You are converting 1.375% to a decimal.
75. What is the meaning of *percent*?
76. What is the percent equation?
77. How could we have used the percent equation to solve Example 5?
78. Explain how the amount $15,107.50 was determined in line 4 of Table 9.2.

For Extra Credit

79. **Depreciation on a new car.** If a new car costs $18,000 and depreciates at a rate of 12% per year, what will be the value of the car in 4 years?

80. **Compounding raises.** If you are given a raise of 8% this year and a raise of 5% the following year, what single raise would give you the same yearly salary in the second year?

81. **Calculating prices.** If a merchant increases the price of a home entertainment system by *x*% and then later reduces the price by *x*%, is the price of the system the same as the original price? If not, what is the relationship between the two prices? Explain your answer by using appropriate examples.

82. Calculating prices. If a merchant reduces the price of a luxury speedboat by $x\%$ and then later increases the price by $x\%$, is the price of the boat the same as the original price? If not, what is the relationship between the two prices? Explain your answer by using appropriate examples.

83. Compounding percents. If you increase an amount by 10% and then again by 20%, is that the same as increasing the amount in one step by 30%? Explain your answer by using appropriate examples.

9.2 Interest

Objectives

1. Understand the simple interest formula.
2. Use the compound interest formula to find future value.
3. Solve the compound interest formula for different unknowns, such as the present value, length, and interest rate of a loan.

The most powerful force in the universe is. . . .

How would you finish this quote? The world-renowned physicist Albert Einstein said,

. . . compound interest.

Are you surprised that of all the forces that he might pick, Einstein chose this one? In this section, we will explain how interest can either work for you—or against you. As you will see, used properly, it can help you build a fortune; used improperly, it can lead you to financial ruin.

If you want to accumulate enough money to buy a newer car or go on a vacation, you could deposit money in a bank account. The bank will use your money to make loans to other customers and pay you interest for using your funds. However, if you borrow money from the bank, say to take a college course, then you will pay interest to the bank. In essence, **interest** is the money that one person (a borrower) pays to another (a lender) to use the lender's money. Savers earn interest; borrowers pay interest.

We will discuss simple and compound interest in this section, and discuss the cost of consumer loans in Section 9.3.

 KEY POINT

Simple interest is a straightforward way to compute interest.

Simple Interest*

The amount you deposit in a bank account is called the **principal**. The bank specifies an **interest rate** for that account as a percentage of your deposit. The rate is usually expressed as an annual rate. For example, a bank may offer an account that has an annual interest rate of 5%. To find the interest that you will earn in such an account, you also need to know how long the deposit will remain in the account. The time is usually stated in years. There is a simple formula that relates principal, interest earned, interest rate, and time. In words,

interest earned = principal × interest rate × time.

When we compute interest this way, it is called **simple interest**.

FORMULA FOR COMPUTING SIMPLE INTEREST We calculate simple interest using the formula

$$I = Prt,$$

where I is the interest earned, P is the principal, r is the interest rate, and t is the time in years.

---

*If you want some practice with basic algebra, see Appendix A.

EXAMPLE 1 *Calculating Simple Interest*

If you deposit $500 in a bank account paying 6% annual interest, how much interest will the deposit earn in 4 years if the bank computes the interest using simple interest?

SOLUTION: In this example:

P is the principal, which is $500

r is the annual interest rate, which is 6% (written as 0.06)

t is the time, which is 4 (years)

Thus, the interest earned is

$$I = Prt = 500 \times 0.06 \times 4 = 120.$$

In 4 years, this account earns $120 in interest.

Now try Exercises 5 to 8. ✳

KEY POINT

Future value equals principal plus interest.

To find the amount that will be in your account at some time in the future, called the **future value** (or sometimes called the **future amount**) we add the principal and the interest earned. We will represent future value by A, so we can say

$$A = \text{principal} + \text{interest} = P + I.$$

If we replace I by Prt, we get the formula $A = P + Prt = P(1 + rt)$.

COMPUTING FUTURE VALUE USING SIMPLE INTEREST To find the future value of an account that pays simple interest, use the formula

$$A = P(1 + rt),$$

where A is the future value, P is the principal, r is the annual interest rate, and t is the time in years.

EXAMPLE 2 *Computing Future Value Using Simple Interest*

Assume that you deposit $1,000 in a bank account paying 3% annual interest and leave the money there for 6 years. Use the simple interest formula to compute the future value of this account.

SOLUTION: We see that $P = 1,000$, $r = 0.03$, and $t = 6$. Therefore,

$$A = \overset{P}{1,000}(1 + (\overset{r}{0.03})(\overset{t}{6})) = 1,000(1 + 0.18) = 1,000(1.18) = 1,180.$$

Thus, your bank account will have $1,180 at the end of 6 years. ✳

In contrast to future value, the principal that you have to invest in an account now to have a specified amount in the account in the future is called the **present value** of the account. Notice that the formula for computing future value has four unknowns. If we want, we can use this formula for finding the present value of an account provided we know the future value, interest rate, and time.

EXAMPLE 3 *Finding the Present Value of an Account*

Assume that you plan to save $2,500 to take a white-water rafting trip in Costa Rica in 2 years. Your bank offers a certificate of deposit (CD) that pays 4% annual interest computed using simple interest. How much must you put in this CD now to have the necessary money in 2 years?

SOLUTION: We can use the formula

$$A = P(1 + rt).$$

We know that $A = 2{,}500$, $r = 4\% = 0.04$, and $t = 2$. Therefore,

$$2{,}500 = P(1 + (0.04)(2)).$$

We can rewrite this equation as

$$2{,}500 = P(1.08).$$

Dividing both sides of the equation by 1.08, we get

$$P = \frac{2{,}500}{1.08} \approx 2314.814815.$$

We will round this *up* to \$2,314.82 to guarantee that if you put this amount in the CD now, in 2 years you will have the \$2,500 you need for your white-water rafting trip.*

Now try Exercises 9 to 14. ❈

Quiz Yourself 5

Redo Example 3, but now assume that you want to save \$2,400 in 4 years and the CD has an annual interest rate of 5%.

 Some Good Advice

In Example 3, we used the earlier formula for computing future value to find the present value rather than stating a new formula to solve this specific problem. You will find it easier to learn a few formulas well and use them, together with simple algebra, to solve new problems rather than trying to memorize separate formulas for every type of problem.

 KEY POINT

Compounding pays interest on previously earned interest.

Compound Interest

It seems fair that if money in a bank account has earned interest, the bank should compute the interest due, add it to the principal, and then pay interest on this new, larger amount. This is in fact the way most bank accounts work. Interest that is paid on principal plus previously earned interest is called **compound interest**. If the interest is added yearly, we say that the interest is *compounded annually*. If the interest is added every three months, we say the interest is *compounded quarterly*. Interest also can be compounded monthly and daily.

EXAMPLE 4   *Calculating Compound Interest the Long Way*

Assume that you want to replace your sailboat with a larger one in 3 years. To save for a down payment for this purchase, you deposit \$2,000 for 3 years in a bank account that pays 10% annual interest,[†] compounded annually. How much will be in the account at the end of 3 years?

SOLUTION: We will perform the compound interest calculations one year at a time in the following table. In compounding the interest, we will use the future value from the previous year as the new principal at the beginning of the year. Notice that the quantity $(1 + rt) = (1 + 0.10 \times 1) = (1.10)$ remains the same throughout the computations.

Quiz Yourself 6

Continue Example 4 to calculate the amount in your account at the end of the fourth year.

Year	Principal (Beginning of Year) P	Future Value (End of Year) $P(1 + rt) = P(1.10)$
1	\$2,000	\$2,000(1.10) = \$2,200
2	\$2,200	\$2,200(1.10) = \$2,420
3	\$2,420	\$2,420(1.10) = \$2,662

❈

---

*When calculating a deposit to accumulate a future amount, we will always round up to the next cent.

[†]An interest rate of 10% would be extraordinarily high. However, we will often choose rates in examples and exercises to keep the computations simple.

PROBLEM SOLVING
Verify Your Answer

You should always check answers to see whether they are reasonable. In Example 4, if we had used simple interest to find the future value, we would have obtained $A = 2{,}000 (1 + (0.10)(3)) = 2{,}000(1.30) = 2{,}600$. The interest we found in Example 4 is a *little* larger because as the interest is added to the principal each year, the bank is paying interest on an increasingly larger principal.

If we were to continue the process that we used in Example 4 for a longer period of time, say for 30 years, it would be very tedious. In Figure 9.2 we look at the same computations in a different way, keeping in mind that the amount in the account at the end of each year is 1.10 times the amount in the account at the beginning of the year.

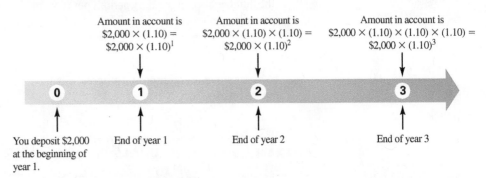

FIGURE 9.2 10% interest being compounded annually.

If we were to continue the pattern shown in Figure 9.2 to compute the future value of the account at the end of 30 years, we would see that

$$A = 2{,}000(1.10)^{30} \approx 2{,}000(17.44940227) \approx 34{,}898.80. \, *$$

This large amount shows how your money can grow if it is compounded over a long period of time.

In general, if we deposit a principal P in an account paying an annual interest rate r for t years, then the future value of the account is given by the formula

money you will
have in the future ⎯⎯⎯ ⎯⎯ money you have now
$$A = P(1 + r)^t.$$

In the example that we just calculated, $P = 2{,}000$, $r = 0.10$, and $t = 30$. It is important to understand that this formula for calculating compound interest only works for the case when r is the *annual interest rate* and t is time being measured in *years*. Do not bother to learn this formula because in just a moment we will give you a similar compounding formula that works for more general situations. **7**

Solving for Unknowns in the Compound Interest Formula

All banks and most other financial institutions compound interest more frequently than once a year. For example, many banks send savings account customers a monthly statement showing the balance in their accounts. So far in our discussion of compounding, we have used a yearly interest rate. If compounding takes place more frequently, then the interest rate must be adjusted accordingly. For example, a yearly interest rate of $12\% = 0.12$

Quiz Yourself

Calculate the future value of an account containing $3,000 for which the annual interest rate is 4% compounded annually for 10 years.

✎ **KEY POINT**

Knowing the principal, the periodic interest rate, and the number of compounding periods, it is easy to determine future value.

---

*To ensure greater accuracy, we often show calculations with eight decimal places. If your calculations do not agree with ours, it may be due to the difference in the way we are rounding our calculations.

corresponds to a monthly interest rate of $\frac{12\%}{12} = \frac{0.12}{12} = 0.01 = 1\%$. If the interest is being compounded quarterly, the quarterly interest rate would then be $\frac{12\%}{4} = \frac{0.12}{4} = 0.03 = 3\%$.

In order to handle situations such as these, we will modify the formula $A = P(1 + r)^t$ slightly.

THE COMPOUND INTEREST FORMULA Assume that an account with principal P is paying an annual interest rate r and compounding is being done m times per year. If the money remains in the account for n time periods, then the future value, A, of the account is given by the formula

$$A = P\left(1 + \frac{r}{m}\right)^n.$$

Notice that in this formula, we have replaced r by $\frac{r}{m}$, which is the annual rate divided by the number of compounding periods per year, and t by n, which is the number of compounding periods.

You can use the compound interest formula for computing compound interest to compare investments.

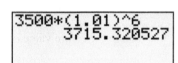

```
3500*(1.01)^6
          3715.320527
```

EXAMPLE 5 *Understanding How "No Payments Until . . ." Works*

You have seen a home fitness center on sale for $3,500 and what really makes the deal attractive is that there is no money down and no payments due for 6 months. Realize that although you do not have to make any payments, the dealer is not loaning you the money for 6 months for nothing. You have borrowed $3,500 and, in 6 months, your payments will be based upon that fact. Assuming that your dealer is charging an annual interest rate of 12%, compounded monthly, what interest will accumulate on your purchase over the next 6 months?

SOLUTION: To determine the interest that has accumulated, we will find the future value of your "loan" (assuming that you make no payments) and subtract $3,500 from that. We will use the formula for calculating future value with $P = 3,500$, $r = 0.12$, $m = 12$, and $n = 6$. Therefore,

monthly interest rate ⌐   ⌐number of months

$$A = P\left(1 + \frac{r}{m}\right)^n = 3,500\left(1 + \frac{0.12}{12}\right)^6 = 3,500(1.01)^6 = 3,715.33.$$

So the accumulated interest is $3,715.33 − $3,500 = $215.33.

Now try Exercises 19 to 26. ✵ **8**

Quiz Yourself **8**

Sarah deposits $1,000 in a CD paying 6% annual interest for 2 years. What is the future value of her account if the interest is compounded quarterly?

✺ ✺ ✺ **HIGHLIGHT**

Between the Numbers—It Doesn't Hurt to Ask

In Example 5, you might ask yourself if you would be better off borrowing the $3,500 from another source that has a lower interest rate and paying for the fitness center outright.

If you have the money, sometimes a dealer might give you a better price if you offer to pay for an item with cash. The trick, of course, is to be able to put money aside so that when you want to make a deal, you are not at the mercy of someone else's money.

— **HIGHLIGHT** 🎇 🎇 🎇

Doing Financial Calculations with a Calculator*

When doing financial computations, often technology can speed up your work. We will use a calculator to reproduce the solution to Example 6.

On my calculator, if we press the [2nd] [Finance] keys, Screen 1 comes up. The letters TVM stand for "Time Value of Money." Then by choosing option 1, we get Screen 2. Now we can enter the values 18 for N, the number of years; 4.8 for I%,

the annual interest rate; 60,000 for FV, the future value; and 4 for C/Y, the number of compounding periods per year. Next we position the cursor over PV (present value) and press the keys [Alpha] [Solve]. The amount −25418.75939 for present value means that we must deposit $25,418.76 now to have the desired $60,000 in 18 years (Screen 3).

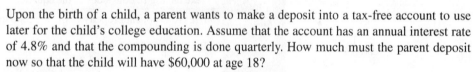

| Screen 1 | Screen 2 | Screen 3 |

Example 6 illustrates a different way to use the compound interest formula.

EXAMPLE 6 *Finding the Present Value for a College Tuition Account*

Upon the birth of a child, a parent wants to make a deposit into a tax-free account to use later for the child's college education. Assume that the account has an annual interest rate of 4.8% and that the compounding is done quarterly. How much must the parent deposit now so that the child will have $60,000 at age 18?

SOLUTION: We will use the compound interest formula $A = P\left(1 + \frac{r}{m}\right)^n$. Because we know $A = 60,000$, $r = 0.048$, $n = 72$, and $m = 4$, we can find the present value by solving the equation

$$60,000 = P\left(1 + \frac{0.048}{4}\right)^{72} = P(1 + 0.012)^{72}$$

for P. Therefore,

$$P = \frac{60,000}{(1.012)^{72}} = \frac{60,000}{2.360461386} \approx 25,418.76.$$

A deposit slightly over $25,400 now will guarantee $60,000 for college in 18 years.

Now try Exercises 33 and 34. 🎇

Although $60,000 may seem like a lot of money, realize that *inflation*, the increase in the price of goods and services, will also cause the cost of a college education to increase. We will consider the effects of inflation in the exercises.

So far we have used the formula $A = P\left(1 + \frac{r}{m}\right)^n$ to find A and P. Sometimes we want to find r or n. To do this, we need to introduce some new techniques.

If you want to solve for n in the formula $A = P\left(1 + \frac{r}{m}\right)^n$, you need to be able to solve an equation of the form $a^x = b$, where a and b are fixed numbers. A property of logarithmic functions enables you to solve such equations. Many calculators have a key labeled either "log" or "log x," which stands for the **common logarithmic function**. Pressing this key

KEY POINT

We use the log function to solve for n in the formula

$$A = P\left(1 + \frac{r}{m}\right)^n.$$

---

*For this example, I am using a TI-83 calculator, but many other calculators have similar features for doing financial calculations. On the TI-83 plus and TI-84, press the [APPS] key and then choose option 1 to get screen 1.

reverses the operation of raising 10 to a power. For example, suppose that you compute $10^5 = 100{,}000$ on your calculator. If you next press the log key, the display will show 5. If you enter 1,000, which is 10 raised to the third power, and press the log key, the display will show 3. Practice finding the log of powers of 10 such as 100 and 1,000,000. If you enter 23 and then press the log key, the display will show 1.361727836. The interpretation of this result is that $10^{1.361727836} = 23$.* The log function has an important property that will help us solve equations of the form $a^x = b$.

EXPONENT PROPERTY OF THE LOG FUNCTION

$$\log y^x = x \log y$$

To understand this property, you should use your calculator to verify the following:

$$\log 4^5 = 5 \log 4$$
$$\log 6^3 = 3 \log 6$$

Example 7 illustrates how to use the exponent property to solve equations.

EXAMPLE 7   *Solving an Equation Using the Exponent Property of the Log Function*

Solve $3^x = 20$.

SOLUTION: We illustrate the steps required to solve this equation.

Step 1	Take the log of both sides of the equation.	$\log 3^x = \log 20$
Step 2	Use the exponent property of the log function.	$x \log 3 = \log 20$
Step 3	Divide both sides by log 3.	$x = \dfrac{\log 20}{\log 3}$
Step 4	Use a calculator to evaluate the right side of the equation (your calculator may give a slightly different answer).	$x = 2.726833028$

Quiz Yourself ⑨

Solve $6^x = 15$.

Now try Exercises 35 to 42. ✳ ⑨

In Example 8, we use the exponent property of the log function to find the time it takes an investment to grow to a certain amount.

EXAMPLE 8   *Saving for Equipment for a Business*

Mara wants to buy lighting equipment from her cousin to start a dance studio. He will sell his equipment for $2,800. She presently has $2,500 and found an investment that will pay her 9% annual interest, compounded monthly. In how many months will Mara be able to pay her cousin for the equipment?

SOLUTION: We know that the future value that Mara must pay her cousin is $A = 2{,}800$. She presently has $2,500 and the monthly interest rate is $\frac{r}{m} = \frac{0.09}{12} = 0.0075$. We must solve the compound interest formula $A = P\left(1 + \frac{r}{m}\right)^n$ for n, which represents the number of months of the compounding. Substituting for A, P, and $\frac{r}{m}$, we get the equation

$$2{,}800 = 2{,}500\left(1 + \frac{0.09}{12}\right)^n.$$

---

*We will not discuss what it means to raise 10 to a power such as 1.361727836.

We solve this equation by the following steps:

$$1.12 = (1.0075)^n$$ Divide both sides of the equation by 2,500 and simplify.

$$\log(1.12) = \log(1.0075)^n$$ Take the log of both sides.

$$\log(1.12) = n\log(1.0075)$$ Use the exponent property of the log function.

Quiz Yourself **10**

Do Example 8 again, but now assume that the interest rate is 6%.

Solving for n, we get the equation

$$n = \frac{\log(1.12)}{\log(1.0075)} \approx 15.17.$$

This means that Mara will have the money she needs by the end of the 16th month. ❈

The last situation that we will consider is how to solve the compound interest equation $A = P\left(1 + \frac{r}{m}\right)^n$ for r. To do this, we have to be able to solve an equation of the form $x^a = b$, where a and b are fixed numbers. We show how to solve such an equation in Example 9.

EXAMPLE 9   *Negotiating a Basketball Contract*

Kobe is negotiating a new basketball contract with the Lakers and expects to retire after playing one more year. In order to reduce his current taxes, his agent has agreed to defer a bonus of $1.4 million to be paid as $1.68 million in 2 years. If the Lakers invest the $1.4 million now, what rate of investment would they need to have $1.68 million to pay Kobe in 2 years? Assume that you want to find an annual interest rate that is compounded monthly.

SOLUTION: To solve this compound interest problem, we again use the formula $A = P\left(1 + \frac{r}{m}\right)^n$. We know that $A = 1.68$, $P = 1.4$, $m = 12$, and $n = 24$.

Substituting for A, P, m, and n, we get the equation

$$1.68 = 1.4\left(1 + \frac{r}{12}\right)^{24}.$$

Dividing both sides of the equation by 1.4 gives us $1.2 = \left(1 + \frac{r}{12}\right)^{24}$. We can get rid of the exponent 24 if we raise both sides of the equation to the $\frac{1}{24}$ power. This gives us the equation

$$(1.2)^{1/24} = \left(\left(1 + \frac{r}{12}\right)^{24}\right)^{1/24} = 1 + \frac{r}{12}.^*$$

Subtracting 1 from both sides of the equation, we get

$$\frac{r}{12} = (1.2)^{1/24} - 1 = 1.00762566 - 1 = 0.00762566.$$

Now, multiplying this equation by 12, we find the annual interest rate, r, to be $12(0.00762566) \approx 0.0915$. Thus, the Lakers need to find an investment that pays an annual interest rate of about 9.15% compounded monthly.

Now try Exercises 43 to 46. ❈

    Some Good Advice

Be careful to distinguish between the situations in Examples 8 and 9. In Example 8, we used the log function to solve an equation of the form $a^x = b$. In Example 9, we solved an equation of the form $x^a = b$ by raising both sides of the equation to the $\frac{1}{a}$ power.

---

*In algebra, $(a^x)^y = a^{xy}$. That is why $\left(\left(1 + \frac{r}{12}\right)^{24}\right)^{1/24} = \left(1 + \frac{r}{12}\right)^{(24)(1/24)} = \left(1 + \frac{r}{12}\right)^1 = 1 + \frac{r}{12}.$

Exercises 9.2

Looking Back*

These exercises follow the general outline of the topics presented in this section and will give you a good overview of the material that you have just studied.

1. How did we find the present value in Example 3?
2. Why did we divide the yearly interest rate of 0.12 by 12 in Example 5?
3. What property of the log function did we use to solve the equation $3^x = 20$ in Example 7?
4. What was our recommendation in the "Between the Numbers" Highlight following Example 5?

Sharpening Your Skills

In Exercises 5–8, use the simple interest formula I = Prt and elementary algebra to find the missing quantities in the table below.

	I	P	r	t
5.		$1,000	8%	3 years
6.	$196		7%	2 years
7.	$700	$3,500		4 years
8.	$1,920	$8,000	6%	

In Exercises 9–14, use the future value formula A = P(1 + rt) and elementary algebra to find the missing quantities in the table below.

	A	P	r	t
9.		$2,500	8%	3 years
10.		$1,600	4%	5 years
11.	$1,770		6%	3 years
12.	$2,332		3%	2 years
13.	$1,400	$1,250		2 years
14.	$966	$840	5%	

In Exercises 15–18, you are given an annual interest rate and the compounding period. Find the interest rate per compounding period.

15. 18%; monthly
16. 8%; quarterly
17. 12%; daily†
18. 10%; daily

In Exercises 19–26, you are given the principal, the annual interest rate, and the compounding period. Use the formula for computing future value using compound interest to determine the value of the account at the end of the specified time period.

19. $5,000, 5%, yearly; 5 years
20. $7,500, 7%, yearly; 6 years
21. $4,000, 8%, quarterly; 2 years
22. $8,000, 4%, quarterly; 3 years
23. $20,000, 8%, monthly; 2 years
24. $10,000, 6%, monthly; 5 years
25. $4,000, 10%, daily; 2 years
26. $6,000, 4%, daily; 3 years

Savings institutions often state two rates in their advertising. One is the nominal yield, *which you can think of as an annual simple interest rate. The other is called the* effective annual yield, *which is the actual interest rate that the account earns due to the compounding. If $1,000 is in an account that pays a nominal yield of 9% and if the compounding is done monthly, then after 1 year, the account would contain $1,093.80, which corresponds to a simple interest rate of 9.38%. We would say that this account has an effective annual yield of 9.38%. In Exercises 27–30, find the effective annual yield for each account.*

27. nominal yield, 7.5%; compounded monthly
28. nominal yield, 10%; compounded twice a year
29. nominal yield, 6%; compounded quarterly
30. nominal yield, 8%; compounded daily

In Exercises 31 and 32, you are given an annual interest rate and the compounding period for two investments. Decide which is the better investment.

31. 5% compounded yearly; 4.95% compounded quarterly
32. 4.75% compounded monthly; 4.70% compounded daily

In Exercises 33 and 34, Ann and Tom want to establish a fund for their grandson's college education. What lump sum must they deposit in each account in order to have $30,000 in the fund at the end of 15 years?

33. **Saving for college.** 6% annual interest rate, compounded quarterly
34. **Saving for college.** 7.5% annual interest rate, compounded monthly

In Exercises 35–42, solve each equation.

35. $3^x = 10$
36. $2^x = 12$
37. $(1.05)^x = 2$
38. $(1.15)^x = 3$
39. $x^3 = 10$
40. $x^2 = 10$
41. $x^4 = 10$
42. $x^4 = 25$

In Exercises 43–46, use the compound interest formula A = P(1 + r)^t and the given information to solve for either t or r. (We are assuming that n = 1.)

43. $A = \$2,500, P = \$2,000, t = 5$
44. $A = \$400, P = \$20, t = 35$
45. $A = \$1,500, P = \$1,000, r = 4\%$
46. $A = \$2,500, P = \$1,000, r = 6\%$

---

*Before doing these exercises, you may find it useful to review the note *How to Succeed at Mathematics* on page xix.
†We will assume there are 365 days in a year.

Applying What You've Learned

47. Buying an entertainment system. You have purchased a home entertainment system for $3,600 and have agreed to pay off the system in 36 monthly payments of $136 each.

   a. What will be the total sum of your payments?

   b. What will be the total amount of interest that you have paid?

48. Buying a car. You have purchased a used car for $6,000 and have agreed to pay off the car in 24 monthly payments of $325 each.

   a. What will be the total sum of your payments?

   b. What will be the total amount of interest that you have paid?

Often, through government-supported programs, students may obtain "bargain" interest rates such as 6% or 8% to attend college. Frequently, payments are not due and interest does not accumulate until you stop attending college. In Exercises 49 and 50, calculate the amount of interest due 1 month after you must begin payments.

49. Borrowing for college. You have borrowed $10,000 at an annual interest rate of 8%.

50. Borrowing for college. You have borrowed $15,000 at an annual interest rate of 6%.

In Exercises 51–54, we will assume that the lender is using simple interest to compute the interest on the loan.

51. Borrowing for a trip. You plan to take a trip to the Grand Canyon in 2 years. You want to buy a certificate of deposit for $1,200 that you will cash in for your trip. What annual interest rate must you obtain on the certificate if you need $1,500 for your trip?

52. Paying interest on late taxes. Jonathan wants to defer payment of his $4,500 tax bill for 4 months. If he must pay an annual interest rate of 15% for doing this, what will his total payment be?

53. Borrowing from a pawn shop. Sanjay has borrowed $400 on his father's watch from the Main Street Pawn Shop. He has agreed to pay off the loan with $425 one month later. What is the annual interest rate that he is being charged?

54. Borrowing from a bail bondsman. If a person accused of a crime does not have sufficient resources, he may have a bail bondsman post bail to be released until a

trial is held. Assume that a bondsman charges a $50 fee plus 8% of the amount of the bail. If a bondsman posts $20,000 for a trial that takes place in 2 months, what is the interest rate being charged by the bondsman? (Treat the $50 fee plus the 8% as interest on a $20,000 loan for two months.)

The computations for dealing with **inflation** *are the same as for determining future value. If an item sells for $100 today and there is an annual inflation rate of 4% for 10 years, the item would then cost* $100(1.04)^{10} = \$148.02$. *The Bureau of Labor Statistics maintains an index called the* **consumer price index** *(CPI), which is a measure of inflation. The accompanying table shows the CPI for several recent years. The CPI of 207.3 for 2007 means that the price of certain basic items such as clothing, food, energy, automobiles, etc. that would have cost $100 in 1982 to 1984, which are the base years for the index, would now cost $207.30.*

Year	2002	2003	2004	2005	2006	2007
CPI	179.9	184.0	188.9	195.3	201.6	207.3
Percent Increase		2.3	2.7	3.4	3.2	2.8

In Exercises 55–58, you are given a year and the price of an item. Use the percent increase in the CPI as the rate of inflation for the next 10 years to calculate the price of that item 10 years later.

55. Inflation. 2004, fast-food meal, $4.65

56. Inflation. 2006, automobile, $17,650

57. Inflation. 2007, gallon of gasoline, $3.25

58. Inflation. 2005, athletic shoes, $96

59. Inflation. From 1992 to 1995, Albania experienced a yearly inflation rate of 226%. Determine the price of the fast-food meal in Exercise 55 after 5 years at a 226% inflation rate.

60. Inflation. The inflation rate in Hungary during the mid-1990s was about 28%. Determine the price of the athletic shoes in Exercise 58 after 10 years at a 28% inflation rate.

61. Comparing investments. Jocelyn purchased 100 shares of Jet Blue stock for $23.75 per share. Eight months later she sold the stock at $24.50 per share.

   a. What annual rate, calculated using simple interest, did she earn on this transaction?

   b. What annual rate would she have to earn in a savings account compounded monthly to earn the same money on her investment?

62. Comparing investments. Dominick purchased a bond for $2,400 to preserve a wildlife sanctuary and 10 months later he sold it for $2,580.

   a. What annual rate, calculated using simple interest, did he earn on this transaction?

   b. What annual rate would he have to earn in a savings account compounded monthly to earn the same money on his investment?

63. Investment earnings. Emily purchased a bond valued at $20,000 for highway construction for $9,420. If the bond pays 7.5% annual interest compounded monthly, how long must she hold it until it reaches its full face value?

64. Investment earnings. Lucas purchased a bond with a face value of $10,000 for $4,200 to build a new sports stadium. If the bond pays 6.5% annual interest compounded monthly, how long must he hold it until it reaches its full face value?

Communicating Mathematics

65. What formula do we use to compute simple interest?

66. What is the difference between simple interest and compound interest?

67. What is the meaning of each variable in the compound interest formula $A = P\left(1 + \frac{r}{m}\right)^{n}$?

68. Explain the relationship between the formulas $A = P(1 + r)^{t}$ and $A = P\left(1 + \frac{r}{m}\right)^{n}$.

69. Under what circumstances will $A = P(1 + r)^{t}$ and $A = P\left(1 + \frac{r}{m}\right)^{n}$ give you the same answers to a compound interest problem?

70. Explain the difference in the techniques that you have to use to solve a problem like Example 8 versus a problem like Example 9.

Using Technology to Investigate Mathematics

71. Get a tutorial from your instructor that explains in more detail how to use a calculator to solve finance problems. Use your calculator to reproduce some of the examples in this section. Your instructor also has Excel spreadsheets available for doing financial computations; use them to reproduce some of the computations in this section.*

72. There are many good interactive financial calculators available on the Internet. Find several and use them to verify some of the computations that we did in this section.

For Extra Credit

Some banks advertise that money in their accounts is compounded continuously. To get an understanding of what this means, apply the compound interest formula using a very large number of compounding periods per year. In Exercises 73 and 74, divide the year into 100,000 compounding periods per year. Apply the compound interest formula for finding future value to approximate what the effective annual yield would be if the compounding were done continuously for the stated nominal yield.

73. nominal yield, 10%

74. nominal yield, 12%

If the principal P is invested in an account that pays an annual interest rate of r% and the compounding is done continuously, then the future value, A, that will be in the account after t years is given by the formula

$$A = Pe^{rt}.$$

The number e is approximately 2.718281828.

75. Use the formula for continuous compounding to find the effective annual yield if the compounding in Exercise 73 is done continuously.

76. Use the formula for continuous compounding to find the effective annual yield if the compounding in Exercise 74 is done continuously.

9.3 | Consumer Loans

Objectives

1. Determine payments for an add-on loan.
2. Compute finance charges on a credit card using the unpaid balance method.
3. Use the average daily balance method to compute credit card charges.
4. Compare credit card finance charge methods.

Debt is a bottomless sea.   —Thomas Carlyle

In the spring of 2008, publications such as *Fortune* and *Money* magazines featured articles highlighting a record U.S. credit card debt of $915 billion, and financial institutions such as Citigroup, American Express, and Bank of America were, to quote *Fortune* magazine, "strapping on their Kevlar vests," anticipating an impending financial explosion.

From ancient times to the present, the Bible, William Shakespeare, Benjamin Franklin, and others have warned about the dangers of unbridled credit. In this section, we will explain the mathematics of credit cards and show you how you can use credit wisely, to avoid drowning in Carlyle's bottomless sea.

Imagine that you have just signed the lease for your first apartment and now all you have to do is furnish it. If you buy living room furniture for $1,100, which you pay for in payments, you are taking out an installment loan. Loans having a fixed number of payments are called *closed-ended credit* agreements (or *installment loans*). Each payment is called an *installment*. The size of your payments is determined by the amount of your purchase and also by the interest rate that the seller is charging. The interest charged on a loan is often called a *finance charge*.

The Add-On Interest Method

KEY POINT

The add-on interest method is a simple way to compute payments on an installment loan.

We use the simple interest formula from Section 9.2 to calculate the finance charge for an installment loan. To determine the payments for an installment loan, we add the simple interest due on the loan to the loan amount and then divide this sum by the number of monthly payments.

> **FORMULA FOR DETERMINING THE MONTHLY PAYMENT OF AN INSTALLMENT LOAN**
>
> $$\text{monthly payment} = \frac{P + I}{n},$$
>
> where P is the amount of the loan, I is the amount of interest due on the loan, and n is the number of monthly payments.

This method is sometimes called the **add-on interest method** because we are adding on the interest due on the loan before determining the payments.

EXAMPLE 1   *Determining Payments for an Add-On Interest Loan*

A new pair of Bose speakers for your home theater system costs $720. If you take out an add-on loan for 2 years at an annual interest rate of 18%, what will be your monthly payments?

SOLUTION: We first use the simple interest formula to calculate the interest:

$$I = Prt = 720(0.18)2 = 259.20.$$

Next, we add the interest to the purchase price:

$$720 + 259.20 = 979.20.$$

To find the monthly payments, we divide this amount by 24:

$$\frac{979.20}{24} = 40.80.$$

Monthly payments are therefore $40.80.

Now try Exercises 5 to 12. ✸ ⑪

Quiz Yourself ⑪

Suppose that you take an installment loan for $360 for 1 year at an annual interest rate of 21%. What are your monthly payments?

In Example 1, the annual interest rate of 18% is quite misleading. If we think about it, the purchase price was $720, so it would be fair to say that you are paying off $720/24 = $30 of the loan amount each month; the other $10.80 is interest. When you reach the last month, although you only owe $30 on the purchase, you are still paying $10.80 in interest. Simple arithmetic shows that 10.80/30 = 0.36. So in a certain sense, the interest rate for the last month of the loan is actually 36%. Because you are paying 36% interest for one month, this is equivalent to an annual interest rate of 12 × 36% = 432%. What we want to point out here is that although simple interest is easy to compute, as you pay off the loan amount, the actual interest you are paying on the outstanding balance is higher than the stated interest rate.

When you use your credit card to pay for gas at a gas station, you are using *open-ended credit*. With open-ended credit, the calculation of finance charges can be more complicated than with closed-ended credit. Although you may be making monthly payments on your loan, you may also be increasing the loan by making further purchases.

There are several ways that credit card companies compute finance charges. We will look at two methods and compare them at the end of this section. You will see that if you understand the method being used to compute your finance charges, you can use this information to reduce the cost of borrowing money.

KEY POINT

The unpaid balance method computes finance charges on the balance at the end of the previous month.

The Unpaid Balance Method

The first method that we will discuss for computing finance charges is called the **unpaid balance method**. With this method, the interest is based on the previous month's balance.

THE UNPAID BALANCE METHOD FOR COMPUTING THE FINANCE CHARGE ON A CREDIT CARD LOAN   This method also uses the simple interest formula $I = Prt$; however,

P = previous month's balance + finance charge + purchases made − returns − payments.

The variable r is the annual interest rate, and $t = \frac{1}{12}$.

EXAMPLE 2   *Using the Unpaid Balance Method for Finding Finance Charges*

Assume that the annual interest rate on your credit card is 18% and your unpaid balance at the beginning of last month was $600. Since then, you purchased ski boots for $130 and sent in a payment of $170.

a) Using the unpaid balance method, what is your credit card bill this month?

b) What is your finance charge next month?

SOLUTION:

a) We will list the items that we need to know to compute this month's balance.

Previous month's balance: $600

Finance charge on last month's balance; $600 \times 0.18 \times \left(\dfrac{1}{12}\right) = \$9$

annual interest rate ⟋   ⎿ Time is 1 month.

Purchases made: $130
Returns: $0
Payment: $170

Therefore, you owe

Previous month's balance + finance charge + purchases made − returns − payments
$$= 600 + 9 + 130 - 0 - 170 = \$569.$$

b) The finance charge for next month will be $\$569 \times 0.18 \times \left(\dfrac{1}{12}\right) = \$8.54$.

Now try Exercises 21 to 26. ❋ **12**

Note that you can use the unpaid balance method to your advantage by making a large purchase early in the billing period and then paying it off just before the billing date. This is not to the credit card company's advantage because you can use the credit card company's money for free for almost a whole month.

It is easy to use credit cards for purchases and so tempting to pay only the minimum payment that appears on your credit card bill that you may find your debt increasing even

Quiz Yourself **12**

Assume that the annual interest rate on your credit card is 21%. Your outstanding balance last month was $300. Since then, you have charged a purchase for $84 and made a payment of $100. What is the outstanding balance on your card at the end of this month? What is next month's finance charge on this balance?

though you are sending in a payment every month. Example 3 illustrates how credit card debt can get out of hand.

EXAMPLE 3 *Paying Off a Credit Card Debt*

Assume that you want to pay off your credit card debt of $6,589 by making the minimum payment of $100 a month. What will your balance be at the end of 1 month? Assume that the annual interest rate on your card is 18% and that the credit card company is using the unpaid balance method to compute your finance charges.

SOLUTION: When you send in your $100, it is credited to your account, so the next month you have an unpaid balance of $6,589 - 100 = \$6,489$. The annual interest rate is 18%, so your monthly interest rate is $\frac{18}{12} = 1.5\%$.

Therefore, at the end of the month you still owe

$$\underset{\text{balance}}{6,489} + \underset{\text{interest}}{(0.015)(6,489)} = 6,489 + 97.34 = \$6,586.34.$$

Thus, your $100 payment has reduced your debt by only $6,589 - 6,586.34 = \$2.66$. ✳

Example 3 illustrates how difficult it is to pay off a large credit card bill. The best practice is to pay off as much of your outstanding balance as you can to avoid paying a large amount of interest. Although it is possible to borrow cash from one company to pay off debts at another, doing this is not reducing the size of your debt. Instead, the debt may still grow at a rate of 18% or more per year.

When you use credit, always look at the annual interest rate. In some cases, if you read the fine print in the agreement, you will find rates as high as 24% or 25%. Also, be very careful when taking a cash advance on your credit card because the interest rate is often much higher than the rate you are charged for making purchases on the card.

KEY POINT

The average daily balance method computes finance charges based on the balance in the account for each day of the month.

The Average Daily Balance Method

A more complicated method for determining the finance charge on a credit card is called the **average daily balance method**, which is one of the most common methods used by credit card companies. With this method, the balance is the average of all daily balances for the previous month.

> **THE AVERAGE DAILY BALANCE METHOD FOR COMPUTING THE FINANCE CHARGE ON A CREDIT CARD LOAN**
>
> 1. Add the outstanding balance for your account for each day of the month.
> 2. Divide the total in step 1 by the number of days in the month to find the average daily balance.
> 3. To find the finance charge, use the formula $I = Prt$, where P is the average daily balance found in step 2, r is the annual interest rate, and t is the number of days in the month divided by 365.

EXAMPLE 4 *Using the Average Daily Balance Method for Finding Finance Charges*

Suppose that you begin the month of September (which has 30 days) with a credit card balance of $240. Assume that your card has an annual interest rate of 18% and that during September the following adjustments are made on your account:

September 11: A payment of $60 is credited to your account.

September 18: You charge $24 for iTune downloads.

September 23: You charge $12 for gasoline.

Use the average daily balance method to compute the finance charge that will appear on your October credit card statement.

SOLUTION: To answer this question, we must first find the average daily balance for September. The easiest way to calculate the balance is to keep a day-by-day record of what you owe the credit card company for each day in September, as we do in Table 9.3.

Day	Balance	Number of Days × Balance
1, 2, 3, 4, 5, 6, 7, 8, 9, 10	$240	$10 \times 240 = 2{,}400$
11, 12, 13, 14, 15, 16, 17	$180	$7 \times 180 = 1{,}260$
18, 19, 20, 21, 22	$204	$5 \times 204 = 1{,}020$
23, 24, 25, 26, 27, 28, 29, 30	$216	$8 \times 216 = 1{,}728$

TABLE 9.3 Daily balances for September.

Quiz Yourself **13**

Recalculate the average daily balance in Example 4, except now assume you bought the iTunes downloads on September 3 instead of September 18. Make a table similar to Table 9.3.

The average daily balance is therefore

$$\frac{(10 \times 240) + (7 \times 180) + (5 \times 204) + (8 \times 216)}{30}$$

$$= \frac{2{,}400 + 1{,}260 + 1{,}020 + 1{,}728}{30} = \frac{6{,}408}{30} = 213.6.$$

We next apply the simple interest formula, where $P = \$213.60$, $r = 0.18$, and $t = \frac{30}{365}$.* Thus, $I = Prt = 213.6(0.18)\left(\frac{30}{365}\right) = 3.16$. Your finance charge on the October statement will be \$3.16.

Now try Exercises 27 to 30. ✵ **13**

As you will see in Example 5, the amount of finance charges you pay on a loan will vary depending on the method used to compute the charges.

Math in Your Life

Will You Be Part of "Generation Broke?"†

You've heard of "Generation X" and "Generation Y" but have you ever heard of "Generation Broke?" Article after article, from *Time Magazine* to *USA Today*, warns of impending financial doom for young adults. Depending on which study you read, the average graduating college senior now owes between $5,000 and $20,000 in student loans and another $3,000 to $4,000 in credit card debt. According to a public policy group in New York called Demos, ". . . young adults are doing everything society tells them to do . . . [but] they can't get ahead because of the debt they went into to get the degree and get the good job."

Demos sees two trends fueling this rise in debt among younger Americans: increasing college costs and aggressive credit card marketing on college campuses. In a report in the *Christian Science Monitor*, one student laments not having had a class in personal financial management, "If I had that type of class, I wouldn't have gotten into such a credit mess."

---

*$t = \frac{30}{365}$ because we are using the credit card for 30 days out of a 365-day year.
†To read the full report, "Generation Broke: The Growth of Debt Among Younger Americans," refer to www.demos-usa.org/pub295.cfm.

HISTORICAL HIGHLIGHT ✺ ✺ ✺

Credit and Interest*

Credit cards were not widely used in the United States until the 1950s when cards such as Diners Club, Carte Blanche, and American Express made the use of plastic money more popular. Today, Americans charge about $1 trillion per year on their cards.

Credit is not a modern idea. Surprisingly, there are ancient Sumerian documents dating back to about 3000 BC that show the regular use of credit in borrowing grain and metal. Interest on these loans was often in the 20% to 30% range—similar to the 18% to 21% charged on many of today's credit cards. As the use of credit increased, so did its

misuse. Many societies wrote laws to prevent its abuse—particularly the charging of unfairly high interest rates, which is called *usury*.

Credit and interest can appear in many diverse forms. The Ifugao tribe of the Philippines charges 100% on a loan. If rice is borrowed, then at the next harvest, the loan must be paid in double. In Vancouver, Canada, the Kwakiutl have a system of credit based on blankets. The rules of interest state that if five blankets are borrowed, in 6 months they become seven. In Northern Siberia, loans are made in reindeer, usually at a 100% interest rate.

Comparing Financing Methods

EXAMPLE 5   *Comparing Methods for Finding Finance Charges*

Suppose that you begin the month of May (which has 31 days) with a credit card balance of $500. The annual interest rate is 21%. On May 11, you use your credit card to pay for a $400 car repair, and on May 29, you make a payment of $500. Calculate the finance charge that will appear on the statement for next month using the two methods we have discussed.

SOLUTION:

Method	P	r	t	Finance Charge $= I = Prt$
Unpaid balance	last month's balance + finance charge − payment + charge for car repair $= 500 + 8.75 + 400 - 500$ $= 408.75$	21%	$\dfrac{1}{12}$	$(408.75)(0.21)\left(\dfrac{1}{12}\right) = \$7.15$
Average daily balance	$\dfrac{10 \times 500 + 18 \times 900 + 3 \times 400}{31}$ $= \dfrac{22{,}400}{31}$ $= 722.58$	21%	$\dfrac{31}{365}$	$(722.58)(0.21)\left(\dfrac{31}{365}\right) = \$12.89$

With the unpaid balance method, the finance charge is $7.15; with the average daily balance method, the finance charge is $12.89. ✺

Example 5 shows that the exact same charges on two different credit cards having the same annual interest rate can result in very different finance charges. If you understand the method your credit card company is using, you may be able to schedule your purchases and payments to minimize your finance charges.

In deciding how to use credit, you must consider many other issues that we have not discussed in this section. Some credit card companies charge an annual fee; others return part of your interest payments. For some credit cards, there is a grace period. If you reduce your balance to zero during this grace period, then you pay no finance

---

*This Historical Highlight is based on S. Homer and R. Sylla, *A History of Interest Rates*, 3rd ed. (Piscataway, NJ: Rutgers University Press, 1991), pp. 21–30.

charges. A credit card may have a low introductory rate that changes to a much higher rate at a later time.

One common enticement is that you can make a purchase and pay no interest payments until several months later. With such deals, however, you must be careful. Often, if you do not pay off the purchase completely at the end of the interest-free period, then all the interest that would have accumulated is added to your balance. It is difficult to understand all the pros and cons of the many different types of credit contracts. However, if you read credit agreements carefully and remember the principles that you learned in this section, you will be an intelligent consumer who will be able to use credit wisely.

Exercises 9.3

Looking Back*

These exercises follow the general outline of the topics presented in this section and will give you a good overview of the material that you have just studied.

1. Describe briefly how we calculated the payments for the add-on interest loan in Example 1.

2. In Example 2, we computed the finance charge from the previous month using the expression *Prt*. What did each variable represent?

3. What does Table 9.3 show in Example 4?

4. In reference to the Math in Your Life on "Generation Broke," what do you think are some of the causes of this phenomenon?

Sharpening Your Skills

In Exercises 5–8, compute the monthly payments for each add-on interest loan. The amount of the loan, the annual interest rate, and the term of the loan are given.

5. $900; 12%; 2 years   6. $840; 10%; 3 years

7. $1,360; 8%; 4 years   8. $1,710; 9%; 3 years

9. **Paying off a computer.** Luis took out an add-on interest loan for $1,280 to buy a new laptop computer. The loan will be paid back in 2 years and the annual interest rate is 9.5%. How much interest will he pay? What are his monthly payments?

10. **Paying off furniture.** Mandy bought furniture costing $1,460 for her new apartment. To pay for it, her bank gave her a 5-year add-on interest loan at an annual interest rate of 10.4%. How much interest will she pay? What are her monthly payments?

11. **Financing equipment.** Angela's bank gave her a 4-year add-on interest loan for $6,480 to pay for new equipment for her antiques restoration business. The annual interest rate is 11.65%. How much interest will she pay? What are her monthly payments?

12. **Paying for a sculpture.** Mikeal purchased an antique sculpture from a gallery for $1,320. The gallery offered him a 3-year add-on loan at an annual rate of 9.75%. How much interest will he pay? What are his monthly payments?

In Exercises 13–16, use the add-on method for determining interest on the loan. Determine the annual interest rate during the last month of the loan.

13. $900; 12%; 2 years

14. $840; 10%; 3 years

15. $1,360; 8%; 4 years

16. $1,710; 9%; 4 years

Applying What You've Learned

17. **Financing a boat.** Ben is buying a new boat for $11,000. The dealer is charging him an annual interest rate of 9.2% and is using the add-on method to compute his monthly payments.

   a. If Ben pays off the boat in 48 months, what are his monthly payments?

   b. If he makes a down payment of $2,000, how much will this reduce his monthly payments?

   c. If he wants to have monthly payments of $200, how large should his down payment be?

18. **Financing a swimming pool.** Mr. Phelps is buying a new swimming pool for $14,000. The dealer is charging him an annual interest rate of 8.5% and is using the add-on method to compute his monthly payments.

   a. If Mr. Phelps pays off the pool in 48 months, what are his monthly payments?

   b. If he makes a down payment of $3,000, how much will this reduce his monthly payments?

   c. If he wants to have monthly payments of $250, how large should his down payment be?

19. **Financing rare coins.** Anna is buying $15,000 worth of rare coins as an investment. The dealer is charging her an annual interest rate of 9.6% and is using the add-on method to compute her monthly payments.

---

*Before doing these exercises, you may find it useful to review the note *How to Succeed at Mathematics* on page xix.

a. If Anna pays off the coins in 36 months, what are her monthly payments?

b. If she makes a down payment of $3,000, how much will this reduce her monthly payments?

c. If she wishes to have monthly payments of $300, how large should her down payment be?

20. Financing a musical instrument. Walt is buying a music synthesizer for his rock band for $6,500. The music store is charging him an annual interest rate of 8.5% and is using the add-on method to compute his monthly payments.

a. If Walt pays off the synthesizer in 24 months, what are his monthly payments?

b. If he makes a down payment of $1,500, how much will this reduce his monthly payments?

c. If he wants to have monthly payments of $150, how large should his down payment be?

In Exercises 21–26, use the unpaid balance method to find the finance charge on the credit card account. Last month's balance, the payment, the annual interest rate, and any other transactions are given.

21. Computing a finance charge. Last month's balance, $475; payment, $225; interest rate, 18%; bought ski jacket, $180; returned camera, $145

22. Computing a finance charge. Last month's balance, $510; payment, $360; interest rate, 21%; bought exercise equipment, $470; bought fish tank, $85

23. Computing a finance charge. Last month's balance, $640; payment: $320; interest rate, 16.5%; bought dog, $140; bought pet supplies, $35; paid veterinarian bill, $75

24. Computing a finance charge. Last month's balance, $340; payment, $180; interest rate, 17.5%; bought coat, $210; bought hat, $28; returned boots, $130

25. Computing a finance charge. Last month's balance, $460; payment, $300; interest rate, 18.8%; bought plane ticket, $140; bought luggage, $135; paid hotel bill, $175

26. Computing a finance charge. Last month's balance, $700; payment, $480; interest rate, 21%; bought ring, $210; bought theater tickets, $142; returned vase, $128

In Exercises 27–30, use the average daily balance method to compute the finance charge on the credit card account for the previous month. The starting balance and transactions on the account for the month are given. Assume an annual interest rate of 21% in each case.

27. Computing a finance charge. Month: August (31 days); previous month's balance: $280

Date	Transaction
August 5	Made payment of $75
August 15	Charged $135 for hiking boots
August 21	Charged $16 for gasoline
August 24	Charged $26 for restaurant meal

28. Computing a finance charge. Month: October (31 days); previous month's balance: $190

Date	Transaction
October 9	Charged $35 for a book
October 11	Charged $20 for gasoline
October 20	Made payment of $110
October 26	Charged $13 for lunch

29. Computing a finance charge. Month: April (30 days); previous month's balance: $240

Date	Transaction
April 3	Charged $135 for a coat
April 13	Made payment of $150
April 23	Charged $30 for DVDs
April 28	Charged $28 for groceries

30. Computing a finance charge. Month: June (30 days); previous month's balance: $350

Date	Transaction
June 9	Made payment of $200
June 15	Charged $15 for gasoline
June 20	Charged $180 for skis
June 26	Made payment of $130

In Exercises 31–34, redo the specified exercise using the unpaid balance method to calculate the finance charges.

31. Exercise 27   **32.** Exercise 28

33. Exercise 29   **34.** Exercise 30

35. Comparing financing methods. Mayesha purchased a large-screen TV for $1,000 and can pay it off in 10 months with an add-on interest loan at an annual rate of 10.5%, or she can use her credit card that has an annual rate of 18%. If she uses her credit card, she will pay $100 per month (beginning next month) plus the finance charges for the month. Assume that Mayesha's credit card company is using the unpaid balance method to compute her finance charges and that she is making no other transactions on her credit card. Which option will have the smaller total finance charges on her loan?

36. Comparing financing methods. Repeat Exercise 35, but now assume that Mayesha purchased an entertainment center for $2,000, the rate for the add-on loan is 9.6%, and she is paying off the loan in 20 months.

37. Accumulated interest. A Home Depot advertises 0% financing for 3 months for purchases made before the new year. The fine print in the advertisement states that if the purchase is not paid off within 3 months, the purchaser must pay interest that has accumulated at a monthly rate of 1.75%. Assume that you buy a refrigerator for $1,150 and make no payments during the next 3 months. How much interest has accumulated on your purchase during this time?

38. Accumulated interest. Repeat Exercise 37, but now assume that the purchase is for $1,450 and the annual interest rate is 24%.

Communicating Mathematics

39. Why is an add-on interest loan called by that name?

40. What was the point of our discussion in the paragraph following Example 1?

41. How can you use the unpaid balance method to your advantage when borrowing?

42. How would you explain informally the difference between computing finance charges with the unpaid balance method and the average daily method to a classmate?

Using Technology to Investigate Mathematics

43. Your instructor has an Excel spreadsheet that will carry out the computations for the average daily balance method. Use this spreadsheet to duplicate the computations in Example 4 and also to solve some of the exercises. *

44. Use the Web to research the terms of some actual credit cards. See if you can determine how the finance charges are computed with those cards. What other terms are in those agreements that we have not discussed in this section?

For Extra Credit

45. In Example 5, we found that the average daily balance method gave the highest finance charges. Explain why this happened.

46. Make up transactions on a hypothetical credit card so that the unpaid balance method will give you lower finance charges than the average daily balance method does. Assume an annual interest rate of 18%.

47. Make up transactions on a hypothetical credit card so that the average daily balance method will give you lower finance charges than the unpaid balance method does. Assume an annual interest rate of 21%.

48. In our discussions about credit, we have ignored the fact that whatever money is not used to pay off a loan can be invested. Assume that you can earn 5% on any money that you do not use for paying off a loan. However, any money you earn as interest is subject to federal, state, and local taxes. Assume that these taxes total 20%. Discuss how that might affect your decision to pay off your credit card debt.

9.4 Annuities

Objectives

1. Calculate the future value of an ordinary annuity.
2. Perform calculations regarding sinking funds.

Somewhere over the rainbow . . . skies are blue, . . . and the dreams that you dare to dream . . . really do come true. —Lyman Frank Baum
(Author of *The Wizard of Oz*)

What are your financial dreams? Do you dream about owning a beautiful house? Visiting some exotic far-away place? Providing a college education for your children? Retiring happily in comfortable surroundings? If you have any long-term plans such as these, to achieve your dreams you will need to have a large sum of money in the future.

In this section, we will discuss how you can do just that by making a series of regular payments over many years to accumulate the money that you will need. This type of investment is called an *annuity*.

KEY POINT

We make regular payments into an annuity.

Annuities

An **annuity** is an interest-bearing account into which we make a series of payments of the same size. If one payment is made at the *end* of every compounding period, the annuity is called an **ordinary annuity**. The **future value of an annuity** is the amount in the account, including interest, after making all payments.

To illustrate the future value of an annuity, suppose that in January you begin making payments of $100 at the end of each month into an account paying 12% yearly interest compounded monthly. How much money will be in this account for a summer vacation beginning on July 1?

This problem is different from those in Section 9.2. In the earlier problems, we deposited a lump sum that earned a stated interest rate for an entire period. In this problem, we are depositing a *series* of payments, and each payment earns interest for a different number of periods.

The January deposit earns interest for February, March, April, May, and June. Using the formula for compound interest, this deposit will grow to

$$100(1 + 0.01)^5 = \$105.10.$$

However, the May deposit earns interest for only 1 month and therefore grows to only

$$100(1 + 0.01)^1 = \$101.$$

The June deposit earns no interest at all. We illustrate this pattern with the timeline in Figure 9.3.

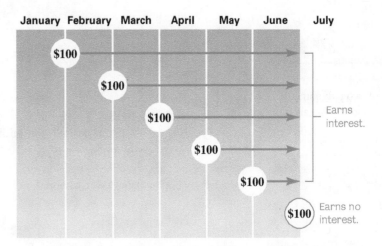

FIGURE 9.3 Timeline for ordinary annuity with deposits at end of January, . . . , June.

If we compute how much each deposit contributes to the account and sum these amounts, we will have the value of the annuity on July 1.

January	$100(1.01)^5 = \$105.10$
February	$100(1.01)^4 = \$104.06$
March	$100(1.01)^3 = \$103.03$
April	$100(1.01)^2 = \$102.01$
May	$100(1.01)^1 = \$101.00$
June	$100(1.01)^0 = \$100.00$
	Total = $615.20

We can express the value of this annuity as

$$100(1.01)^5 + 100(1.01)^4 + 100(1.01)^3 + 100(1.01)^2 + 100(1.01)^1 + 100.$$

By factoring out the 100, we can write the value of the annuity in the form

$$100[(1.01)^5 + (1.01)^4 + (1.01)^3 + (1.01)^2 + (1.01)^1 + 1]. \qquad (1)$$

Notice that although you deposited $100 at the end of each month for *six* months, the first deposit earned interest for *five* months, the second deposit earned interest for *four* months, and so on.

Following this pattern, it is clear that if you had deposited the $100 in a vacation savings account at the end of each month for 10 months, the value of the annuity would have been

$$100[(1.01)^9 + (1.01)^8 + \cdots + (1.01)^2 + (1.01)^1 + 1]. \qquad (2)$$

Notice that in equation (1) we have an expression of the form $x^5 + x^4 + x^3 + x^2 + x^1 + 1$, and in equation (2) we have an expression of the form $x^9 + x^8 + \cdots + x^2 + x^1 + 1$. Fortunately, there is a way to write these lengthy expressions in a simpler form.

EXAMPLE 1 *Simplifying Annuity Computations*

Show that $x^5 + x^4 + x^3 + x^2 + x^1 + 1 = \dfrac{x^6 - 1}{x - 1}$.

SOLUTION: To show this relationship, we multiply the polynomials $x^5 + x^4 + x^3 + x^2 + x^1 + 1$ and $x - 1$ in the usual way.

$$
\begin{array}{r}
x^5 + x^4 + x^3 + x^2 + x^1 + 1 \\
\times\, x - 1 \\
\hline
x^6 + x^5 + x^4 + x^3 + x^2 + x^1 \\
-\, x^5 - x^4 - x^3 - x^2 - x^1 - 1 \\
\hline
x^6 \qquad\qquad\qquad\qquad\qquad -1
\end{array}
$$

This result shows that $(x^5 + x^4 + x^3 + x^2 + x^1 + 1)(x - 1) = x^6 - 1$. Dividing this equation by $x - 1$, we obtain our desired relationship.

Now try Exercises 3 to 4. ❊ **14**

Following the pattern of Example 1, we can prove that

$$x^n + x^{n-1} + x^{n-2} + \cdots + x^2 + x^1 + 1 = \frac{x^{n+1} - 1}{x - 1}. \qquad (3)$$

Returning to our vacation savings account example, we can think of 1.01 as x in equation (1). Then we can use equation (3) to simplify our calculations. Because

$$(1.01)^5 + (1.01)^4 + (1.01)^3 + (1.01)^2 + (1.01)^1 + 1$$
$$= \frac{(1.01)^6 - 1}{1.01 - 1} = \frac{1.061520151 - 1}{1.01 - 1} = \frac{0.061520151}{0.01} \approx 6.1520,$$

we can write

$$100[(1.01)^5 + (1.01)^4 + (1.01)^3 + (1.01)^2 + (1.01)^1 + 1] \approx 100(6.1520) = \$615.20.$$

This is the same amount that we found earlier.

Doing similar computations, we find that the 10-month vacation savings account annuity has a value of

$$100[(1.01)^9 + (1.01)^8 + \cdots + (1.01)^2 + (1.01)^1 + 1]$$
$$= 100\left[\frac{(1.01)^{10} - 1}{1.01 - 1}\right] \approx 100(10.4622) = \$1,046.22.$$

We can generalize the patterns that we have just seen in a formula for finding the future value of an annuity.

Quiz Yourself **14**

Write $x^3 + x^2 + x^1 + 1$ as a quotient of two polynomials. (Do computations that are similar to those we did in Example 1.)

KEY POINT

The future value of an annuity depends on the size of the payment, the interest rate, and the number of payments.

> **FORMULA FOR FINDING THE FUTURE VALUE OF AN ORDINARY ANNUITY** Assume that we are making *n* regular payments, *R*, into an ordinary annuity. The interest is being compounded *m* times a year and deposits are made at the end of each compounding period. The future value (or amount), *A*, of this annuity at the end of the *n* periods is given by the equation
>
> $$A = R \frac{\left(1 + \dfrac{r}{m}\right)^n - 1}{\dfrac{r}{m}}.$$

To calculate this expression, you should do the following steps:

1st: Find $\frac{r}{m}$ and add 1.

2nd: Raise $1 + \frac{r}{m}$ to the *n* power and then subtract 1.

3rd: Divide the amount that you found in step 2 by $\frac{r}{m}$.

4th: Multiply the quantity that you found in step 3 by *R*.

EXAMPLE 2 *Finding the Future Value of an Ordinary Annuity*

Assume that we make a payment of $50 at the end of each month into an account paying a 6% annual interest rate, compounded monthly. How much will be in that account after 3 years?

SOLUTION: This account is an ordinary annuity. The payment *R* is 50, the monthly rate $\frac{r}{m}$ is $\frac{6\%}{12} = \frac{0.06}{12} = 0.005$, and the number of payments *n* is $3 \times 12 = 36$. Using the formula for finding the future value of an ordinary annuity, we get

$$A = 50 \left[\frac{(1.005)^{36} - 1}{0.005} \right] = 50 \left(\frac{1.19668053 - 1}{0.005} \right)$$

$$= 50 \left(\frac{0.19668053}{0.005} \right)$$

$$= 50(39.336105) \approx \$1,966.81.*$$

Now try Exercises 7 to 16. ✻ **15**

N=36
I%=6
PV=0
PMT=50
·FV=■1966.805248
P/Y=12
C/Y=12
PMT:**END** BEGIN

TI-83 screen verifies calculations in Example 2.

Quiz Yourself **15**

Redo Example 2, except now assume that you are depositing $75 per month for 2 years.

If you make regular payments into an annuity for many years, the value of the annuity can become enormous due to the compounding of interest. Figure 9.4 shows that if the annual interest rate is 6.6%, then in roughly 19 years, the amount of interest that the annuity has earned exceeds the amount of the deposits. The fact that the interest curve is rising so rapidly indicates that the future value of your account is also growing rapidly.

KEY POINT

With a sinking fund, we make payments to save a specified amount.

Sinking Funds

You may want to save regularly to have a fixed amount available in the future. For example, you may want to save $1,800 to travel to Jamaica in 2 years. The question is, how much should you save each month to accomplish this? The account that you establish for

---

*When using your calculator, you should hold off on rounding your answers as long as possible. If you round off too soon, your answers will differ slightly from the answers in this text.

❈ ❈ ❈ HIGHLIGHT

Between the Numbers—Whom Do You "Trust"?

The "trust" that we are referring to is the Social Security trust fund. When you first started working, you may have been dismayed to see a deduction from your first paycheck labeled FICA, which is an acronym for the Federal Insurance Contributions Act. This law mandates that workers must contribute a certain amount of their wages to the Social Security trust fund.

When you contribute to Social Security, you are not actually saving your money for *your retirement*, but your taxes are paying for *someone else's retirement*. The idea is that when you retire, younger workers will then pay for your retirement. However, some see a huge problem with this. Right now, roughly 50 million Americans receive Social Security benefits with contributions supported by approximately 200 million

U.S. workers. If we think of this as a ratio, every person on Social Security is supported by 4 workers. In 1950, the ratio was 16 workers for every Social Security beneficiary. It is projected that by 2030, the ratio will be 2 workers for every beneficiary and the fund will be in trouble. So what can you do to protect your retirement?

The government has been encouraging people to make plans for their retirement by establishing tax-deferred annuities to guarantee that when they retire they will have money to supplement Social Security benefits. *Tax deferred* means that the money you set aside in the annuity is not taxed now but at a later date when you start withdrawing from the annuity. As you will see in the exercises, there can be a huge financial benefit to saving this way.

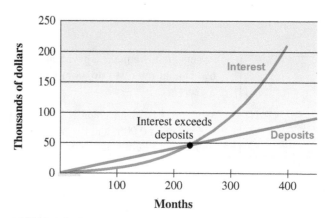

FIGURE 9.4 At an annual rate of 6.6%, the amount of interest earned in an ordinary annuity exceeds the amount of deposits in about 230 months.

your deposits is called a **sinking fund**. You could estimate the amount to save each month by simply dividing 1,800 by 24 months to get $\frac{1,800}{24} = \$75$ per month. Because your estimate ignores the interest that your deposits will generate, the actual amount you would need to put aside each month is somewhat less. Knowing exactly how much you need to save each month could be important if you were on a tight budget.

Because a sinking fund is a special type of annuity, it is not necessary to find a new formula to answer this question. We can use the formula for calculating the future value of an ordinary annuity that we have stated earlier. In this case, we know the value of A and we want to find R.*

EXAMPLE 3 *Calculating Payments for a Sinking Fund*

Assume that you wish to save $1,800 in a sinking fund in 2 years. The account pays 6% compounded quarterly and you will also make payments quarterly. What should be your monthly payment?

---

*In making payments into a sinking fund, we will always round the payment *up* to the next cent.

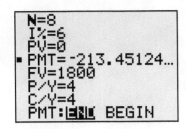

TI-83 screen verifies calculations in Example 3.

 *Quiz Yourself* **16**

What payments must you make to a sinking fund that pays 9% yearly interest compounded monthly if you want to save $2,500 in 2 years?

KEY POINT

We use the log function to find how long it takes for an annuity to accumulate a specified value.

SOLUTION: Recall the formula for finding the future value of an ordinary annuity:

$$A = R\frac{\left(1 + \frac{r}{m}\right)^n - 1}{\frac{r}{m}}. \tag{4}$$

We want the value A of the annuity to be $1,800, the monthly rate $\frac{r}{m}$ is $\frac{6\%}{4} = \frac{0.06}{4} = 0.015$, and the number of payments n is $2 \times 4 = 8$. Substituting these values in equation (4), we get

$$1,800 = R\frac{(1 + 0.015)^8 - 1}{0.015} = R(8.432839106).$$

Dividing both sides of the equation by 8.432839106, we get the monthly payment

$$R = \frac{1,800}{8.43289106} \approx \$213.46.$$

Now try Exercises 17 to 20. ❊ **16**

 *Some Good Advice*

You may be tempted to memorize a new formula to solve sinking fund problems. This is not necessary, because once you have learned to solve annuity problems, you can use the same formula (and a little bit of algebra) to solve sinking fund problems.

Sometimes in working with annuities, we want to know how long it will take to save a certain amount. That is, in the annuity formula we want to find n. This problem is a little more complicated than those we have solved so far. To solve such problems, we will use the exponent property for the log function, which we introduced in Section 9.3. We will show you how to use this property in Example 4.

EXAMPLE 4   *Finding the Time Required to Accumulate $1,000,000*

Suppose you have decided to retire as soon as you have saved $1,000,000. Your plan is to put $200 each month into an ordinary annuity that pays an annual interest rate of 8%. In how many years will you be able to retire?

SOLUTION: We can use the future value formula for an ordinary annuity to solve this problem:

$$A = R\frac{\left(1 + \frac{r}{m}\right)^n - 1}{\frac{r}{m}}$$

Here, A is the future value of $1,000,000, $\frac{r}{m}$ is the monthly interest rate of $\frac{0.08}{12} \approx 0.00667$, and R is 200. We must find n, the number of months for which you will be making deposits. Therefore, we must solve for n in the following equation:

$$1,000,000 = 200\left[\frac{(1 + 0.00667)^n - 1}{0.00667}\right]$$

We begin by multiplying both sides of the equation by 0.00667:

$$6,670 = 200[(1 + 0.00667)^n - 1].$$

Next, we divide both sides of the equation by 200 and then add 1 to both sides of the equation:

$$34.35 = (1.00667)^n.$$

Then we take the log of both sides:

$$\log 34.35 = \log(1.00667)^n.$$

Now we use the exponent property of the log function to simplify the equation:

$$\log 34.35 = n \log 1.00667.$$

We divide by $\log 1.00667$ and use a calculator to find n:

$$n = \frac{\log 34.35}{\log 1.00667} = 531.991532 \approx 532.$$

This tells how many months it will take you to save $1,000,000. Dividing 532 by 12 gives us $\frac{532}{12} = 44.33$ years until your retirement.

Now try Exercises 29 to 34. ✻ **17**

Quiz Yourself **17**

If you put $150 per month into an ordinary annuity that pays an annual interest rate of 9%, how long will it take for the annuity to have a value of $100,000?

Exercises 9.4

Looking Back*

These exercises follow the general outline of the topics presented in this section and will give you a good overview of the material that you have just studied.

1. To calculate the future value of the annuity in Example 2, we used the expression

$$R\frac{\left(1+\frac{r}{m}\right)^n - 1}{\frac{r}{m}}.$$ What is the meaning of $\frac{r}{m}$? What is the meaning of m? What is R?

2. What implications do you see of the situation presented in the Highlight regarding the Social Security trust fund?

Sharpening Your Skills

In Exercises 3 and 4, simplify each algebraic expression, as in Example 1.

3. $x^7 + x^6 + \cdots + x^2 + x^1 + 1$

4. $x^8 + x^7 + \cdots + x^2 + x^1 + 1$

Exercises 5 and 6 are based on the vacation account example at the beginning of this section. Assume that, beginning in January, you make payments at the end of each month into an account paying the specified yearly interest. Interest is compounded monthly. How much will you have available for your vacation by the specified date?

5. Monthly payment, $100; yearly interest rate, 6%; August 1

6. Monthly payment, $200; yearly interest rate, 3%; May 1

In Exercises 7 and –16, find the value of each ordinary annuity at the end of the indicated time period. The payment R, frequency of deposits m (which is the same as the frequency of compounding), annual interest rate r, and the time t are given.

7. Amount, $200; monthly; 3%; 8 years

8. Amount, $450; monthly; 2.4%; 10 years

9. Amount, $400; monthly; 9%; 4 years

10. Amount, $350; monthly; 10%; 10 years

11. Amount, $600; monthly; 9.5%; 8 years

12. Amount, $500; monthly; 7.5%; 12 years

13. Amount, $500; quarterly; 8%; 5 years

14. Amount, $750; quarterly; 9%; 3 years

15. Amount, $280; quarterly; 3.6%; 6 years

16. Amount, $250; quarterly; 4.8%; 18 years

In Exercises 17–20, find the monthly payment R needed to have a sinking fund accumulate the future value A. The yearly interest rate r and the time t is given. Interest is compounded monthly. Round your answer up to the next cent.

17. $A = \$2,000$; $r = 6\%$; $t = 1$

18. $A = \$10,000$; $r = 12\%$; $t = 5$

19. $A = \$5,000$; $r = 7.5\%$; $t = 2$

20. $A = \$8,000$; $r = 4.5\%$; $t = 3$

Solve each equation for x.

21. $3^x = 20$ **22.** $5^x = 15$

23. $8^x = 10$ **24.** $20^x = 100$

25. $\dfrac{8^x - 5}{6} = 20$ **26.** $\dfrac{4^x + 6}{3} = 10$

27. $\dfrac{8^x + 2}{5} = 12$ **28.** $\dfrac{5^x - 8}{10} = 14$

In Exercises 29–34, use the formula for finding the future value of an ordinary annuity,

$$A = R\frac{\left(1+\frac{r}{m}\right)^n - 1}{\frac{r}{m}},$$

*Before doing these exercises, you may find it useful to review the note *How to Succeed at Mathematics* on page xix.

to solve for n. *You are given A, R, and r. Assume that payments are made monthly and that the interest rate is an annual rate.*

29. $A = \$10,000$; $R = 200$; $r = 9\%$

30. $A = \$12,000$; $R = 400$; $r = 8\%$

31. $A = \$5,000$; $R = 150$; $r = 6\%$

32. $A = \$8,000$; $R = 400$; $r = 5\%$

33. $A = \$6,000$; $R = 250$; $r = 7.5\%$

34. $A = \$7,500$; $R = 100$; $r = 8.5\%$

Applying What You've Learned

In Exercises 35–40, assume that the compounding is being done monthly.

35. Saving for a scooter. Matt is saving to buy a new Vespa. If he deposits $75 at the end of each month in an account that pays an annual interest rate of 6.5%, how much will he have saved in 30 months?

36. Saving for a trip. Angelina wants to save for an African safari. She is putting $200 each month in an ordinary annuity that pays an annual interest rate of 9%. If she makes payments for 2 years, how much will she have saved for her trip?

37. Saving for a car. Kristy Joe deposits $150 each month in an ordinary annuity to save for a new car. If the annuity pays a monthly interest rate of 0.85%, how much will she be able to save in 3 years?

38. Saving for retirement. Cohutta is saving for his retirement in 10 years by putting $500 each month into an ordinary annuity. If the annuity has an annual interest rate of 9.35%, how much will he have when he retires?

39. Saving for a vacation home. Wendy has set up an ordinary annuity to save for a retirement home in Florida in 15 years. If her monthly payments are $400 and the annuity has an annual interest rate of 6.5%, what will be the value of the annuity when she retires?

40. Saving for retirement. Thiep has set up an ordinary annuity to save for his retirement in 20 years. If his monthly payments are $350 and the annuity has an annual interest rate of 7.5%, what will be the value of the annuity when he retires?

41. Saving for a condominium. Kanye wants to save $14,000 in 8 years by making monthly payments into an ordinary annuity for a down payment on a condominium at the shore. If the annuity pays 0.7% monthly interest, what will his monthly payment be?

42. Saving to start a business. Victory is making monthly payments into an annuity that pays 0.8% monthly interest to save enough for a down payment to start her own business. If she wants to save $10,000 in 5 years, what should her monthly payments be?

43. Saving for consumer goods. Sandra Lee is making monthly payments into an annuity. She wants to have $600 in the fund to buy a new convection range in 6 months, and the account pays 8.2% annual interest. What are her monthly payments to the account?

44. Saving for consumer goods. Lennox is making monthly payments into an annuity. He wishes to have $1,150 in 10 months to buy exercise equipment. His account pays 9% annual interest. What are his monthly payments to the account?

Tax-deferred annuities work like this: If, for example, you plan to set aside $400 per month for your retirement in 30 years in a tax-deferred plan, the $400 is not taxed now, so all of the $400 is invested each month. In a nondeferred plan, the $400 is first taxed and then the remainder is invested. So, if your tax bracket is 25%, after you pay taxes, you would have only 75% of the $400 to invest each month. However, in the tax-deferred plan, all of your money is taxed when you withdraw the money. In the nondeferred plan, only the interest that you have earned is taxed.

In Exercises 45–50, we give the amount you are setting aside each month, your current tax rate, the number of years you will contribute to the annuity, and your tax rate when you begin withdrawing from the annuity. Answer the following questions for each situation:

a) *Find the value of the tax-deferred and the nondeferred accounts.*

b) *Calculate the interest that was earned in both accounts. This will be the value of the account minus the payments you made.*

c) *If you withdraw all money from each account and pay the relevant taxes, which account is better and by how much?*

	Monthly Payment	Number of Years	Annual Interest Rate	Current Tax Rate	Future Tax Rate
45.	$300	30	6%	25%	18%
46.	$400	25	4.5%	25%	15%
47.	$400	20	4%	30%	30%
48.	$600	30	4.6%	25%	25%
49.	$500	35	3.4%	25%	30%
50.	$500	30	4.8%	18%	25%

In Exercises 51–54, assume that monthly deposits are being placed in an ordinary annuity and interest is compounded monthly.

51. Saving for a fire truck. The Reliance Volunteer Fire Company wants to take advantage of a state program to save money to purchase a new fire truck. The truck will cost $400,000, and members of the finance committee estimate that with community and state contributions, they can save $5,000 per month in an account paying 10.8% annual interest. How long will it take to save for the truck?

52. Saving for new equipment. BioCon, a bioengineering company, must replace its water treatment equipment within 2 years. The new equipment will cost $80,000, and the company will transfer $3,800 per month into a special account that pays 9.2% interest. How long will it take to save for this new equipment?

53. **Saving for a condominium.** Kirsten wants to save $30,000 for a down payment on a condominium at a ski resort. She feels that she can save $550 per month in an account that has a 7.8% annual interest rate. How long will it take to acquire her down payment?

54. **Saving for a business.** Leo needs to save $25,000 for a down payment to start a photo restoration business. He intends to save $300 per month in an account that pays an annual interest rate of 6%. How long will it take for him to save for the down payment?

Communicating Mathematics

55. What property of the log function would you use to solve an equation of the form $y = a^x$ for x?

56. What is similar about the problem of finding the future value of an annuity and finding the payments to make into a sinking fund? How are the two problems related?

Using Technology to Investigate Mathematics

57. See your instructor for tutorials for the TI-83 to do financial calculations. Use your calculator to reproduce some of the examples in this section.*

58. You can find many interactive annuity calculators on the Internet. Some implement the calculations that you have learned in this section and others implement other types of annuity problems. Find some interesting annuity calculators, experiment with them, and report on your findings.

For Extra Credit

59. **Saving for retirement.** Reconsider Exercise 38. Suppose that Cohutta had started his annuity 10 years earlier. What would his monthly payments have been to accumulate the same future value in his annuity as you found in Exercise 38?

60. **Saving for retirement.** Reconsider Exercise 40. Suppose that Thiep had started his annuity 10 years earlier. What would his monthly payments have been to accumulate the same future value in his annuity as you found in Exercise 40?

61. **Saving for retirement.** Carlos began to save for his retirement at age 25, and for 10 years he put $200 per month into an ordinary annuity at an annual interest rate of 6%. After the 10 years, he could no longer make payments, so he placed the value of the annuity into another account that paid 6% annual interest compounded monthly. He left the money in this account for 30 years until he was ready to retire. How much did he have for retirement?

62. **Saving for retirement.** If Carlos had waited until age 45 to think about retirement and then decided to put money into an ordinary annuity for 20 years, what would his monthly payments have to be to accumulate the same amount for retirement as you found in Exercise 61? (We assume that the interest rate for the annuity is the same.)

63. **Saving for retirement.** Examine your solutions to Exercises 61 and 62. What do you notice? Explain why this is so.

64. **Comparing annuities.** The difference between an *annuity due* and an ordinary annuity is that with an annuity due, the payment is made at the *beginning* of the month rather than at the end of the month. This means that each payment generates one more month of interest than with an ordinary annuity.

   a. How does this change the formula for finding the future value of an annuity?

   b. Use this formula to find the value of the annuity in Example 2, assuming that the annuity is an annuity due.

9.5 Amortization

Objectives

1. Calculate the payment to pay off an amortized loan.
2. Construct an amortization schedule.
3. Find the present value of an annuity.
4. Calculate the unpaid balance on a loan.

Congratulations! You just bought a new home—it's lovely—and in a good neighborhood. Only 360 more payments and it's all yours. When you make such a large purchase, you usually have to take out a loan that you repay in monthly payments. The process of paying off a loan (plus interest) by making a series of regular, equal payments is called **amortization**, and such a loan is called an **amortized loan**.

   If you were to make such a purchase, one of the first questions you might ask is, "What are my monthly payments?" Of course, the lender can answer this question, but you may find it interesting to learn the mathematics involved with paying off a mortgage so that you can answer that question yourself.

Amortization

✎ KEY POINT

Paying off a loan with regular payments is called amortization.

Assume that you have purchased a new car and after your down payment, you borrowed $10,000 from a bank to pay for the car. Also assume that you have agreed to pay off this loan by making equal monthly payments for 4 years. Let's look at this transaction from two points of view:

Banker's point of view: Instead of thinking about your payments, the banker might think of this transaction as a future value problem in which she is making a $10,000 loan to you now and compounding the interest monthly for 4 years. At the end of 4 years, she expects to be paid the full amount due. Recall from Section 9.2 that this future value is

$$A = P\left(1 + \frac{r}{m}\right)^n.$$

Your point of view: For the time being, you could also ignore the question of monthly payments and choose to pay the banker in full with one payment at the end of 4 years. In order to have this money available, you could make monthly payments into a sinking fund to have the amount A available in 4 years. As you saw in Section 9.4, the formula for doing this is

$$A = R\frac{\left(1 + \frac{r}{m}\right)^n - 1}{\frac{r}{m}}.$$

Thus, to find your monthly payment, we will set the amount the banker expects to receive equal to the amount that you will save in the sinking fund and then solve for R.

FORMULA FOR FINDING PAYMENTS ON AN AMORTIZED LOAN
Assume that you borrow an amount P, which you will repay by taking out an amortized loan. You will make m periodic payments per year for n total payments and the annual interest rate is r. Then, you can find your payment by solving for R in the equation

$$P\left(1 + \frac{r}{m}\right)^n = R\left(\frac{\left(1 + \frac{r}{m}\right)^n - 1}{\frac{r}{m}}\right).^*$$

Do not let this equation intimidate you. You have done the calculation on the left side many times in Section 9.2 and the computation on the right side in Section 9.4. Once you find these two numbers, you do a simple division to solve for R, as you will see in Example 1.

EXAMPLE 1 *Determining the Payments on an Amortized Loan*

Assume that you have taken out an amortized loan for $10,000 to buy a new car. The yearly interest rate is 18% and you have agreed to pay off the loan in 4 years. What is your monthly payment?

---

*Certainly we could do the necessary algebra to solve this equation for R. Then we could use this new formula for solving problems to find the monthly payments for amortized loans. We chose not to do this because our philosophy is to minimize the number of formulas that you have to memorize to solve the problems in this chapter. We will round payments on a loan *up* to the next cent.

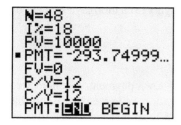

TI-83 calculator confirms our computations in Example 1.

What would your payments be in Example 1 if you agree to pay off the loan in 5 years?

SOLUTION: We will use the preceding equation. The values of the variables in this equation are

$$P = 10,000$$
$$n = 12 \times 4 = 48$$
$$\frac{r}{m} = \frac{18\%}{12} = 0.015$$

We must solve for R in the equation

monthly interest rate ⎯⎯⎯⎯⎯⎯⎯⎯⎯⎯⎯⎯⎯ number of payments

$$10,000(1 + 0.015)^{48} = R\left[\frac{(1 + 0.015)^{48} - 1}{0.015}\right].$$

amount of loan ⎯⎯⎯⎯⎯

If we calculate the numerical expressions on both sides of this equation as we did in Sections 9.2 and 9.4, we get

$$20,434.78289 = R(69.56521929).$$

Therefore, your monthly payment is

$$R = \frac{20,434.78289}{69.56521929} \approx \$293.75.$$

Now try Exercises 3 to 10. ❋ **18**

Amortization Schedules

Payments that a borrower makes on an amortized loan partly pay off the principal and partly pay interest on the outstanding principal. As the principal is reduced, each successive payment pays more toward principal and less toward interest. A list showing payment-by-payment how much is going to principal and interest is called an **amortization schedule**. We illustrate such a schedule in Example 2.

EXAMPLE 2   *Constructing an Amortization Schedule*

To expand your business selling collectibles on the Internet, you need a loan of $5,000. Your banker loans you the money at a 12% annual interest rate, which you agree to pay back in three equal monthly installments of $1,700.12.* Construct an amortization schedule for this loan.

SOLUTION: At the end of the first month, you have borrowed $5,000 for 1 month at a 1% monthly interest rate. So using the simple interest formula, the interest that you owe the bank is

$$\overset{P}{\$5,000} \times \overset{r}{0.01} \times \overset{t}{1} = \overset{I}{\$50}.$$

Your payment is $1,700.12; therefore, $50 pays the interest, and the rest, $1,700.12 − $50 = $1,650.12, is applied to the principal.

For the second month, you are now borrowing $5,000 − $1,650.12 = $3,349.88 at 1% monthly interest. We complete the computations for the payments on this loan in Table 9.4.

Payment Number	Amount of Payment	Interest Payment	Applied to Principal	Balance
				$5,000.00
1	$1,700.12	$50.00	$1,650.12	$3,349.88
2	$1,700.12	$33.50	$1,666.62	$1,683.26
3	$1,700.12	$16.83	$1,683.29	−$0.03

TABLE 9.4 An amortization schedule.

---

*We used the method from Example 1 to calculate the exact payment to be $1,700.110557. Because we increase this ever so slightly to $1,700.12, after the third payment we have overpaid by $0.03.

As expected, we ended with a negative balance because the payment of $1,700.12 is a fraction of a cent larger than it needs to be. In an actual banking situation, the bank would adjust the final payment so that the final balance is exactly $0.00. ✺

Example 3 illustrates how discouraging it can be when you make your first payment on a mortgage for a house and realize how little of your payment goes toward paying the principal.

EXAMPLE 3   *Constructing an Amortization Schedule*

Assume that you have saved money for a down payment on your dream house, but you still need to borrow $120,000 from your bank to complete the deal. The bank offers you a 30-year mortgage at an annual rate of 7%. The monthly payment is $798.37. Construct an amortization schedule for the first three payments on this loan.

SOLUTION: We compute Table 9.5* as we did Table 9.4 in Example 2.

Payment Number	Amount of Payment	Interest Payment	Applied to Principal	Balance
				$120,000.00
1	$798.37	$700.00	$98.37	$119,901.63
2	$798.37	$699.43	$98.94	$119,802.69
3	$798.37	$698.85	$99.52	$119,703.17

TABLE 9.5 Making an amortization schedule for a lengthy mortgage.

Quiz Yourself ⑲

Compute the fourth line of Table 9.5.

You see that for such a lengthy amortized loan, the early payments are mostly interest. Fortunately, because the debt is being reduced, each month a little more of the payment goes toward principal and a little less toward interest.

Now try Exercises 11 to 14. ✺ ⑲

HIGHLIGHT ✺ ✺ ✺

Between the Numbers—Can They Really Do That to You?

How would you feel if you took out a $200,000 mortgage for a house, faithfully made all of your payments on time, and at the end of 1 year owed $201,118? Incredibly, this can actually happen if you have an adjustable rate mortgage, or ARM. Some ARMs allow you to make payments that *do not even cover the interest* on the loan, so the amount you owe increases even though you make your payments on time.

ARMs can have other very serious problems for the consumer. With an ARM, it is possible to start with a low interest rate, say 4%, and with yearly increases after several years *your interest rate could be much higher.* Mortgage lenders use an index, often tied to government securities, to determine how much to increase your interest rate. There are many different types of ARMs—some limit the rate increase from year to year, and others limit the maximum rate that can be charged. However, even with these limits, your monthly payments in an ARM could increase from $900 to $1,400 over a 3-year period, causing you great financial distress.

The *Consumer Handbook on Adjustable Rate Mortgages*, available from the Federal Reserve Board, is an excellent guide to ARMs and contains numerous examples, cautions, and a worksheet to help you make sensible decisions regarding mortgages.

---

*If you verify these computations by hand, your answers may differ slightly from ours due to a difference in the way we are rounding off our intermediate calculations.

HIGHLIGHT ❋ ❋ ❋

Using a Spreadsheet to Make an Amortization Schedule

A spreadsheet can create an amortization schedule in the blink of an eye. The following is a spreadsheet that calculates the schedule for an amortized loan for $10,000 with 60 monthly payments of $202.77. We first show the spreadsheet displaying the formulas in the cells of the spreadsheet.

	A	B	C	D	E	F
1	End of Month	Payment	Interest	Principal	Balance	
2	0	$202.77			$10,000	
3	1	$202.77	E2*0.08/12	B3 – C3	E2 – D3	
4	2	$202.77	E3*0.08/12	B4 – C4	E3 – D4	
5	3	$202.77	E4*0.08/12	B5 – C5	E4 – D5	
6	4	$202.77	E5*0.08/12	B6 – C6	E5 – D6	
7	5	$202.77	.	.	.	
8	6	$202.77	.	.	.	
9	7	$202.77	.	.	.	

Here is the same spreadsheet when the formulas in the spreadsheet are evaluated.

	A	B	C	D	E	F
1	End of Month	Payment	Interest	Principal	Balance	
2	0	$202.77			$10,000.00	
3	1	$202.77	$66.67	$136.10	$9,863.90	
4	2	$202.77	$65.76	$137.01	$9,726.89	
5	3	$202.77	$64.85	$137.92	$9,588.96	
6	4	$202.77	$63.93	$138.84	$9,450.12	
7	5	$202.77	.	.		.
8	6	$202.77	.	.		.
9	7	$202.77	.	.		.

To generate a new schedule for a mortgage, all we have to do is change the formulas in several cells and the entire spreadsheet will be recalculated.

KEY POINT

We use the formula for finding the size of monthly payments to determine the present value of an annuity.

Finding the Present Value of an Annuity

When buying a car, your budget determines the size of the monthly payments you can afford, and that determines how much you can pay for the car you buy. Assume that you can afford car payments of $200 per month for 4 years and your bank will grant you a car loan at an annual rate of 12%. We can think of this as a future value of an annuity problem where R is 200, $\frac{r}{m}$ is 1%, and n is 48 months. We know from Section 9.4 that the future value of this annuity is

$$A = 200 \left[\frac{(1 + 0.01)^{48} - 1}{0.01} \right] = \$12,244.52.$$

This result does not mean that now you can afford a $12,000 car! This amount is the *future value* of your annuity, not what that amount of money would be worth in the *present*.

> **DEFINITION** If we know the monthly payment, the interest rate, and the number of payments, then the amount we can borrow is called the **present value of the annuity**.

We can find the present value of an annuity by setting the expression for the future value of an account using compound interest equal to the expression for finding the future value of an annuity and solving for the present value P.

> **FINDING THE PRESENT VALUE OF AN ANNUITY**   Assume that you are making m periodic payments per year for n total payments into an annuity that pays an annual interest rate of r. Also assume that each of your payments is R. Then to find the present value of your annuity, solve for P in the equation
>
> $$P\left(1+\frac{r}{m}\right)^{n} = R\left(\frac{\left(1+\frac{r}{m}\right)^{n}-1}{\frac{r}{m}}\right).$$

Again, you have done the computations on both sides of this equation many times in Sections 9.2 and 9.4.

EXAMPLE 4   *Determining the Price You Can Afford for a Car*

If you can afford to spend \$200 each month on car payments and the bank offers you a 4-year car loan with an annual rate of 12%, what is the present value of this annuity?

SOLUTION: To solve this problem, we can use the formula for finding payments on an amortized loan:

$$P\left(1+\frac{r}{m}\right)^{n} = R\left(\frac{\left(1+\frac{r}{m}\right)^{n}-1}{\frac{r}{m}}\right). \tag{1}$$

We know $R = 200$, $\frac{r}{m} = 1\% = 0.01$, and $n = 48$ months. If we substitute these for the variables in equation (1), we get

$$P(1+0.01)^{48} = 200\left[\frac{(1+0.01)^{48}-1}{0.01}\right]. \tag{2}$$

Calculating the numerical expressions on both sides of equation (2) gives us

$$P(1.612226078) = 12{,}244.52155.$$

Now dividing both sides of this equation by 1.612226078, we find

$$P = \left[\frac{12{,}244.52155}{1.612226078}\right] \approx \$7{,}594.79.$$

You may find this answer surprising, but the mathematics of this problem are clear. If you can only afford payments of \$200 per month, then you can only afford to finance a car loan for about \$7,600!

Now try Exercises 25 to 30. ❋ **20**

Finding the Unpaid Balance of a Loan

During times when interest rates are high, people are forced to borrow money at these high rates if they want to buy a car or a house on credit. If interest rates decline, then it is wise to consider paying off the remaining debt on the first loan by taking out a second loan at a

---

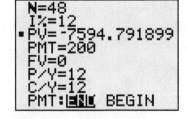

N=48
I%=12
▪PV=-7594.791899
PMT=200
FV=0
P/Y=12
C/Y=12
PMT:**END** BEGIN

TI-83 screen confirms our computations in Example 4.

Quiz Yourself **20**

Redo Example 4, but now assume that you can afford payments of \$250 per month.

✎ **KEY POINT**

To refinance a loan, we must know the unpaid balance on the loan.

lower interest rate. This procedure is called **refinancing** the loan. To understand refinancing, we must be able to compute how much debt remains on a loan after a certain number of payments have been made.

EXAMPLE 5   *Finding the Unpaid Balance on a Loan*

a) Assume that you take out a 30-year mortgage for $100,000 at an annual interest rate of 9%. If, after 10 years, interest rates drop and you want to refinance, how much remains to be paid on your mortgage?

b) If you can refinance your mortgage for the remaining 20 years at an annual interest rate of 7.2%, what will your monthly payments be?

c) How much will you save in interest in 20 years by paying the lower rate?

SOLUTION:

a) Doing the same kind of calculations as we did in Example 1, we find that the monthly payment is $804.63.

   Your monthly payment was based on the assumption that you would be paying the loan for 30 years. Therefore, after 10 years, you will not have accumulated enough in your annuity to pay off the banker. This means that the amount you owe, $P\left(1 + \frac{r}{m}\right)^n$, must be larger than the amount that you have accumulated in your sinking fund,

$$R\left(\frac{\left(1 + \dfrac{r}{m}\right)^n - 1}{\dfrac{r}{m}}\right).$$

The unpaid balance U on the loan is therefore

what you have accumulated

what you owe

$$U = \overbrace{P\left(1 + \frac{r}{m}\right)^n}^{} - R\overbrace{\left(\frac{\left(1 + \dfrac{r}{m}\right)^n - 1}{\dfrac{r}{m}}\right)}^{}{}^*. \qquad (3)$$

It is important to recognize in equation (3) that only 10 years have elapsed, so $n = 12 \times 10 = 120$, not 360.

   We can now substitute the values $P = \$100,000$, $\frac{r}{m} = 0.09/12 = 0.0075$, $n = 120$, and $R = \$804.63$ in equation (3).

10 years   10 years

$$U = 100,000(1 + 0.0075)^{120} - 804.63\left[\frac{(1 + 0.0075)^{120} - 1}{0.0075}\right] = \$89,428.32.$$

Therefore, you still owe $89,428.32 on this mortgage.

b) Because you have a balance of $89,428.32 on your mortgage, in effect you are now taking out a new mortgage for this amount at an annual interest rate of 7.2% for the remaining 20 years. In this case, $P = \$89,428.32$, $n = 12 \times 20 = 240$, and $\frac{r}{m} = 0.072/12 = 0.006$.

   We now solve for the monthly payment R in the equation

new monthly
interest rate

amount borrowed
for second loan   20 years

$$89,428.32(1 + 0.006)^{240} = R\left[\frac{(1 + 0.006)^{240} - 1}{0.006}\right]$$

---

*The unpaid balance appears in the balance column of an amortization table.

If we calculate the numerical expressions on both sides of this equation as we did in Sections 9.2 and 9.4, we get

$$375,829.1355 = R(533.7623389).$$

Therefore, your new monthly payment is

$$R = \frac{375,829.1355}{533.7623389} \approx \$704.12.$$

Therefore, by refinancing, you are able to reduce your monthly mortgage payment by $804.63 − $704.12 = $100.51 per month.

c) If you make monthly payments on the unpaid balance for 20 years at the old interest rate, your total payments will be 240 × $804.63 = $193,111.20. If you make monthly payments for 20 years at the new interest rate, you will pay 240 × $704.12 = $168,988.80. The difference

$$\$193,111.20 - \$168,988.80 = \$24,122.40*$$

is the amount that you save in interest over 20 years at the reduced rate.

Now try Exercises 31 to 36. ❋

Often, when refinancing a mortgage you must pay a refinancing fee. The refinancing fee is often calculated as a percentage of the balance remaining on the mortgage. Suppose in Example 5 that you had to pay a 2% refinancing fee. Two percent of $89,428.32 is $1,788.57. You would gain this fee back in 18 months with the reduced payments on the loan. In this case, it is clear that after 18 months, you would benefit from the refinancing.

Exercises 9.5

Looking Back†

These exercises follow the general outline of the topics presented in this section and will give you a good overview of the material that you have just studied.

1. What does the left side of the first equation in Example 1 represent? What does the right side represent?

2. After reading the Highlight on adjustable rate mortgages, name two possible dangers of ARMs.

Sharpening Your Skills

Solve the equation

$$P\left(1 + \frac{r}{m}\right)^n = R\left(\frac{\left(1 + \frac{r}{m}\right)^n - 1}{\frac{r}{m}}\right)$$

for R to find the monthly payment necessary to pay off the loan. You are given the loan amount, the annual interest rate, and the length of the loan.

3. Amount, $5,000; rate, 10%; time, 4 years

4. Amount, $6,000; rate, 8%; time, 3 years

5. Amount, $8,000; rate, 7.5%; time, 4 years

6. Amount, $10,000; rate, 8.4%; time, 4 years

7. Amount, $12,500; rate, 8.25%; time, 4 years

8. Amount, $10,500; rate, 9.75%; time, 4 years

9. Amount, $1,900; rate, 8%; time, 18 months

10. Amount, $1,050; rate, 6.5%; time, 15 months

In Exercises 11–14, complete the first three lines of an amortization schedule for each loan. Your answer should look like Table 9.4.

11. The loan described in Exercise 3

12. The loan described in Exercise 5

13. The loan described in Exercise 7

14. The loan described in Exercise 9

Applying What You've Learned

15. **Paying off a mortgage.** Assume that you have taken out a 30-year mortgage for $100,000 at an annual rate of 7%.

   a. Construct the first three lines of an amortization schedule for this mortgage.

   b. Assume that you have decided to pay an extra $100 per month to pay off the mortgage more quickly. Find the first three lines of your payment schedule under this assumption.

   c. What is the difference in interest that you will pay on the mortgage during the fourth month if you pay the extra $100 per month versus paying only the required payment?

---

*Note that you can find this amount more quickly by multiplying the difference in mortgage payments, $100.51, by 240 months.

†Before doing these exercises, you may find it useful to review the note *How to Succeed at Mathematics* on page xix.

16. Paying off a mortgage. Repeat Exercise 15, but assume that the mortgage is a 20-year mortgage for $80,000 and the annual rate is 8%.

In Exercises 17–20, a) the monthly payment for each amortized loan and b) the total interest paid on the loan. Assume that all interest rates are annual rates.

17. Paying off a boat. Wilfredo bought a new boat for $13,500. He paid $2,000 for the down payment and financed the rest for 4 years at an interest rate of 7.2%.

18. Paying off a car. Beatrice bought a new car for $14,800. She received $3,500 as a trade-in on her old car and took out a 4 year loan at 8.4% to pay the rest.

19. Paying off a consumer debt. Franklin's new skis cost $350. After his down payment of $75, he financed the remainder at 18% for 5 months.

20. Paying off a consumer debt. Richard's used motorcycle cost $3,500. He paid $1,100 down and financed the rest at 8.5% for 2 years.

In Exercises 21–24, assume that all mortgages are 30-year, adjustable rate mortgages. In each situation, use the additional information given to calculate the monthly payment on the mortgage a) in year one and b) in year five.*

21. $P = \$200,000$; beginning interest rate, 4%; rate increases 2% per year

22. $P = \$180,000$; beginning interest rate, 3.5%; rate increases 7% by year five

23. $P = \$220,000$; beginning interest rate, 4.4%; rate increases 2%, then 2%, then 1%, then 1.8%

24. $P = \$160,000$; beginning interest rate, 3.6%; rate increases 2%, then 1.6%, then 1.8%, then 2%

In Exercises 25–30, find the present value of each annuity. Assume that all rates are annual rates.

25. The value of a lottery prize. Marcus has won a $1,000,000 state lottery. He can take his prize as either 20 yearly payments of $50,000 or a lump sum of $425,000. Which is the better option? Assume an interest rate of 10%.

26. The value of a lottery prize. Belinda has won a $3,400,000 lottery. She can take her prize as either 20 yearly payments of $170,000 or a lump sum of $1,500,000. Which is the better option? Assume an interest rate of 10%.

27. Present value of a car. If Addison can afford car payments of $350 per month for 4 years, what is the price of a car that she can afford now? Assume an interest rate of 10.8%.

28. Present value of a car. If Pete can afford car payments of $250 per month for 5 years, what is the price of a car that he can afford now? Assume an interest rate of 9.6%.

29. Planning for retirement. Shane has a retirement plan with an insurance company. He can choose to be paid either $350 per month for 20 years, or he can receive a lump sum of $40,000. Which is the better option? Assume an interest rate of 9%.

30. Planning for retirement. Nico has a retirement plan with an investment company. She can choose to be paid either $400 per month for 10 years, or she can receive a lump sum of $30,000. Which is the better option? Assume an interest rate of 9%.

In Exercises 31–36, find the unpaid balance on each loan.

31. Paying off a loan early. You have taken an amortized loan at 8.5% for 5 years to pay off your new car, which cost $12,000. After 3 years, you decide to pay off the loan.

32. Paying off a loan early. In order to pay for new scuba equipment, you took an amortized loan for $1,800 at 11%, which you agreed to repay in 3 years. After 18 payments, you decide to pay off the loan.

33. Paying off a mortgage early. The MacGuffs took out a 30-year mortgage for $120,000 on their vacation home at an annual interest rate of 7%. They decide to refinance the mortgage after 8 years.

34. Paying off a mortgage early. In order to modernize their restaurant, the Buccos took out a 25-year mortgage for $135,000 at an annual interest rate of 6%. They decide to refinance the mortgage after 10 years.

35. Paying off a loan early. Garrett took out an amortized loan for $8,000 for 2 years at 8% to finish culinary school. After 12 payments, he decided to pay off the loan.

36. Paying off a loan early. Sheila borrowed $14,000 to invest in her floral shop. She took out an amortized loan at 6% for 5 years. After making payments for 1 year, she decided to pay off the loan.

---

*To keep these exercises simple, during year five, use the same values for P and n as you used in year one. Technically, to get a more exact answer, you should take into account that by year five, some of the principal would have been paid off and also that only 26 years of payments remain. Ignoring these does not affect the spirit of the exercise because during the first few years, most of your mortgage payments are going towards interest.

In Exercises 37–42, you are given the amount of an amortized loan P, the annual interest rate r, the number of payments of the loan n, and the monthly payment R. After the specified number of months, the borrower decides to refinance at the new interest rate for the remaining length of the loan.

a) *What is the new monthly payment?*

b) *How much does the borrower save on interest?*

37. $P = \$10,000$; $r = 8\%$; $n = 48$; $R = \$244.13$; refinance after 24 months at an interest rate of 6.5%.

38. $P = \$20,000$; $r = 9\%$; $n = 48$; $R = \$497.71$; refinance after 12 months at an interest rate of 7%.

39. $P = \$100,000$; $r = 8\%$; $n = 240$; $R = \$836.45$; refinance after 60 months at an interest rate of 7%.

40. $P = \$100,000$; $r = 9.5\%$; $n = 360$; $R = \$840.86$; refinance after 120 months at an interest rate of 7.5%.

41. $P = \$40,000$; $r = 8\%$; $n = 48$; $R = \$976.52$; refinance after 24 months at an interest rate of 7.5%.

42. $P = \$50,000$; $r = 10\%$; $n = 60$; $R = \$1,062.36$; refinance after 24 months at an interest rate of 9.5%.

Communicating Mathematics

43. In the formula for finding the payments on an amortized loan, where have you seen the expressions on the left and right sides of the equation before?

44. What does Example 5 show you with regard to the benefit of refinancing a loan?

45. What do the words *amortize* and *mortality* have in common? In light of the Three-Way Principle, how does this help you understand the word *amortization*?

46. Why is the interest payment on the mortgage decreasing in Table 9.4?

Using Technology to Investigate Mathematics

47. Ask your instructor for tutorials and spreadsheets to perform the amortization computations that we did in this section. Duplicate some of the results that we obtained in our examples.✳

48. Find mortgage calculators on the Internet and use them to reproduce some of the examples that we explained in this section. Report on your findings.

For Extra Credit

49. In deciding to refinance at a lower interest rate, how does it affect your payments if you decide to refinance early in the loan period versus later in the loan period? For example, for a 60-month loan, would the new payments be larger, smaller, or the same if you refinance after 12 months instead of 36 months? Make up numerical examples to answer this question. Explain your answer.

50. Some mortgage agreements allow the borrower to make payments that are larger than what is required. Because this extra money goes toward reducing principal, increasing your payments may allow you to pay off the mortgage many years earlier, thus saving a great amount of interest. Assume you take out a 30-year amortized loan at 8% for $100,000 and your monthly payments will be $733.77. Suppose that instead of making the specified payment, you increase it by $100 to $833.77. How much do you save on interest over the life of the loan if you make the larger payment?

Looking Deeper

9.6 Annual Percentage Rate

Objectives

1. Calculate the annual percentage rate from a table.
2. Estimate the annual percentage rate.

A fool and his money are soon parted.   —Dutch Proverb

Have you ever heard of that saying? It certainly applies when you are borrowing money. Because the mathematics of borrowing money is complicated, there are unscrupulous money lenders who will try to take advantage of you. That is why Congress passed a law requiring lenders to inform consumers of the true cost of borrowing money.

The Annual Percentage Rate

To illustrate the problem, assume that you agree to repay a loan for $3,000 (plus the interest) in three yearly payments using an add-on interest rate of 10%. What is your true interest rate?

It depends on how you look at this agreement. Using the add-on method described in Section 9.2, we compute the interest using the formula $I = Prt = (3{,}000)(0.10)(3) = \$900$. Thus the amount to be repaid in three equal installments is $3{,}000 + 900 = \$3{,}900$. Each payment is therefore $\frac{3{,}900}{3} = \$1{,}300$, of which \$1,000 is being paid on the principal and \$300 is interest. Therefore, for the first year of your loan, you have borrowed \$3,000 and paid \$300 in interest. Solving the equation $300 = (3{,}000)(r)(1)$, we see that your interest rate is actually 10%.

At the end of the second year, you make another payment of \$1,300, of which \$1,000 goes to reduce the principal and \$300 is interest. Thus, for the second year you have paid \$300 interest on a \$2,000 loan. Solving the equation $300 = (2{,}000)(r)(1)$ for r, we find $r = 0.15$. So, in reality, the interest rate on your loan for the second year is 15%.

But, it gets worse! At the end of the third year, you make the final payment of \$1,300. For this last year you have paid \$300 interest on the \$1,000 remaining on the balance of the loan. Solving the equation $300 = (1{,}000)(r)(1)$ for r, we find $r = 0.30$. Now the interest rate is 30%.

What is the true interest rate?

The "true" interest rate we are looking for is called the **annual percentage rate**, or APR, which we will denote by a. Looking at our previous calculations, we see that

interest for the first year + interest for the second year + interest for the third year = \$900.

Using the interest formula $I = Prt$, we can rewrite this as

$$(3{,}000)(a)(1) + (2{,}000)(a)(1) + (1{,}000)(a)(1) = 900.$$

Collecting like terms, we get $(6{,}000)(a)(1) = 900$. Solving this equation gives us $a = 0.15$. Thus, the annual percentage rate is 15%. You can verify that if you borrow \$3,000 for 1 year at 15% and then \$2,000 for 1 year at 15% and then \$1,000 for 1 year at 15%, the total interest for the 3 years is \$900.

 Some Good Advice

In doing these calculations, it is easy to make a minor computational error that will throw the answer off by a large amount. To detect such errors, always ask yourself, does the answer seem reasonable?

Suppose that we borrowed \$6,000 at a simple add-on interest rate of 10% and agreed to repay it by making 60 monthly payments. In calculating the APR, we should remember that we are repaying \$100 per month, so we have really borrowed \$6,000 for 1 month, \$5,900 for 1 month, \$5,800 for 1 month, etc. Instead of having three terms on the left side of the equation as we did previously, we would have 60 terms. To avoid such lengthy computations, lenders use tables similar to Table 9.6 to determine the APR. Because most loans are repaid with monthly payments, for the remainder of this section on APR, to keep the discussion simple, we will only consider payment plans having monthly payments.

Number of Payments	APR						
	10%	11%	12%	13%	14%	15%	16%
	Finance Charge per $100						
6	\$2.94	\$3.23	\$3.53	\$3.83	\$4.12	\$4.42	\$4.72
12	\$5.50	\$6.06	\$6.62	\$7.18	\$7.74	\$8.31	\$8.88
24	\$10.75	\$11.86	\$12.98	\$14.10	\$15.23	\$16.37	\$17.51
36	\$16.16	\$17.86	\$19.57	\$21.30	\$23.04	\$24.80	\$26.57
48	\$21.74	\$24.06	\$26.40	\$28.77	\$31.17	\$33.59	\$36.03

TABLE 9.6 Finding the annual percentage rate.*

---

*We have kept this table simple to emphasize how it is used. A real table would have more columns for the APR, such as 14.5% and 14.25%.

In order to use Table 9.6, you must first know the **finance charge** on a loan, which is the total amount the borrower pays to use the money. This amount may include interest and fees. Then you must find the finance charge per $100 of the amount financed. To find this, divide the finance charge by the amount financed and multiply by 100. For example, if you borrow $780 and pay a finance charge of $148.20, then the finance charge per $100 of the amount financed is

$$\frac{\text{finance charge}}{\text{amount borrowed}} \times 100 = \frac{148.20}{780} \times 100 = 0.19 \times 100 = \$19.$$

USING TABLE 9.6 TO FIND THE APR ON A LOAN

1. Find the finance charge on the loan if it is not already given to you.

2. Determine the finance charge per $100 on the loan.

3. Use the line of Table 9.6 that corresponds to the number of payments to find the number closest to the amount found in step 2.

4. The top of the column containing the number found in step 3 is the APR.

EXAMPLE 1   *Using the APR Table*

Hector has agreed to pay off a $3,500 loan by making 24 monthly payments. If the total finance charge on his loan is $460, what is the APR he is being charged?

SOLUTION: The finance charge per $100 financed is

$$\frac{\text{finance charge}}{\text{amount borrowed}} \times 100 = \frac{460}{3,500} \times 100 \approx 0.1314 \times 100 \approx \$13.14.$$

Because Hector is making 24 monthly payments, we use the row in Table 9.6 for 24 payments, as we show in Figure 9.5. Reading across this line, we find that the closest amount to $13.14 is $12.98. The top of this column shows the approximate APR for Hector's loan, which is 12%.

Now try Exercises 5 to 12. ❋ **21**

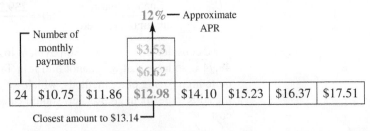

FIGURE 9.5 Using Table 9.6 to find the APR for Hector's loan.

We can find the APR if we know the number and size of payments on a loan.

EXAMPLE 2   *Finding the APR Using Table 9.6*

Jessica is considering buying a car costing $11,850. The terms of the sale require a down payment of $2,000 and the rest to be paid off by making 48 monthly payments of $250 each. What APR will she be paying on the car financing?

SOLUTION: The amount being financed is the purchase price minus the down payment, which is $11,850 - 2,000 = \$9,850$. Because her payments amount to $48 \times 250 = \$12,000$,

---

Quiz Yourself **21**

Assume that Jason will repay a loan for $11,250 by making 36 payments. Assume that the finance charge is $1,998.

a) What is the finance charge per $100 financed?

b) What is the APR?

this makes the finance charge equal to 12,000 − 9,850 = $2,150. The finance charge per $100 financed is therefore

$$\frac{\text{finance charge}}{\text{amount borrowed}} \times 100 = \frac{2,150}{9,850} \times 100 \approx 0.2183 \times 100 = \$21.83.$$

We now look at the row for 48 payments in Table 9.6. The number in this row that is closest to $21.83 is $21.74. Looking at the top of this column, we find that the APR for this car financing is about 10%.

Now try Exercises 17 to 24. ✳ **22**

Quiz Yourself **22**

In Example 2, assume that Jessica's payments are $265 instead of $250. What is the APR that she is being charged?

Because the Consumer Credit Protection Act was passed in 1968, it is not as common for lenders to offer add-on interest loans because they must reveal the APR. One way merchants can avoid having to state the APR is by offering the consumer the opportunity to rent rather than purchase the product outright. With a "rent-to-own" contract, because there is no loan, the merchant does not have to reveal the APR. If we consider these rental agreements as loans, we would often find that the APRs are outrageously high.

Knowing the APR enables consumers to determine the best deal when shopping for a loan.

EXAMPLE 3   *Computing the Cost of "Renting to Own"*

Jeff is considering renting a TV from a nearby rent-to-own store. He can rent the TV, which he saw priced at $479 in a local store, for $19.95 a month. If he rents the TV for 36 months, then the TV is his to keep. Analyze this rental agreement to determine whether Jeff is making a wise decision.

SOLUTION: There is really not much difference here between what Jeff is considering and purchasing the TV at another store with an agreement to make monthly payments of $19.95. Of course, with the rent-to-own agreement, Jeff can stop renting before 36 months. If Jeff were to rent the TV until he owned it, he would make 36 payments of $19.95, so he would pay a total of 36 × 19.95 = $718.20. His finance charge would be 718.20 − 479 = $239.20. The finance charge per $100 financed is therefore

$$\frac{\text{finance charge}}{\text{amount borrowed}} \times 100 = \frac{239.20}{479} \times 100 \approx 0.4994 \times 100 = \$49.94.$$

If we consider his rental as a 36-payment loan, we can try to use Table 9.6. Unfortunately, 49.94 is so large that we cannot find it in Table 9.6, which implies that the interest rate is quite high. Using other methods, which we explain in the Highlight on page 443, we find the APR to be about 28.5%. Jeff should carefully consider whether this rental is worth the cost. ✳

Math in Your Life

Short of Cash? We Can Help

If you are short of cash and were to search the Internet for "payday loans," you could find many sites that will offer you a very short-term loan to tide you over until your next payday. One site that I found will loan you $100 for 7 days provided you are willing to then pay back $125. If you take the time to check the page where the company states its annual percentage rates, you would find that you are going to be charged an APR of 1,303.57%.

Another way of looking at this loan, is to consider what would happen if you were not to repay this loan for 1 year. The loan P is $100, the weekly interest rate r is 0.25, and time t is 52 weeks. So, applying the compound interest formula, at the end of the year you would owe

$$P(1 + r)^t = 100(1.25)^{52} \approx \$10,947,644,25.$$

That's right, your $100 loan would have grown to a debt of almost $11 million!

HIGHLIGHT ✸ ✸ ✸

Using a Graphing Calculator to Find an APR

If we consider Jeff's rental in Example 3 as a loan with payments of $19.95 per month, then we can reason as we did in Section 9.5 when determining payments on a mortgage. Recall that we thought of the banker offering a loan where interest was computed monthly and we thought of the borrower as paying it off by making monthly payments into an annuity. The equation that we used was

$$P\left(1 + \frac{r}{m}\right)^n = R\left(\frac{\left(1 + \frac{r}{m}\right)^n - 1}{\frac{r}{m}}\right).$$

Knowing P, r, m, and n, it was easy to solve for R. The situation here is different. We know P, m, n, and R and we need to solve for r, which is quite difficult. However, using a calculator, such as the TI-83 we can solve for r as we show in the accompanying screen. Thus, the APR is roughly 28.5%.

```
N=36
·I%=28.52782389
 PV=479
 PMT=-19.95
 FV=0
 P/Y=12
 C/Y=12
 PMT:END BEGIN
```

Estimating the APR

As you saw in Example 3, it is difficult to calculate an APR without using technology; however, there is a formula that gives a good estimate of an APR for the special case of an add-on interest loan.

> **FORMULA TO APPROXIMATE THE ANNUAL PERCENTAGE RATE**
> We can approximate the annual percentage rate for an add-on interest loan by using the formula
>
> $$APR \approx \frac{2nr}{n+1},$$
>
> where r is the annual interest rate and n is the number of payments.

EXAMPLE 4 *Estimating an APR*

Quiz Yourself ㉓

Use the formula to approximate the APR for an add-on interest loan for $5,500 at an annual interest rate of 9.6% that will be repaid in 48 months.

Minxia must borrow $4,000 to pay tuition for her last year in college. Her bank will give her an add-on interest loan at 7.7% for 3 years. Use the formula above to estimate Minxia's APR.

SOLUTION: In this problem, $n = 3 \times 12 = 36$ and $r = 7.7\% = 0.077$. So Minxia's annual percentage rate is

$$APR \approx \frac{2nr}{n+1} = \frac{2 \times 36 \times 0.077}{36 + 1} = \frac{5.544}{37} = 0.1499 = 14.99\%.$$

Now try Exercises 13 to 16. ✳ ㉓

Exercises [9.6]

Looking Back*

These exercises follow the general outline of the topics presented in this section and will give you a good overview of the material that you have just studied.

1. In our example on page 439, how did we argue that the interest rate for the last year of the loan was 30%?

2. In Example 2, how did we find the finance charge per $100 on Jessica's loan?

Sharpening Your Skills

In Exercises 3 and 4, use an approach similar to the discussion preceding Example 1 to find the APR of the loan. Realize that Table 9.6 does not apply to these situations because the payments are not monthly. You are given the amount of the loan, the number and type of payments, and the add-on interest rate.

3. Loan amount, $6,000; three yearly payments; rate = 8%

4. Loan amount, $8,000; four yearly payments; rate = 12%

*Before doing these exercises, you may find it useful to review the note *How to Succeed at Mathematics* on page xix.

Find the finance charge per $100 for each loan.

5. Loan, $1,800; finance charge, $270

6. Loan, $3,000; finance charge, $840

7. Loan, $2,000; finance charge, $260

8. Loan, $5,000; finance charge, $1,125

Use Table 9.6 to find the APR to the nearest whole percent. Assume that all interest rates are annual rates.

9. Finding the APR on a loan. Michael has agreed to pay off a $3,000 loan by making 24 monthly payments. The total finance charge on his loan is $420.

10. Finding the APR on a loan. Daisy has agreed to pay off a $4,500 loan by making 24 monthly payments. The total finance charge on her loan is $600.

11. Finding the APR on a loan. Luisa pays a finance charge of $165 on a 6-month, $4,000 loan.

12. Finding the APR on a loan. Wesley pays a finance charge of $310 on a 12-month, $5,000 loan.

In Exercises 13–16, estimate the annual percentage rate for the add-on loan using the given number of payments and annual interest rate. Use the formula on page 443.

13. $n = 36$; $r = 6.4\%$ **14.** $n = 48$; $r = 4.8\%$

15. $n = 42$; $r = 7\%$ **16.** $n = 30$; $r = 8\%$

Applying What You've Learned

Use Table 9.6 to find the APR to the nearest whole percent. Assume that all interest rates are annual rates.

17. Finding the APR on a remodeling loan. Thiep took out a $10,000 add-on loan to remodel his house and will repay it by making 24 payments of $485.

18. Finding the APR on a car loan. Diana took out an $8,000 add-on loan to buy a car and will repay it by making 36 payments of $270.

19. Finding the APR on a consumer loan. Pete took out a $4,500 add-on loan to buy a sound system for his band and will repay it by making 48 payments of $116.50.

20. Finding the APR on a consumer loan. Amanda took out a $1,500 add-on loan to buy a new computer and will repay it by making 24 payments of $71.25.

21. Finding the APR on a travel loan. Emily took out a 24-month, $2,000 add-on loan at an interest rate of 8% to go to China.

22. Finding the APR on a vehicle loan. John took out a 48-month, $26,000 add-on loan at an interest rate of 7.9% to pay off his truck.

23. Finding the APR on a loan. What is the APR of a 36-month add-on loan with an interest rate of 8.2%?

24. Finding the APR on a loan. What is the APR of a 48-month add-on loan with an interest rate of 8.75%?

In Exercises 25–28, decide which has the better APR to repay a $5,000 loan. Assume that you are making monthly payments.

25. a. An add-on interest loan at 8.4% for 3 years

   b. 24 payments of $230

26. a. An add-on interest loan at 7.2% for 2 years

   b. 36 payments of $165

27. a. An add-on interest loan at 8.9% for 4 years

   b. 36 payments of $165

28. a. An add-on interest loan at 8.4% for 1 year

   b. 24 payments of $240

In Exercises 29 and 30, think of the rent-to-own agreement as though it were an add-on loan. If the consumer rents until the item is paid for, find the finance charge per $100 financed. Although Table 9.6 does not contain enough columns to estimate the APR, guess as to what you think it might be.

29. Evaluating a rent-to-own agreement. Marcus rents a TV worth $375 for monthly payments of $18.75. After 2 years, he will own the TV.

30. Evaluating a rent-to-own agreement. Maria rents furniture worth $1,375 for monthly payments of $49. After 3 years, she will own the furniture.

Communicating Mathematics

31. How do you use Table 9.6 to find the APR on a loan?

32. In what way is a rent-to-own agreement different from an add-on interest loan?

Using Technology to Investigate Mathematics

33. Ask your instructor for a tutorial to show you how to find the APR with a graphing calculator. Use your calculator to reproduce the computations in Example 3 and in Exercises 29 and 30.*

34. Search the Internet for payday loans or other types of loans such as car loans and mortgages. Try to find the APR on these loans and report on your findings.

For Extra Credit

35. We often see advertisements stating that we can consolidate our loans and have more manageable payments. The advertiser may do this for us by extending the length of our loans. Consider an add-on loan for $1,000 at an interest rate of 10% for 3 years and then for 4 years. How does this affect the APR? Is it more financially sound to pay off loans in a short period of time or a longer period of time? (Here we are only thinking about the APR—of course, there may be other considerations.)

36. Is the APR affected by the size of the loan?

CHAPTER SUMMARY*

SECTION	SUMMARY	EXAMPLE
SECTION 9.1	The word **percent** is derived from the Latin "per centum," which means "per hundred." Examining what numbers are in the tenths and hundredths place in a decimal will allow you to **convert a decimal to a percent** properly. Deciding which numbers to put in the tenths and hundredths place will help you to **convert a percent to a decimal** properly.	Discussion, p. 396 Examples 1–3, pp. 396–397
	Percent of change is given by $$\text{percent of change} = \frac{\text{new amount} - \text{base amount}}{\text{base amount}}.$$	Examples 4 and 5, p. 398
	Many percent problems are based on the equation percent $\times$ base = amount. This equation is used to solve many applied problems.	Example 6, p. 399 Examples 7 and 8, pp. 399, 400
	Calculating with percents often occurs when **calculating taxes**.	Example 9, p. 401
SECTION 9.2	**Interest** is the money that a borrower pays to use a lender's money. The amount borrowed is called the **principal**. The **interest rate** is specified as a percentage of the principal. We use the formula $I = Prt$, where I is the interest, P is the principal, r is the interest rate, and t is the time. The equation $A = P(1 + rt)$ computes the **future value** of an account using simple interest. A is the future value (or amount), P is the principal, r is the interest rate, and t is the time. We find the **present value** of an account by solving the equation $A = P(1 + r\,t)$ for P.	Discussion, p. 404 Example 1, p. 405 Example 2, p. 405 Example 3, p. 405
	To find A, the **future value** of an account using **compound interest**, we use the formula $A = P\left(1 + \dfrac{r}{m}\right)^n$, where P is the **principal**, r is the annual **interest rate**, m is the number of **compounding periods** per year, and n is the total number of compounding periods.	Discussion, pp. 407, 408 Example 5, p. 408
	We find **present value** by solving the compound interest equation for P.	Example 6, p. 409
	The **common logarithmic function** reverses the operation of raising 10 to a power.	Example 7, p. 410
	To solve for n in the compound interest formula, take the log of both sides of the equation and use the exponent property of the log function. To solve for $\dfrac{r}{m}$, divide both sides of the equation $A = P\left(1 + \dfrac{r}{m}\right)^n$ by P, raise both sides of the resulting equation to the $\dfrac{1}{n}$ power, and then subtract 1 from both sides.	Example 8, p. 410 Example 9, p. 411
SECTION 9.3	When using the **add-on interest method** to compute the monthly payments on a loan, we use the following formula: payment $= \dfrac{P + I}{n}$, where P is the amount of the loan, I is the interest due on the loan, and n is the number of monthly payments.	Example 1, p. 415
	The **unpaid balance method** for computing finance charges uses the simple interest formula $I = Prt$, where P = previous month's balance + finance charge + purchases made − returns − payments. The variable r is the annual interest rate and $t = \frac{1}{12}$.	Example 2, p. 416
	Use the **average daily balance method** to compute a finance charge: 1. Add the outstanding balances for your account for each day of the previous month. 2. Divide this total by the number of days in the previous month. 3. Use the formula $I = Prt$, where P is the average daily balance found in step 2, r is the annual interest rate, and t the number of days in the previous month divided by 365.	Example 4, p. 417
	The exact same charges on two different credit cards may result in different finance charges.	Example 5, p. 419

*Before studying this chapter's material, it would be useful to reread the note *How to Succeed at Mathematics* on page xix.

SECTION 9.4

When we make a series of regular payments into an interest-bearing account, this account is called an **annuity**. If payments are made at the end of every compounding period, the annuity is called an **ordinary annuity**. The **interest** in an annuity is compounded with the same frequency as the payments. The sum of all the deposits plus all interest is called the **future value** of the account.

Discussion, p. 423

Assume that we are making a regular payment, R, at the end of each compounding period for an annuity that has an annual interest rate, r, which is being compounded m times per year. Then the value of the annuity after n compounding periods is

Example 2, p. 425

$$A = R\frac{\left(1+\frac{r}{m}\right)^n - 1}{\frac{r}{m}}.$$

A **sinking fund** is an account into which we make regular payments for the purpose of saving some specified amount in the future. The interest is compounded with the same frequency as the payments. To find the regular **payments** that must be made into a sinking fund to save the amount A, solve for R in the following equation:

Discussion, p. 425

Example 3, p. 426

$$A = R\frac{\left(1+\frac{r}{m}\right)^n - 1}{\frac{r}{m}}.$$

SECTION 9.5

The process of paying off a loan (plus interest) by making a series of regular equal payments is called **amortization**, and such a loan is called an **amortized loan**. We assume that P is the amount **borrowed**, r is the annual **interest rate**, m is the **number** of compounding periods per year, n is the total number of compounding periods, and R is the **payment** that is made regularly.

Discussion, p. 430

To find the regular **payment** due on an amortized loan, solve for R in the following equation:

Example 1, p. 431

$$P\left(1+\frac{r}{m}\right)^n = R\frac{\left(1+\frac{r}{m}\right)^n - 1}{\frac{r}{m}}.$$

A list showing payment by payment how much applies to principal and interest on an amortized loan is called an **amortization** schedule.

Examples 2 and 3, pp. 432, 433

To find the **present value** of your annuity, solve for P in the following equation:

Example 4, p. 435

$$P\left(1+\frac{r}{m}\right)^n = R\frac{\left(1+\frac{r}{m}\right)^n - 1}{\frac{r}{m}}.$$

The **unpaid balance**, U, on a loan after n payments is

Example 5, p. 436

$$U = P\left(1+\frac{r}{m}\right)^n - R\frac{\left(1+\frac{r}{m}\right)^n - 1}{\frac{r}{m}}.$$

SECTION 9.6	The **annual percentage rate**, or **APR**, is a standardized version of the "true" interest rate on a loan.	Discussion, pp. 439–440
	To use the APR table to calculate an annual percentage rate, we first find the **finance charge per $100** of the amount financed, which equals $\dfrac{\text{finance charge}}{\text{amount borrowed}} \times 100$. We can then use Table 9.6 to find the APR.	Example 1, p. 441
		Example 2, p. 441
	We can **estimate** the annual percentage rate for an add-on loan using the formula $\text{APR} = \dfrac{2nr}{n+1}$, where n is the number of payments and r is the annual interest rate.	Example 4, p. 443

CHAPTER REVIEW EXERCISES

Section 9.1

1. Convert 0.1245 to a percent.

2. Convert 1.365 percent to a decimal.

3. Convert $\frac{11}{16}$ to a percent.

4. 2,890 is what percent of 3,400?

5. In 2007, M&M sales were $238.4 million, which was 13.2% of the total chocolate candy sales. What was the total amount spent on chocolate candy in 2007?

6. Use Table 9.2 to calculate the federal income tax that Maribel owes if her taxable income is $56,400.

Section 9.2

7. Find the future value of an account paying simple interest if $P = \$1,500$, $r = 9\%$, and $t = 2$ years.

8. You have agreed to pay off an $8,000 car loan with 24 monthly payments of $400 each. Use the simple interest formula to determine the interest rate that you are being charged.

9. Jacob wants to defer his income taxes of $11,400 for 6 months. If he must pay an 18% penalty (compounded monthly) to do this, what will his tax bill be?

10. Palma wants to establish a fund for her granddaughter's college education. What lump sum must she deposit in an account that pays an annual interest rate of 6%, compounded monthly, if she wants to have $10,000 in 10 years?

11. If you invest $1,000 in an account that pays an annual interest rate of 6.4%, compounded monthly, how long will it take for your money to double?

12. If $A = \$1,400$, $P = \$1,200$, and $t = 5$, solve $A = P(1 + r)^t$ for r.

Section 9.3

13. Bernie purchased a riding lawn mower for $1,320. The store offered him a 3-year add-on loan at an annual rate of 8.25%. How much interest will he pay? What are his monthly payments?

14. Use the unpaid balance method to calculate the finance charge on Joanna's credit account if last month's balance was $1,350, she made a payment of $375, she bought hiking boots for $120, and she returned a jacket for $140. Assume an annual interest rate of 21%.

15. Calculate the finance charges for the following credit card account for August (which has 31 days) using the average daily balance method. July's balance was $275 and the annual interest rate is 18%.

Date	Transaction
August 6	Made payment of $75
August 12	Charged $115 for clothes
August 19	Charged $20 for gasoline
August 24	Charged $16 for lunch

Section 9.4

16. Piers is saving for his retirement by putting $175 each month into an ordinary annuity. If the annuity pays an annual interest rate of 9.35%, how much will he save for his retirement in 10 years?

17. Find the monthly payment needed to have a sinking fund accumulate to $2,000 in 36 months if the annual interest rate is 6%.

18. Solve $\dfrac{3^x - 4}{2} = 10$ for x.

19. You are making monthly payments of $300 into an annuity that pays 9% annual interest. How long will it take to accumulate $10,000?

20. Assume that you are saving $350 a month in a retirement annuity that has an interest rate of 4.2%. Assume that your income taxes for the life of the annuity are 25% and that they drop to 18% when you retire. How much more do you earn in 30 years in a tax-deferred account than a nondeferred one?

Section 9.5

21. Find the monthly payment necessary to pay off a 4-year amortized loan of $5,000 if the annual interest rate is 10%.

22. Complete the first two lines of an amortization schedule for a 20-year, $100,000 mortgage if the annual interest rate is 8%.

23. Jesse has won a $1,000,000 state lottery. She can take her prize as either 20 yearly payments of $50,000 or a lump sum of $500,000. Which is the better option? Assume an interest rate of 8%.

24. You have taken an amortized loan at 7.5% for 5 years to pay off your new car, which cost $13,000. After 2 years, you decide to pay off the loan. What is your unpaid balance?

25. Assume that you borrow $180,000 in a 30-year adjustable rate mortgage with an initial interest rate of 4.5%. The interest rate increases over 4 years to 12.5%. What are your monthly payments in the first year? The fifth year?

Section 9.6

26. Ann took out a $1,800 add-on loan for a professional-quality color printer, which she will repay with 12 payments of $163. Use Table 9.6 to find her interest rate to the nearest percent.

27. Use the formula on page 443 to estimate the annual percentage rate on a loan that has an annual interest rate of 8% that will be repaid in 20 months.

CHAPTER TEST

1. Convert 0.3624 to a percent.

2. Convert 23.45 percent to a decimal.

3. Convert $\frac{7}{16}$ to a percent.

4. Use the unpaid balance method to calculate the finance charge on Marion's credit account if last month's balance was $950, she made a payment of $270, and she bought a ski parka for $217 and gloves for $23. Assume an annual interest rate of 24%.

5. Find the future value of an account paying simple interest if $P = \$3,400$, $r = 2.5\%$, and $t = 3$ years.

6. 994 is what percent of 2,840?

7. Best Buy is selling an MP3 player that normally sells for $169.99 for $149.99. What is the percent of the reduction on the price of this player?

8. Hiro took out a $1,600 add-on loan for a handmade, split-bamboo, Japanese fly-fishing rod that he will repay with 24 payments of $75. Use Table 9.6 to find his interest rate to the nearest percent.

9. You are paying off your large-screen projection TV that cost $3,000 with 24 monthly payments of $162.50. What is the annual simple interest rate that you are being charged?

10. If Danica deposits $4,000 in an account that has an interest rate of 3.6% that is compounded monthly, what is the value of the account in 4 years?

11. If you invest $1,000 in an account that pays an interest rate of 4.8% compounded monthly, how long will it take for your money to double?

12. Assume that you borrow $220,000 in a 30-year adjustable rate mortgage with an initial interest rate of 3.2%. The interest rate increases 1.5% per year for the next 4 years. What are your monthly payments in the first year? The fifth year?

13. José wants to establish a trust for his nephew who is now 3 years old. He will deposit a lump sum in an account with an annual interest rate of 4.2% compounded monthly. How much must he deposit now if he wants his nephew to have $15,000 when he turns 21?

14. To pay for scuba diving equipment costing $1,560, Carmen took out a 2-year add-on interest loan at an annual rate of 10.5%. How much interest will he pay? What are his monthly payments?

15. If $A = \$2,400$, $P = \$2,100$, and $t = 3$, solve $A = P(1 + r)^t$ for r.

16. From 2005 to 2006, the price of a new home rose from $250 thousand to $257 thousand. What was the percent of increase?

17. Calculate the finance charges for the following credit card account for April (which has 30 days) using the average daily balance method. March's balance was $425, and the annual interest rate is 21%.

Date	Transaction
April 4	Made payment of $85
April 10	Charged $25 for gasoline
April 15	Charged $15 for lunch
April 25	Charged $80 for concert tickets

18. Grace is saving for her son's college education by putting $200 each month into an ordinary annuity. If the annuity pays an annual interest rate of 5.15%, how much will she have saved in 8 years?

19. Solve $\frac{5^x - 4}{3} = 10$ for x.

20. Use the formula on page 443 to estimate the annual percentage rate on a loan that has an annual interest rate of 8% that will be repaid in 20 months.

21. Find the monthly payment needed to have a sinking fund accumulate to $1,800 in 36 months if the annual interest rate is 4%.

22. Find the monthly payment necessary to pay off an 8-year amortized loan of $20,000 if the annual interest rate is 9%.

23. Assume that you are making monthly payments of $450 into an annuity that pays 3.75% annual interest. How long will it take to accumulate $9,000?

24. Use Table 9.2 to calculate the federal income tax that Jakob owes if his taxable income is $48,600.

25. Mike has won the $1,000,000 prize on *Deal or No Deal*. He can take his prize as a lump sum of $750,000 or as a regular annuity with 10 yearly payments of $100,000. Which is the better option? Assume an annual interest rate of 4%.

26. Assume that you have taken out a 20-year amortized loan of $140,000 at an annual interest rate of 7.5%.

a. What is the monthly payment on your loan?

b. Write the first two lines of the amortization table for this loan.

27. Estelle has taken an amortized loan at 9.6% for 5 years to pay off her new car, which costs $16,500.

a. What is her monthly payment on the loan?

b. After 2 years, she decides to pay off the loan. What is her unpaid balance?

GROUP EXERCISES

1. Get federal income tax tables for filing single, married filing jointly, and married filing separately and investigate if there are any advantages for a married couple to file one way versus the other.

2. Go to the Web site www.federalreserve.gov/pubs/arms/arms_english.htm or some other Web site to learn more about adjustable rate mortgages. Also, try to find actual examples of current mortgage offers either online or by going to financial institutions. There are many varieties of ARMs other than the ones we have discussed. Make up new examples illustrating the dangers of ARMs.

Geometry

Ancient and Modern Mathematics Embrace

Geometry is all around us. If you stop to think about it for a moment, I believe you would agree with this statement because when you look around you see all kinds of geometric objects such as lines, rectangles, and spheres. But surprisingly, geometry is also inside of us, we wear it, we watch it at the movies and play with it on our Xboxes, Wiis, and PlayStations. And, if you were to fly from Florida to the Philippines, you would find it strange that geometry tells the pilot the best route goes through Alaska.* Also, geometry tells us that the paths that streams and rivers take in flowing from the mountains to the sea are geometrically similar to the paths that bacteria take while growing in a petri dish and the way airways branch inside our lungs.

(continued)

*See http://gc.kls2.com/ for an interactive site that will calculate flight paths such as this which contradict our intuition.

In this chapter, you will first study the classical geometry of points, lines, angles, and solids that the Greeks used as the basis for surveying, mapmaking, and architecture. But intertwined with that discussion, we will introduce you to a type of "curved" geometry that we use to navigate on a spherical Earth and that Albert Einstein used to describe our curved universe.

Finally in this chapter, we will show you a modern type of geometry where lines are neither straight nor curved, but rather have an infinite number of "wiggles." Scientists use this fractal geometry to describe the roughness of mountain peaks and shorelines, the ups and downs of the stock market, and the irregular beating of a healthy heart. ●

10.1 Lines, Angles, and Circles

Objectives

1. Understand the basic properties of geometric objects such as points, lines, and planes.
2. Work with the fundamental properties of angles.
3. Solve problems involving the relationships among angles, arcs, and circles.

Before we begin this section, let's take a moment to think about the future. I don't mean my future—or your future—or even a thousand years from now. Let's try to imagine 2,300 years into the future. What "important" ideas that you struggle to learn the night before a big exam in one of your courses will still be relevant then? It's hard to grasp the size of that question.

If you were to look backwards instead, you would see one idea that has shaped mathematics and science for over 2,000 years—the method of deductive reasoning that was put forth in the most famous textbook in the history of the world—*Elements* by Euclid of Alexandria. *Elements*, which was written around 300 BC, is an introduction to elementary mathematics—including number theory and geometry—that gave mathematicians a method of reasoning which we still use today.

✎ **KEY POINT**

Two lines in the plane are either parallel or intersecting.

Points, Lines, and Planes

Euclid begins his discussion of geometry with intuitive descriptions of three *undefined* terms, saying that a **point** is "that which has no part," a **line** has "length but no breadth," and a **plane** has "length and breadth only."

To discuss some of the basic properties of lines and angles, we need to introduce some terminology and notation. We will label points with capital letters, such as A, B, and C, and lines with lowercase letters, such as l and m, or we may include subscripts, such as l_1 or l_2.

As we show in Figure 10.1, any point on a line divides the line into three parts—the point and two *half lines*. A **ray** is a half line with its endpoint included. In Figure 10.1(b), the open dot means that the point A is not included in the half line, whereas the solid dot in Figure 10.1(c) means that A is part of the ray. A piece of a line joining two points and including the points is called a **line segment**. ❶

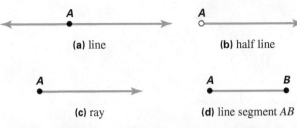

(a) line   **(b)** half line   **(c)** ray   **(d)** line segment AB

FIGURE 10.1 Some basic terminology regarding lines.

Although we do not try to define precisely what a plane is, you can think of it as being an infinite two-dimensional surface such as an infinitely large flat sheet of paper.

According to Euclid's geometry, lines either intersect or are parallel. **Parallel lines** are lines that lie on the same plane and have no points in common. In Figure 10.3, lines l_1 and l_2 are parallel. We express this as $l_1 \| l_2$. If two different lines lying on the same plane are not parallel, then they have a single point in common and are called **intersecting lines**. In Figure 10.3, lines l_3 and l_4 are intersecting lines.

Quiz Yourself **1** *

Identify each object shown in Figure 10.2.

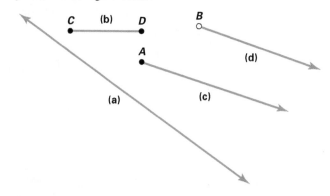

FIGURE 10.2 Line terminology.

parallel lines   intersecting lines

FIGURE 10.3 Parallel lines and intersecting lines.

Angles

Two rays having a common endpoint form an **angle**. In Figure 10.4, we form an angle by rotating ray *AB*, called the **initial side**, about point *B* to finish in the position corresponding to ray *BC*, called the **terminal side**. We use the symbol ∠ to denote an angle; therefore, we can call the angle in Figure 10.4 ∠*ABC*, or simply ∠*B*. Point *B* is called the **vertex** of the angle.

 **KEY POINT**

We measure angles in degrees.

We measure angles in units called *degrees*.[†] The symbol ° represents the word *degrees*. If you rotate the initial side of an angle one complete revolution about the vertex so that the terminal side coincides with the initial side, you will have formed a 360° angle, as we show in Figure 10.5(a). If you rotate the initial side only $\frac{1}{360}$ of the way around the vertex to reach the terminal side, that angle has size 1°. A 36° angle is shown in Figure 10.5(b).

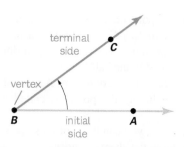

FIGURE 10.4 An angle formed by rotating a ray about point *B*.

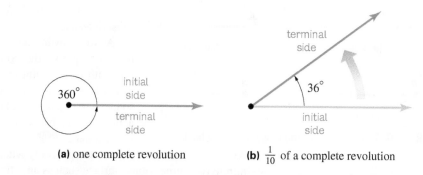

(a) one complete revolution   **(b)** $\frac{1}{10}$ of a complete revolution

FIGURE 10.5 We form a 36° angle by rotating the initial side $\frac{1}{10}$ of the way around the vertex.

---

*Quiz Yourself answers begin on page 778.
[†]There are other possible units that are used to measure angles, such as radians. We will not discuss these other measures in this book.

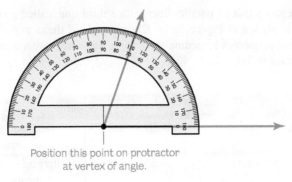

Position this point on protractor
at vertex of angle.

FIGURE 10.6 A protractor measuring a 70° angle.

Figure 10.6 shows a tool called a *protractor* measuring a 70° angle. We write the measure (in degrees) of ∠ABC as m∠ABC.

Certain types of angles occur so often that we give them special names (Figure 10.7). An angle whose measure is between 0° and 90° is called an **acute angle**. A **right angle** has a measure of 90°. We indicate a right angle by placing a square at the vertex of the angle, as shown in Figure 10.7. An **obtuse angle** has a measure between 90° and 180°, and a **straight angle** has a measure of 180°.

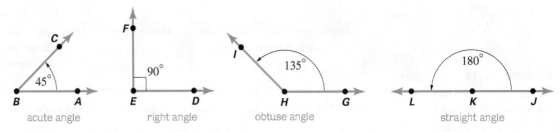

FIGURE 10.7 Some special types of angles.

Two intersecting lines form two pairs of angles called **vertical angles**. Figure 10.8 shows one pair of vertical angles, *ABC* and *EBD*.* Vertical angles have the following important property.

> **PROPERTY OF VERTICAL ANGLES** Vertical angles have equal measures.

We call a pair of angles **complementary** if the sum of their measures is 90°. Two angles having an angle sum of 180° are called **supplementary** angles. In Figure 10.8, angles *PQR* and *RQS* are complementary, and angles *WXY* and *YXZ* are supplementary angles. Two lines that intersect forming right angles are called **perpendicular lines**. ❷

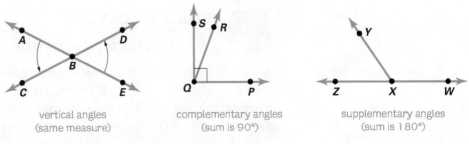

FIGURE 10.8 Some special pairs of angles.

Quiz Yourself ❷

Identify the angles shown in Figure 10.9.

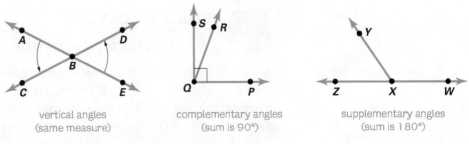

(a)   **(b)**   **(c)**   **(d)**   **(e)**

FIGURE 10.9

---

*DBA and CBE would be another pair of vertical angles.

KEY POINT

Parallel lines cut by a transversal form several pairs of equal angles.

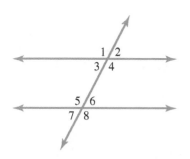

FIGURE 10.10 Special pairs of angles are formed when a transversal cuts parallel lines.

If we intersect a pair of parallel lines with a third line, called a **transversal**, we form eight angles, as shown in Figure 10.10. Certain pairs of these angles have special names and also special properties regarding their angle measures. We summarize some of these special properties in Table 10.1. **3**

Type of Angles	Examples	Property
Corresponding angles	Angles 1 and 5	Corresponding angles have equal measures.
Alternate interior angles	Angles 3 and 6	Alternate interior angles have equal measures.
Alternate exterior angles	Angles 1 and 8	Alternate exterior angles have equal measures.
Interior angles on the same side of the transversal	Angles 3 and 5	Interior angles on the same side of the transversal are supplementary angles (sum of measures is 180°).

TABLE 10.1 Properties of pairs of angles formed by cutting parallel lines with a transversal.

 **3**

Fill in the blanks using angles other than those mentioned in Table 10.1 to make the following statements true:

a) Angles 2 and _____ are alternate exterior angles.

b) Angles 4 and _____ are corresponding angles.

c) Angles 4 and _____ are interior angles on the same side of the transversal.

d) Angles 5 and _____ are alternate interior angles.

PROBLEM SOLVING
The Analogies Principle

As we said in Section 1.1, it is easier to remember new mathematical terminology if you think about what the words mean in English. For example, when you use the term *alternate interior angles*, you are talking about "alternate" angles—one angle is on each side of the transversal—that are "interior"—inside, or between the parallel lines.

EXAMPLE 1   *Finding Measures of Angles*

In Figure 10.11, assume that lines l and m are parallel. Also assume that $m\angle A = 51°$ and $m\angle B = 76°$.

a) Find the measure of angle 9.   b) Find the measure of angle 2.

SOLUTION:

a) Angles 8 and B are equal because they are corresponding angles. Thus, $m\angle 8 = 76°$. Angles A, 8, and 9 form a straight angle, so

$$m\angle A + m\angle 8 + m\angle 9 = 180°.$$

Substituting the measures of angles A and 8 gives the equation

$$51° + 76° + m\angle 9 = 180°.$$

FIGURE 10.11 Finding measures of angles.

Use Figure 10.11 to find a) the measure of angle 7 and b) the measure of angle 6.

✏ **KEY POINT**

There is a correspondence between the measure of central angles and the length of arcs of circles.

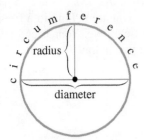

FIGURE 10.12 Radius (red), diameter (red), and circumference (blue) of a circle.

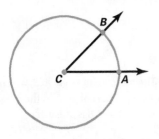

FIGURE 10.13 Angle *ACB* is a central angle.

Length of arc *AB* is proportional to measure of ∠*ACB*.

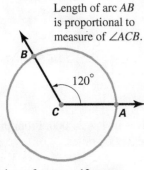

circumference = 12 meters

FIGURE 10.14 The measure of ∠*ACB* determines the length of arc *AB*.

Solving for $m\angle 9$, we get

$$m\angle 9 = 180° - 51° - 76° = 53°.$$

b) Because interior angles on the same side of the transversal are supplementary, we have $m\angle A + m\angle 2 = 180°$. Substituting 51° for $m\angle A$, we get $51° + m\angle 2 = 180°$. Subtracting 51° from both sides, we get $m\angle 2 = 180° - 51° = 129°$.

Now try Exercises 33 to 38. ✻ **4**

Circles

Circles are common geometric objects that have many useful applications.

> **DEFINITIONS** A **circle** is the set of all points lying on a plane that are located at a fixed distance, called the **radius**,* from a given point called the **center**. A **diameter** of a circle is a line segment passing through the center with both endpoints lying on the circle. The **circumference** is the distance around the circle. (See Figure 10.12.)

An angle that has its vertex at the center of a circle is called a **central angle** (see Figure 10.13). In Figure 10.13, the length of the arc between A and B is proportional to the central angle *ACB*. By this we mean that we have the following ratio:

$$\frac{\text{the measure of angle } ACB}{360°} = \frac{\text{length of arc } AB}{\text{circumference of circle}}.$$

For example, if $m\angle ACB = 60°$, then the length of the arc from A to B is $\frac{60}{360} = \frac{1}{6}$ of the circumference of the circle.

EXAMPLE 2 *Using a Central Angle to Measure the Length of an Arc of a Circle*

Assume that a circle has a circumference of 12 meters. If central angle *ACB* has measure of 120°, then what is the length of the arc from A to B?

SOLUTION: It is a good problem-solving strategy to draw a diagram, as we do in Figure 10.14. We can now use the ratio

$$\underset{\underset{\text{12 meters}}{|}}{\frac{\text{length of arc } AB}{\text{circumference of circle}}} = \overset{\overset{120°}{|}}{\frac{\text{the measure of angle } ACB}{360°}}$$

to solve the problem. This gives us the equation

$$\frac{\text{length of arc } AB}{12} = \frac{120}{360} = \frac{1}{3}.$$

Multiplying both sides by 12, we get that the length of arc $AB = \frac{1}{3} \cdot 12 = 4$ meters.

Now try Exercises 39 to 44. ✻ **5**

Surprisingly, we can use the small amount of geometry we have developed so far to solve meaningful problems.

---

*We will use the word *radius* in two ways. (1) It is the *distance* between the center and any point on the circle. (2) It is a *line segment* joining the center to any point on the circle.

Quiz Yourself ⑤

Assume that a circle has a circumference of 40 inches. If a central angle has measure of 45°, what is the length of the arc of the circle determined by the sides of the angle?

EXAMPLE 3   *Finding the Circumference of Earth*

How can you use elementary geometry to estimate the circumference of Earth?*

SOLUTION: Consider Figure 10.15 below. Assume that lines l and m are parallel and cut by the transversal t. The point C is the center of the circle. Therefore, angles α and β are equal.

From our earlier discussion of central angles, we see that we have the following ratio:

$$\frac{\text{measure of angle } \beta}{360 \text{ degrees}} = \frac{\text{length of arc cut by sides of } \beta}{\text{total circumference of circle}}.$$

With this observation, it is easy to measure the circumference of Earth. Begin by placing a vertical pole in the ground and waiting until high noon when the rays of the Sun and the pole form an angle of 0°. Suppose at that very moment, you are talking to a friend who lives 1,000 miles away and who also has a similar vertical pole. Your friend tells you that the Sun's rays make an angle of 15° with his pole. If you redraw Figure 10.15 as in Figure 10.16, you will see how to find your answer.

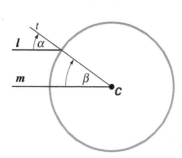

FIGURE 10.15 $\alpha = \beta$ because $l \parallel m$ and α and β are corresponding angles.

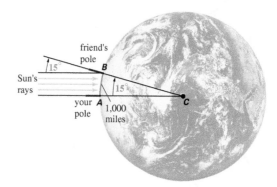

FIGURE 10.16 The measure of angle *ACB*, which is 15°, is the same fractional part of 360° as the length of the arc between *A* and *B* is of Earth's circumference.

Denote the circumference of Earth by c and set up the following ratio:

$$\frac{15°}{360°} = \frac{1,000}{c}. \tag{1}$$

Cross multiplying equation (1) results in the equation

$$15c = 360(1,000). \tag{2}$$

Dividing both sides of equation (2) by 15 and simplifying gives us $c = 24,000$. From this calculation, you can estimate the circumference of Earth to be 24,000 miles.

Now try Exercises 55 and 56. ✵

---

*Although Earth is not a perfect sphere, we will assume that it is in order to simplify our calculations.

HISTORICAL HIGHLIGHT ✻ ✻ ✻

Non-Euclidean Geometry (Part 1)

Several years ago I had the opportunity to fly to France to visit my sister. As the jetliner climbed to an altitude of over 6 miles, a monitor displayed the path the flight was taking from Newark, New Jersey, to Paris. Surprisingly, instead of flying straight across the ocean, the plane went to the north towards Greenland and after several hours into the flight, it was clear that the flight path was curved. This might surprise you as well, because as we all know—the shortest distance between two points is a straight line—or is it? Although this statement *is true* for points on a plane, *it is not true* for other surfaces. On a sphere, the shortest distance between two points is an arc of a *great circle.** A great circle, as shown in Figure 10.17, is a circle on a sphere that has the same center as the sphere. Therefore, in spherical geometry, we think of a "line" as a great circle.

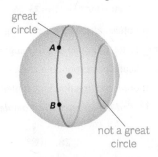

FIGURE 10.17 The distance between points *A* and *B* on a sphere is an arc of a great circle.

There can be no parallel lines in spherical geometry because any two great circles on a sphere intersect in two points. In Figure 10.18, the two great circles intersect at points *P* and *Q*.

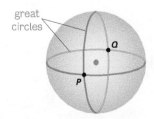

FIGURE 10.18 Two great circles intersect at points *P* and *Q*.

Notice that what we consider to be lines and what properties these lines have depends on the surface on which we are drawing the lines.

Euclid's fifth postulate[†] states that through a point not on a given line there is *exactly one* line that is parallel to the given line, as we show in Figure 10.19.

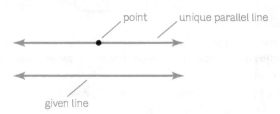

FIGURE 10.19 Euclid's fifth postulate.

However, for centuries mathematicians speculated that Euclid's fifth postulate could be proved from his other postulates. Unable to prove the fifth postulate, mathematicians decided to take another approach. They asked: "What if we assume that the fifth postulate is false? What would our geometry be like?"

There are two ways to deny the fifth postulate:

1) Assume that for a line and a point not on that line, there are no lines parallel to the given line.

2) Assume that for a line and a point not on that line, there are at least two lines parallel to the given line.

The first approach led to geometries such as spherical geometry that we mentioned previously. Around 1850, the great German mathematician Bernhard Riemann invented such a geometry.

In the early part of the nineteenth century, Karl Friedrich Gauss from Germany, Janos Bolyai from Hungary, and Nicolai Lobachevsky from Russia each independently developed a geometry using the second approach. We can visualize this type of geometry on a surface called a *pseudosphere*. To form a pseudosphere, we rotate a curve called a *tractrix* about a line, as shown in Figure 10.20.

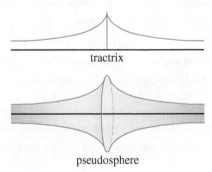

FIGURE 10.20 A pseudosphere is a model of a non-Euclidean geometry.

The surface looks somewhat like the bells of two trumpets joined together. We will discuss these non-Euclidean geometries further in Section 10.2.

---

*Arcs of circles that are not great circles will not give the shortest distance between two points on the surface of a sphere.
[†]This postulate was an assumption made by Euclid about geometry that could not be proved.

Exercises 10.1

Looking Back*

These exercises follow the general outline of the topics presented in this section and will give you a good overview of the material that you have just studied.

1. Use Figure 10.7 to name the type of angle described by each of the following angle measures:

   a. between 0° and 90°   **b.** 90°

   c. between 90° and 180°   **d.** 180°

2. Use Figure 10.10 to find an example of each of the following other than the examples mentioned in Table 10.1:

   a. corresponding angles

   b. alternate interior angles

3. In solving Example 2, what relationship were we using between the length of the arc *AB* and the central angle *ACB*?

4. What is the shortest distance between two points on a sphere?

Sharpening Your Skills

In Exercises 5–12, match each term with the numbered angles in the given figure. There may be several correct answers. We will state only one in the answer key. Lines l and m are parallel.

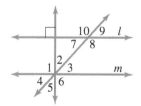

Figure for Exercises 5–12

5. vertical angles   6. complementary angles

7. alternate interior angles   8. right angle

9. obtuse angle   10. corresponding angles

11. supplementary angles   12. acute angle

In Exercises 13–22, determine whether each statement is true or false. Remember by the Always Principle that if a statement is true, it must always be true without exception. If you believe that a statement is false, you should try to find a counterexample.

13. Two lines lying on the same plane that do not intersect are parallel.

14. At least two of the angles formed by two intersecting lines are equal.

15. If two angles are complementary, then they must be equal.

16. If two angles (with measure greater than 0°) are complementary, then each must be an acute angle.

17. If two equal angles are supplementary, then each is a right angle.

18. An obtuse angle cannot be complementary to another angle.

19. An angle cannot be the complement of one angle and the supplement of another angle at the same time.

20. Four of the angles formed when parallel lines are cut by a transversal are equal.

21. The supplement of an acute angle must be an acute angle.

22. Alternate interior angles must be acute angles.

Use the given figure to answer Exercises 23–26. There may be several correct answers. We will state only one in the answer key.

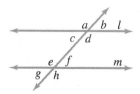

Figure for Exercises 23–26

23. Find a pair of obtuse, alternate interior angles.

24. Find a pair of acute, alternate exterior angles.

25. Find a pair of acute, corresponding angles.

26. Find a pair of obtuse, corresponding angles.

In Exercises 27–32, find the measure of a complementary angle and a supplementary angle for each angle.

27. 30°   28. 108°

29. 120°   30. 45°

31. 51.2°   32. 110.4°

In Exercises 33–38, find the measures of angles a, b, and c in each figure. In Exercises 35–38, lines l and m are parallel.

33.

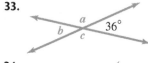

34.

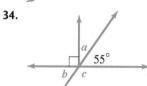

35.

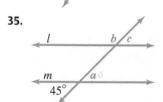

36.

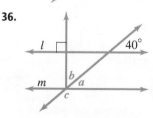

---

*Before doing these exercises, you may find it useful to review the note *How to Succeed at Mathematics* on page xix.

37.

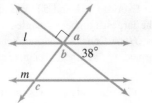

38.

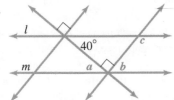

In Exercises 39–44, you are given two of the following three pieces of information: the circumference of the circle, the measure of the central angle ACB, and the length of arc AB. Find the third piece of information.

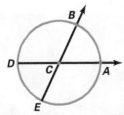

Figure for Exercises 39–44

39. circumference = 24 feet; $m\angle ACB = 90°$

40. circumference = 150 centimeters; $m\angle ACB = 72°$

41. circumference = 12 meters; length of arc $AB = 4$ meters

42. circumference = 240 inches; length of arc $AB = 40$ inches

43. $m\angle ACB = 30°$; length of arc $AB = 100$ millimeters

44. $m\angle ACB = 120°$; length of arc $AB = 9$ feet

Applying What You've Learned

Continuing the situation from Exercises 39–44, use the given information to answer Exercises 45–48.

45. circumference = 18 feet; $m\angle ACB = 60°$. Find the length of arc BD.

46. $m\angle ACB = 30°$; length of arc $AE = 10$ meters. Find the circumference.

47. circumference = 30 inches; length of arc $DE = 3$ inches. Find $m\angle BCD$.

48. circumference = 120 centimeters; length of arc $AB = 12$ centimeters. Find $m\angle DCE$.

In Exercises 49–52, solve for x. Assume that lines l and m are parallel.

49.   **50.**

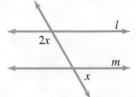   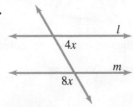

51.   **52.**

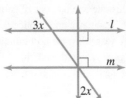   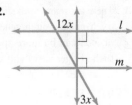

53. Two lines in a plane can intersect forming four angles (some may have the same measure). What is the greatest number of angles we can form using three lines?

54. Solve Exercise 53 for four lines.

55. In Example 3, your friend has erred in measuring the angle the vertical pole makes with the Sun's rays because the correct circumference of Earth is closer to 25,000 miles than 24,000 miles. If we use the circumference of 25,000 miles in Example 3, what should the angle measurement taken by your friend have been?

56. Reconsider Example 3. Assume that you do not know how far your friend is from you. At high noon, your time, your friend tells you that the Sun's rays make an 18° angle with the vertical pole he has in the ground. Assume that the true circumference of Earth is 25,000 miles. How far away is your friend?

Communicating Mathematics

57. What is the difference between supplementary and complementary angles?

58. When a pair of parallel lines is cut by a transversal, name three types of angles that are pairwise equal.

59. Explain how you remember the meaning of *alternate exterior angles.*

60. Explain how you remember the meaning of *interior angles on the same side of the transversal.*

In Exercises 61–64, use the fact that two intersecting lines form four angles.

61. Can all of the four angles be equal? Explain your answer.

62. Can all of the four angles be acute? Explain your answer.

63. What is the largest number of angles that can be obtuse? Explain your answer.

64. Could three of these angles be acute and one of them be obtuse? Explain your answer.

65. Can alternate interior angles be complementary? Explain.

66. Can alternate interior angles be supplementary? Explain.

Using Technology to Investigate Mathematics

67. You can find many interactive applets that illustrate the ideas of this section. For example, I found applets that illustrate Euclid's elements, tutorials that illustrate various properties of parallel lines and angles, and so forth. Search the Internet for some applets and duplicate some of the computations of this section. Report on your findings.

68. There are many Web sites that illustrate applications of geometry. You can search generally for "geometry and applications," or, you can be more specific by searching for combinations such as "geometry and art" or "geometry and medicine." Find some sites illustrating interesting applications of geometry and report on your findings.

For Extra Credit

69. Draw a diagram that has four lines and six points and in which each line passes through exactly three of the six points.

70. Draw a diagram that has 5 lines and 10 points and in which each line passes through exactly 4 of the 10 points.

71. Consider your solutions to Exercises 53 and 54. Without drawing a diagram, find the largest number of angles that can be formed by 10 lines. (*Hint:* Consider the number of intersections that can be formed by five lines, six lines, and so on.)

72. A boat lost at sea has a radio that transmits a distress signal. Anyone receiving the signal can determine the direction of the signal, but not the distance. Explain why if one ship receives the signal, it cannot notify a search plane of the exact location of the boat. If two different ships receive the signal, the exact location of the boat can now be determined. Explain how to find the boat's position with the information from both ships.

10.2 Polygons

Objectives

1. Understand the basic terminology and properties of polygons.
2. Solve problems involving angle relationships of polygons.
3. Use similar polygons to solve problems.
4. Be aware of some differences between Euclidean and non-Euclidean geometries.

Have you noticed the great number of geometric figures that you encounter each day? They are literally all around you. You see them in magazine ads, TV commercials, clothing design, art, architecture, product design, and religious symbols, as well as in many other places. In this section, we will build on our previous discussion of lines and angles to study a familiar class of geometric objects called *polygons*.

 **KEY POINT**

Polygons are special types of plane figures made up of line segments.

Polygons

We begin with a few definitions (see Figures 10.21 and 10.22).

> **DEFINITIONS** A plane figure is **closed** if we can draw it without lifting the pencil and if the starting and ending points are the same. A plane figure is **simple** if we can draw it without lifting the pencil and in drawing it we never pass through the same point twice, with the possible exception of the starting and ending points.

closed and simple   simple, not closed   closed, not simple   not simple, not closed

FIGURE 10.21 Closed and simple plane figures.

DEFINITIONS A **polygon** is a simple, closed plane figure consisting only of line segments, called **edges**, such that no two consecutive edges lie on the same line. We call an endpoint of an edge a **vertex** (plural, *vertices*). A polygon is **regular** if all of its edges are the same length and all of its angles have the same measure.

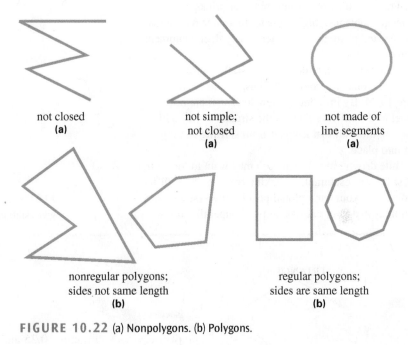

FIGURE 10.22 (a) Nonpolygons. (b) Polygons.

Number of Sides	Name of Polygon
3	Triangle
4	Quadrilateral
5	Pentagon
6	Hexagon
7	Heptagon
8	Octagon
9	Nonagon
10	Decagon

TABLE 10.2 Names of polygons.

We classify polygons according to the number of their sides. Table 10.2 lists the names of polygons having up to 10 sides.

There is another property that a polygon may have regarding its shape.

DEFINITION A polygon is **convex** if for any two points *X* and *Y* inside the polygon, the entire line segment *XY* also lies inside the polygon.

Figure 10.23 shows a convex and a nonconvex polygon.

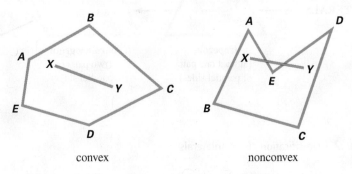

FIGURE 10.23 A convex and a nonconvex polygon.

❉ ❉ ❉ HIGHLIGHT

Geometry in Everyday Things

If the floor to your new apartment is not perfectly even, you might consider buying a coffee table with three legs instead of four. Any three points always lie on a plane, so the three-legged table won't wobble and spill your drinks, but the four-legged table just might. It is for this same reason that surveyors and photographers often steady their equipment on three-legged tripods.

When carpenters build a new wall, they often nail a board diagonally across the beams, as shown in Figure 10.24. By introducing new lines that are not parallel to the existing lines in the structure, they add rigidity to the wall that keeps it from shifting as they lift it into place.

While driving in your car, you may want to locate the nearest Italian restaurant. By taking readings from different locations, your car's global positioning system (GPS) determines that your car lies on two nonparallel lines.

Because these lines intersect in a unique point, the system can find your exact location and direct you to the nearest restaurant.

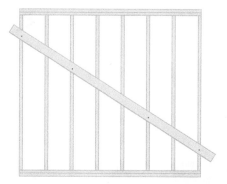

FIGURE.10.24 The diagonal board gives stability to the frame.

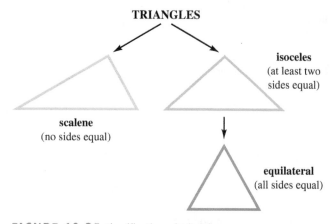

FIGURE 10.25 Classification of triangles.

Figures 10.25 and 10.26 show some special types of triangles and quadrilaterals. In these figures, an object following an arrow has all the properties of the objects preceding the arrow. For example, in Figure 10.25 we see that every equilateral triangle is also an isoceles triangle. Note that an isoceles triangle may not necessarily be an equilateral triangle.

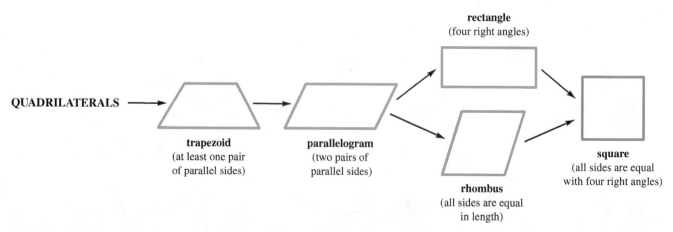

FIGURE 10.26 Classification of quadrilaterals.*

---

*Some define a trapezoid to be a quadrilateral that has *exactly one* pair of parallel sides. According to this alternate definition, a parallelogram would not be a trapezoid.

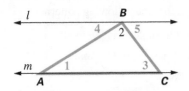

FIGURE 10.27 Lines *l* and *m* are parallel lines cut by transversals that form equal alternate interior angles.

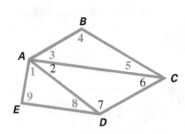

FIGURE 10.28 A pentagon divided into a collection of triangles.

Polygons and Angles

We can use polygons to solve real-life problems such as designing a deck or building a house. However, to do this, we often need to know the sum of measures of the interior angles of the polygons. For example, imagine how difficult it would be to design a hexagon-shaped gazebo without knowing the measure of the interior angles of the floor.

EXAMPLE 1 *The Angle Sum of a Triangle Is 180°*

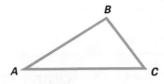

Find the sum of the measures of the interior angles in $\triangle ABC$. (The notation $\triangle ABC$ is read "triangle *ABC*.")

SOLUTION: We begin by constructing a line *m* that contains line segment *AC* and a second line *l* through point *B* that is parallel to *m*, as shown in Figure 10.27.

Because angles 1 and 4 are alternate interior angles, they are equal. Similarly, angles 3 and 5 are equal. Therefore, the sum of the measures of angles 1, 2, and 3 equals the sum of the measures of angles 4, 2, and 5, which is 180°. ✳

Now that we know the sum of the angles of a triangle, we can use this information to find the interior angle sum of other polygons.

EXAMPLE 2 *The Angle Sum of a Pentagon*

Find the interior angle sum of the convex pentagon *ABCDE*.

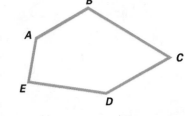

SOLUTION: Because we already know the interior angle sum for a triangle, it makes sense to divide the pentagon into a collection of triangles, as shown in Figure 10.28.

Notice in Figure 10.28 that $\angle A$ is made up of three smaller angles 1, 2, and 3. Also, $\angle C$ consists of angles 5 and 6 and $\angle D$ is made up of angles 7 and 8.

The sum of the angles of the pentagon is

$$m\angle A + m\angle B + m\angle C + m\angle D + m\angle E.$$

If we replace $m\angle A$ by $m\angle 1 + m\angle 2 + m\angle 3$, $m\angle C$ by $m\angle 5 + m\angle 6$, and $m\angle D$ by $m\angle 7 + m\angle 8$, we see that the angle sum of the pentagon is

$$m\angle 1 + m\angle 2 + m\angle 3 + \cdots + m\angle 9.$$

This is the same as the angle sum of the three triangles $\triangle AED$, $\triangle ADC$, and $\triangle ACB$, which equals $3 \times 180° = 540°$.

Now try Exercises 19 to 24. ✳ **6**

Quiz Yourself 6

Apply the method used in Example 2 to find the interior angle sum of quadrilateral *ABCD*.

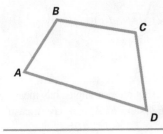

 PROBLEM SOLVING

Convert a New Problem to an Earlier One

As we mentioned in Section 1.1, you can often solve a new problem by relating it to one that you have seen before. We solved the problem in Example 2 by relating it to the earlier problem of finding the angle sum of a triangle.

KEY POINT

The number of sides of a polygon determines the sum of the measures of its interior angles.

Table 10.3 summarizes what you have seen so far about the angle sum of polygons.

Polygon	Number of Sides	Interior Angle Sum
Triangle	3	$180° = 1 \times 180°$
Quadrilateral	4	$360° = 2 \times 180°$
Pentagon	5	$540° = 3 \times 180°$

TABLE 10.3 Interior angle sum of polygons.

We can generalize this pattern to n-sided convex polygons.

> **ANGLE SUM OF A POLYGON** The sum of the measures of the interior angles of a convex polygon having n sides is $(n-2) \times 180°$.

If a polygon is regular, we can say a little more about the angles of the polygon. Because each angle of a regular polygon has the same measure, we find the following pattern:

each interior angle of a regular triangle (an equilateral triangle) has $\frac{180°}{3} = 60°$,

each interior angle of a regular quadrilateral (a square) has $\frac{360°}{4} = 90°$, and

each interior angle of a regular pentagon has $\frac{540°}{5} = 108°$.

We can also generalize this pattern.

> **INTERIOR ANGLES OF A REGULAR POLYGON** Each interior angle of a regular polygon with n sides has measure $\frac{(n-2) \times 180°}{n}$. **7**

Quiz Yourself **7**

Find the measure of each interior angle of a regular octagon.

Although many word-processing and computer illustration programs have graphics capabilities, you often need to understand basic geometry in order to draw a figure exactly the way you want it to look.

EXAMPLE 3 *Designing a Logo*

Imagine that *Dancing with the Stars* is taking its act on tour to your city and your advertising company has been hired to design a giant star-shaped billboard to advertise this event. Determine the angle measure of each point of the star.

SOLUTION: Consider the star in Figure 10.29.

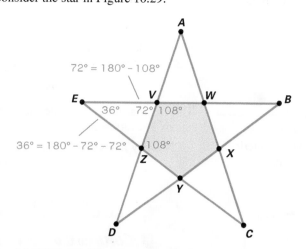

FIGURE 10.29 Constructing the five-point star.

The shaded pentagon *VWXYZ* is a regular pentagon, so each of its interior angles has measure $\frac{(5-2) \times 180°}{5} = 108°$. Because a straight angle equals 180°, $\angle EZV$ and EVZ each have measure $180° - 108° = 72°$. This means that angle E has measure $180° - 72° - 72° = 36°$. ❀

KEY POINT

Similar polygons have proportional sides and equal angles.

Similar Polygons

If you were hired to design a new open-air theater for your campus, you would first have to build a scale model of the project before a decision could be made to commit money for your project. As a graphic artist, you might create a small, preliminary version of an advertisement before enlarging it to billboard size. Similarly, fashion designers often make small sample garments that are later resized after they have sold the designs to stores. In each case, we are working with objects that have the same shape but different sizes. Likewise, in geometry, we often work with similar figures.

> **DEFINITION** Two polygons are **similar** if their corresponding sides are proportional and their corresponding angles are equal.

Polygons *A* and *B* in Figure 10.30 are similar. Sometimes it is useful to know if two triangles are similar. It can be proved in geometry that if one triangle has two angles equal to two angles in a second triangle, then the two triangles are similar. We will use this fact in Example 4.

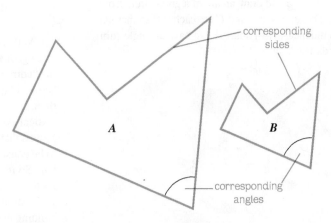

FIGURE 10.30 *A* and *B* are similar polygons.

EXAMPLE 4 *Using Similar Triangles to Build a Wilderness Bridge*

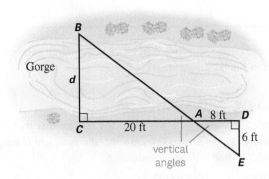

FIGURE 10.31 Building a bridge.

Yau-Man and James, racing against other teams in a wilderness survival contest, encounter a deep gorge whose bridge is missing. They plan to cross by cutting a tree to fall across the gorge to use as a temporary bridge. They have measured the distances in two right triangles, as shown in Figure 10.31. Use this information to find the distance, *d*, across the gorge.

SOLUTION: Angles *BAC* and *DAE* are vertical angles and therefore equal. Also, angles *D* and *C* are right angles, so they also are equal. Therefore, triangles *ACB* and *ADE* are similar, and so their corresponding sides are proportional. This gives us the ratio

$$\frac{\text{length of } BC}{\text{length of } ED} = \frac{\text{length of } AC}{\text{length of } AD}.$$

Substituting for these four lengths, we get $\frac{d}{6} = \frac{20}{8}$. Cross multiplying gives the equation $d \cdot 8 = 6 \cdot 20 = 120$. Dividing both sides of the equation by 8 gives us $d = \frac{120}{8} = 15$. Therefore, a 15-foot tree will do the job. ❋

❊ ❊ ❊ HISTORICAL HIGHLIGHT

Non-Euclidean Geometry (Part 2)

Because the fundamental axioms of non-Euclidean geometry are different from Euclid's axioms, it is not surprising that when we rephrase well-known Euclidean geometry theorems in non-Euclidean terms, they sound somewhat strange. The Euclidean theorem that the interior angle sum of a triangle is 180° in Riemannian geometry becomes

the interior angle sum of a triangle is greater than 180°.

If we consider the surface of a sphere, it is not hard to understand why this theorem should be true. Figure 10.32 shows a triangle whose interior angle sum is greater than 180°. Imagine beginning at the top of the sphere, the North Pole so to speak (call this point *A*), and draw an arc of a great circle to meet another great circle that is horizontal, comparable to the equator. Call this point *B*. Make a right angle, draw an arc along this "equator" to point *C*, and then make a right angle and draw an arc of a great circle from *C* back to *A*. The angles at *B* and *C* are each 90° so that when we add in the measure of angle *A*, we have an angle sum that exceeds 180°.

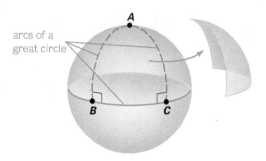

FIGURE 10.32 Triangle with angle sum greater than 180°.

On a pseudosphere, which has a shape like two bells of a trumpet, triangles look something like the curved triangle drawn in Figure 10.33. In this type of non-Euclidean geometry, triangles have an interior angle sum that is less than 180°.

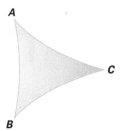

FIGURE 10.33
Triangle with an angle sum less than 180°.

At this point, you might be wondering which of the three geometries (Euclid's, Riemann's, Lobachevsky's) is the "correct" geometry. The answer is that there is no one "correct" geometry. Mathematicians have proved that all three types of geometries are perfectly consistent mathematical systems. Even more remarkable, they have also proved that for any one of these non-Euclidean geometries to be consistent, the other two types must also be consistent. So in this sense, no one of the geometries is better. As to which geometry we use, it all depends on what application we have in mind. For surveying land and building buildings, Euclidean geometry is appropriate; however, Einstein found that to understand the vastness of the universe, non-Euclidean geometry is a better tool.

Exercises 〔 **10.2** 〕

Looking Back*

These exercises follow the general outline of the topics presented in this section and will give you a good overview of the material that you have just studied.

1. What property did we use in Example 1 involving parallel lines cut by a transversal? What information did that property give us?

2. How did we arrive at the fact that the sum of the interior angles of the pentagon in Example 2 was 540°?

3. In Example 3, how did we determine that $m\angle EVZ = 72°$?

4. State one difference between triangles in Euclidean geometry and non-Euclidean geometry.

Sharpening Your Skills

In Exercises 5–10, determine whether each statement is true or false. Remember by the Always Principle that if a statement is true, it must always be true without exception.

5. A trapezoid is a parallelogram.

6. A rhombus is a parallelogram.

7. A regular polygon is convex.

---

*Before doing these exercises, you may find it useful to review the note *How to Succeed at Mathematics* on page xix.

8. If two polygons have corresponding angles equal, then the polygons are similar.

9. If two polygons have corresponding sides equal, then the polygons are similar.

10. A convex polygon can have an interior angle sum of 400°.

In Exercises 11–14, state whether each figure is a polygon. For those that are not polygons, state what part of the definition fails.

11.

12.

13.

14.

In Exercises 15–18, use the information that we give you to find the measures of angles A, B, *and* C *in* △ABC. *All measures are in degrees.*

15. $m\angle B = 2m\angle A, m\angle C = 3m\angle A$

16. $m\angle B = m\angle A, m\angle C = 5 + 3m\angle A$

17. $m\angle B = m\angle A + 10, m\angle C = 2m\angle A - 10$

18. $m\angle B = 3m\angle A, m\angle C = 2m\angle A + m\angle B$

19. If we divide a regular hexagon into triangles as we did in Example 2, how many triangles will there be? What will be the interior angle sum of the hexagon?

20. If we divide a regular octagon into triangles as we did in Example 2, how many triangles will there be? What will be the interior angle sum of the hexagon?

21. What is the measure of an interior angle of a regular 20-sided polygon?

22. What is the measure of an interior angle of a regular 12-sided polygon?

23. If each interior angle of a regular polygon measures 160°, how many sides does the polygon have?

24. If each interior angle of a regular polygon measures 135°, how many sides does the polygon have?

In Exercises 25 to 28, assume that each of the triangles in a pair are similar. Find length x.

25.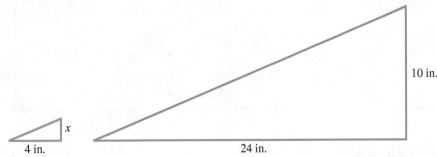

26.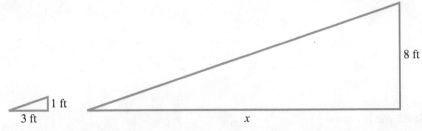

27.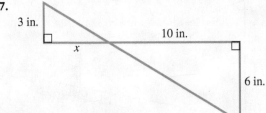

28.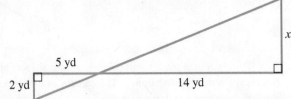

In Exercises 29–32, assume that in each pair the figures are similar. Given the lengths of sides and measures of angles in the left figure, what information do you know about the right figure?

29.

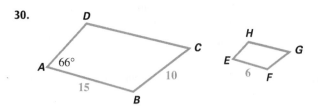

30.

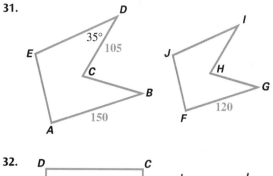

31.

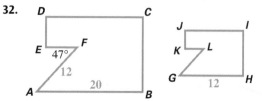

32.

Applying What You've Learned

33. The Russians erected the world's largest full-figure statue, *Motherland*, which is 270 feet tall, as a World War II memorial. If at a certain time of day, a 6-foot person casts a 10-foot shadow, how long will the statue's shadow be?

34. If Yao Ming, the 7-foot 6-inch center of the Houston Rockets casts a shadow of 18 feet 9 inches and Chauncy Billups, guard with the Detroit Pistons, standing beside him casts a shadow of 15 feet, $7\frac{1}{2}$ inches, how tall is Billups?

35. How wide is the river below at point *A*?

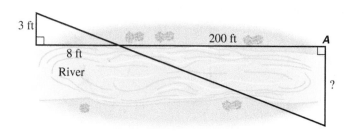

36. How wide is the river below at point *A*?

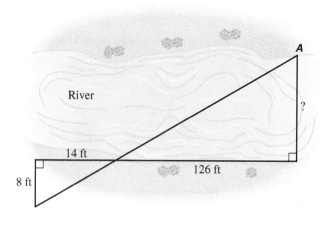

37. If triangles *ABC* and *ADE* are similar in this diagram, what is the length of the pond?

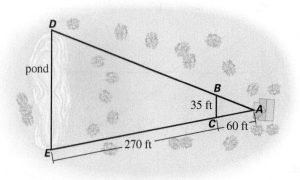

38. Jack Bauer wants to place a surveillance camera at location *C* to observe activity at location *X*. The camera cannot be seen directly from position *X* because of a large clump of bushes.

The camera will take pictures by aiming at a building, *M*, with shiny, mirror-like sides, as shown in the diagram. How far should the camera be positioned from point *I* for this setup to work?

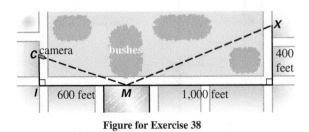

Figure for Exercise 38

Some Japanese furniture makers construct elegant wooden furniture without using any glue or mechanical fasteners. To assemble the furniture, the pieces of wood must be cut precisely so that they fit together tightly.

39. A furniture maker is constructing a chair using a horizontal beam with a cross section in the shape of a regular pentagon. The beam must fit into a notch cut into a support post so that an angle of the beam fits exactly in a notch cut in the post, as shown in the given diagram. What should the measure of the indicated angles be so that the beam fits exactly in the notch?

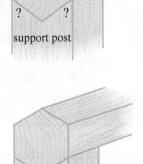

40. Repeat Exercise 39, but now assume that the horizontal beam has a cross section in the shape of a regular hexagon. The beam will rest in the support post as shown in the given diagram.

41. A gazebo has a floor in the shape of a regular hexagon with each side measuring 10 feet. The floor requires two supports, as shown, that measure roughly 17.4 feet. If we plan to build a slightly larger gazebo with 12-foot sides, how long must the support beams be?

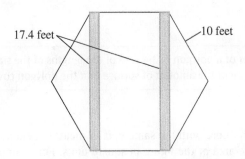

42. If the longest support beams in Exercise 41 that we can purchase are 15 feet, what would the length of the sides of the gazebo be?

Communicating Mathematics

43. What is the difference between an isosceles and an equilateral triangle?

44. What information do you know about the angles and the sides of similar polygons?

45. Can an isoceles triangle also be a scalene triangle? Explain.

46. Can an isoceles triangle also be an equilateral triangle? Explain.

47. What is the difference between a rhombus and a square?

48. What is the difference between a trapezoid and a parallelogram?

Using Technology to Investigate Mathematics

49. Search the Web for applications of geometry in different cultures. For example, you can find interesting sites if you search for "geometry and native American" or "geometry and Chinese." Find a site that interests you and report on your findings.

50. There are sites on the Internet devoted to non-Euclidean geometry. Some have applets that allow you to construct various geometric figures. Find such a site, run some of the applets, and report on your findings.

For Extra Credit

In Exercises 51–54, if it is possible to construct a triangle of the type described, then explain how you might draw one. If it is impossible to construct the triangle described, explain why it is impossible.

51. A scalene triangle with two acute angles

52. A right triangle that also has an obtuse angle

53. An equilateral triangle that has all obtuse angles

54. An equilateral triangle that has all acute angles

55. Make up a description of a triangle as we did in Exercises 51–54 that is impossible to construct.

56. Make up a description of a triangle as we did in Exercises 51–54 that is possible to construct.

57. What happens to the measure of the interior angles of a regular *n*-sided polygon as *n* gets larger and larger? Explain your answer.

58. The English surveyors Mason and Dixon surveyed the famous Mason–Dixon line between Maryland and Pennsylvania using a level made from wood in the shape of the letter A,* as shown in the given diagram. A string with a weight hangs from the tip of the level. Explain

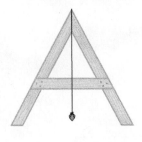

---

*J. E. Thompson, *Geometry for the Practical Worker* (New York: Van Nostrand Reinhold, 1982), p. 82.

how you would build such a level and also explain how it would work. Be sure to discuss lengths of line segments and measures of angles.

59. Generalize Exercises 39 and 40. If the cross beam has a cross section in the shape of a regular polygon with *n* sides, what would be the measure of the indicated angles for the support beam? Assume that one vertex of the end of the cross beam points directly down, as was the case in Exercises 39 and 40.

60. In building scaffolding, often the scaffolding has many triangles, as shown in figure (a). What advantage do you see in using scaffolding of type (a) versus type (b)? (*Hint:* There is a fundamental property that triangles have that rectangles do not have.)

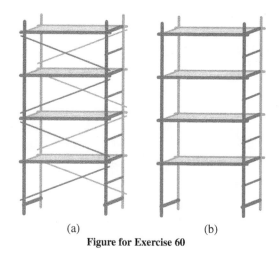

(a)   (b)

Figure for Exercise 60

10.3 Perimeter and Area

Objectives

1. Calculate the perimeter and area of geometric objects.
2. Understand how area formulas for geometric figures are related.
3. Use the Pythagorean theorem to solve problems involving right triangles.
4. Calculate the circumference and area of circles.

It's good that your vacation is coming up because you sure have a lot of jobs to get done around the house. Your new puppy Max is a lot of fun, but he just won't stay in the yard, so you'll have to think about getting a fence. Your dining room could use some touching up. Some fresh paint and decorative molding would certainly brighten up the room. Also, the deck is looking a little shabby and could use a new coat of sealer. If you have time, it would also be good to look into what size solar panels to have installed to take the bite out of your heating bill. What should you do first?

Perimeter and Area

Well, the first thing that you will need to do to get these jobs done is to recall some basic facts about perimeter and area.

> **DEFINITIONS** The **perimeter** of a polygon is the sum of the lengths of the sides of the polygon. The **area** is a measure of the amount of surface that the polygon covers.

We measure the perimeter of a figure with the same unit of measurement as we measure the sides, and we measure the area of the figure in square units. For example, as we see in Figure 10.34, a rectangle with length 6 feet and width 4 feet, has a perimeter of $6 + 4 + 6 + 4 = 20$ feet, and the area is $6 \times 4 = 24$ square feet.

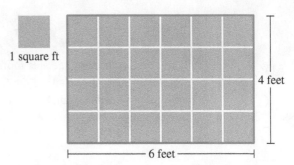

FIGURE 10.34 The perimeter of the rectangle is 20 feet; the area is 24 square feet.

The following are general formulas for calculating the perimeter and area of rectangles.

> **PERIMETER AND AREA OF A RECTANGLE** If a rectangle has length *l* and width *w*, then the perimeter of the rectangle is $P = 2l + 2w$ and the area is $A = l \cdot w$.

KEY POINT

We can use the formula for the area of a rectangle to derive formulas for the area of other polygons.

Deriving Area Formulas

Knowing how to do a calculation for one type of geometric figure often leads us to a method for doing that same computation for another type of figure. For example, once we know the formula for the area of a rectangle, we can easily derive the formula for the area of a parallelogram.

Consider the parallelogram in Figure 10.35(a), which has height *h* and base *b*. If we cut off the blue triangle on the left, slide it over, and attach it to the right side of the parallelogram, we get the rectangle shown in Figure 10.35(b). We know that the area of this rectangle is $h \cdot b$, so therefore the area of the parallelogram is also $h \cdot b$.

> **AREA OF A PARALLELOGRAM** The area of a parallelogram with height *h* and base *b* is $A = h \cdot b$.

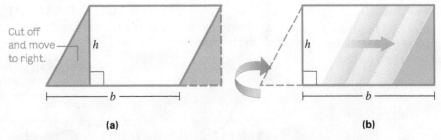

(a)   **(b)**

FIGURE 10.35 (a) Parallelogram. (b) The area of the parallelogram = the area of the rectangle = $h \cdot b$.

We next use the formula for the area of a parallelogram to derive the formula for the area of a triangle. In Figure 10.36, triangle *ABC* has height *h* and base *b*. It is easy to see that the area of △*ABC* is exactly one-half of the area of the parallelogram *AXBC*, which has area $h \cdot b$. Therefore, △*ABC* has area $\frac{1}{2}h \cdot b$.

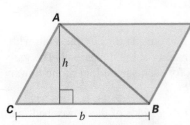

FIGURE 10.36 The area of △*ABC* is one-half the area of the parallelogram, or $\frac{1}{2}h \cdot b$.

> **AREA OF A TRIANGLE** A triangle with height *h* and base *b* has area $A = \frac{1}{2}h \cdot b$.

Some Good Advice

If you practice deriving the area formulas as we have developed them, it will be easier for you to remember the details of the formulas. For example, remembering that a triangle is one-half of a parallelogram helps you recall that there is a factor of $\frac{1}{2}$ in the formula for the area of a triangle.

EXAMPLE 1   *The Area of a Playground*

a) Figure 10.37 shows a recreation area in the shape of a parallelogram. If a pound of grass seed covers 100 square yards, how much grass seed is needed to seed the entire area?

b) Suppose that we want to seed only the triangular area *ACD*. How much grass seed will be needed then?

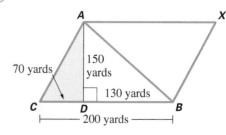

FIGURE 10.37 Recreation area shaped like a parallelogram.

SOLUTION:

a) The area of the parallelogram is $A = h \cdot b = 150 \cdot 200 = 30{,}000$ square yards. Dividing this area by 100, we see that 300 pounds of grass seed are needed for the entire recreation area.

b) Triangle *ACD* is a triangle with base 70 yards and height 150 yards. The area of this triangle is $\frac{1}{2}h \cdot b = \frac{1}{2} \cdot 150 \cdot 70 = 5{,}250$ square yards. Dividing this by 100 we get 52.5, which is the number of pounds of grass seed required for this area.

Now try Exercises 11 and 12. ❋ **8**

Quiz Yourself **8**

Find the area of the given triangle.

Sometimes we don't know the height of a triangle, but we do know the length of all three sides. In this case we can use Heron's formula to find the area of the triangle. Because this formula is not as intuitively clear as the formula we developed earlier, we will state it without proof.

✎ **KEY POINT**

Heron's formula uses the lengths of the sides of a triangle to find its area.

> **HERON'S FORMULA FOR THE AREA OF A TRIANGLE** Suppose that a triangle has sides *a*, *b*, and *c*. We define the quantity $s = \frac{1}{2}(a + b + c)$. Then the area of the triangle is
> $$A = \sqrt{s(s-a)(s-b)(s-c)}.$$

EXAMPLE 2   *Finding the Area of a Triangular Flower Bed Using Heron's Formula*

A gardener wants to fill a triangular flower bed outside the city museum with yellow tulips. Figure 10.38 shows the dimensions of the flower bed. The gardener estimates that he will need four bulbs for each square foot of the flower bed. How many dozen bulbs should he buy?

SOLUTION: Because we know the length of the sides of the flower bed, we can use Heron's formula. First we find

$$s = \frac{1}{2}(a + b + c) = \frac{1}{2}(18 + 12 + 24) = 27.$$

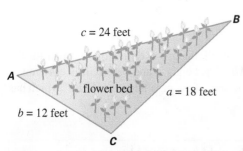

FIGURE 10.38 Triangular flower bed.

Then the area of the flower bed is

$$A = \sqrt{s(s-a)(s-b)(s-c)} = \sqrt{27(9)(15)(3)} = \sqrt{10{,}935} \approx 105 \text{ square feet.}$$

Therefore, the gardener needs about $105 \times 4 = 420 = 35$ dozen bulbs.

Now try Exercises 31 to 36. ✳

We can use the area formula for a triangle to develop area formulas for other figures such as the trapezoid shown in Figure 10.39 (a).

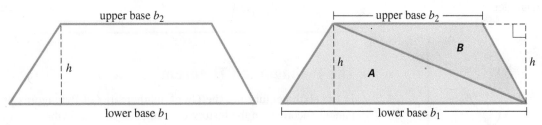

FIGURE 10.39 (a) A trapezoid. (b) The area of the trapezoid is the sum of the area of triangles A and B.

We will begin by dividing this trapezoid into two triangles, as we show in Figure 10.39 (b). Triangle A has base b_1 and height h, so the area of triangle A is $\frac{1}{2}b_1 \cdot h$. Similarly, triangle B has base b_2 and height h, so its area is $\frac{1}{2}b_2 \cdot h$. The area of the trapezoid is the area of A plus the area of B, which equals $\frac{1}{2}b_1 \cdot h + \frac{1}{2}b_2 \cdot h = \frac{1}{2}(b_1 + b_2) \times h$.

AREA OF A TRAPEZOID   A trapezoid with lower base b_1, upper base b_2, and height h has area

$$A = \frac{1}{2}(b_1 + b_2) \times h.$$

EXAMPLE 3   *Finding the Area of Trapezoids in the Base of a Statue*

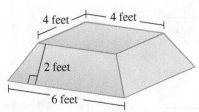

FIGURE 10.40 Base for statue formed by one square and four trapezoids.

A sculptor has created a statue for the lobby of the town's historical society building. Because the building is old and the town engineer wants to reduce the weight of the platform the statue will rest on, he recommends a hollow base instead of a solid one. The platform will be formed by joining four congruent trapezoids and one square, as shown in Figure 10.40. To determine which material will be best for the platform, the sculptor needs to know the surface area of the platform. Use the formulas we have developed so far to determine this surface area.

SOLUTION: We know that the area of the top of the platform is $4 \times 4 = 16$ square feet. Each side is a trapezoid with lower base 6 feet, upper base 4 feet, and height 2. Therefore, using the formula for the area of a trapezoid, the area of each face is

$$\frac{1}{2}(b_1 + b_2) \times h = \frac{1}{2}(6 + 4) \times 2 = 10 \text{ square feet.}$$

The total area of the four trapezoidal sides plus the top is $4 \times 10 + 16 = 56$ square feet.

Now try Exercises 9 and 10. ✳ **9**

Quiz Yourself **9**

Find the area of the given trapezoid.

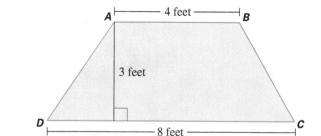

✎ **KEY POINT**

We can use the Pythagorean theorem to find measurements involving right triangles.

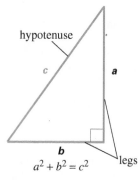

FIGURE 10.42 The Pythagorean theorem.

The Pythagorean Theorem

In the sixth century BC, the Greek mathematician Pythagoras proved one of the most famous theorems in the history of mathematics. The Pythagorean theorem states that the sum of the squares of the lengths of the legs of a right triangle equals the square of the length of the hypotenuse.

> **THE PYTHAGOREAN THEOREM** If a and b are the legs of a right triangle and c is the hypotenuse (the side opposite the right angle, shown in red) then $a^2 + b^2 = c^2$ (see Figure 10.42).

Math in Your Life

That Geometry Looks Lovely on You*

A serious clothing designer needs to understand the basic notions of plane geometry that you are studying in this chapter. Two common methods of pattern making that designers use are the flat pattern method and draping.

A designer using the flat pattern method may begin with a generic pattern called a *bodice sloper*, as shown in Figure 10.41. This sloper is a rectangle from which various geometric shapes have been removed. By modifying this basic sloper, the designer can then create a blouse or a jacket. For women's clothes, there are also slopers for skirts, pants, and sleeves.

In draping, the designer drapes fabric cut into various shapes, such as rectangles, circles, and half circles, on a dress form or on a live model. A talented designer who creates fashions this way must have a good intuitive understanding of geometry.

So, you see that not only is geometry "all around us" but we wear it every day.

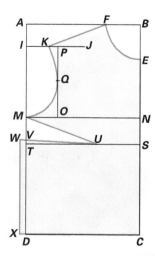

FIGURE 10.41 A bodice sloper.

---

*This example is based on the article "The Drafter, the Draper, the Flat Pattern," *Threads Magazine*, no. 11, June/July 1987, pp. 33–37.

If we know the lengths of any two sides of a right triangle, we can use the Pythagorean theorem to find the length of the third side.

EXAMPLE 4   *Using the Pythagorean Theorem*

Use the lengths of the two given sides to find the length of the third side in the triangles in Figure 10.43.

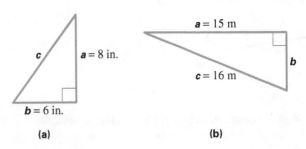

FIGURE 10.43 Using the Pythagorean theorem.

SOLUTION:

a) We are given $a = 8$ and $b = 6$, so we must find c. If we substitute the values for a and b in the Pythagorean theorem, we get

$$c^2 = 8^2 + 6^2 = 64 + 36 = 100.$$

Therefore, $c = \sqrt{100} = 10$ inches.

b) In this case, we are given that $a = 15$ and $c = 16$, and we must find b. Substituting these values in the Pythagorean theorem, we get

$$15^2 + b^2 = 16^2,$$

or

$$225 + b^2 = 256.$$

So,

$$b^2 = 256 - 225 = 31.$$

This means that

$$b = \sqrt{31} \approx 5.57 \text{ meters.}$$

Now try Exercises 37 to 42. ❄ ⑩

Quiz Yourself ⑩

Assume that the hypotenuse of a right triangle measures 20 inches and one leg measures 10 inches. What is the length of the other leg?

To solve a problem, it may be necessary to use the Pythagorean theorem several times, as we demonstrate in Example 5.

EXAMPLE 5   *Using the Pythagorean Theorem to Find the Height of a Pyramid*

The Great Pyramid, near Cairo, Egypt, is the tomb of the Egyptian pharaoh Khufu (also called Cheops by the Greeks) and was considered to be one of the seven wonders of the ancient world. An archaeologist wants to determine the height of this pyramid. This pyramid has a square base measuring 230 meters on each side, and she has found the distance from one corner of the base to the tip of the pyramid to be 219 meters. What is the height of the pyramid?

SOLUTION: If we imagine this pyramid to be hollow, we could drop a string with a weight from the tip of the pyramid, point T, to point M, which is the middle of the base. If we then drew a line segment from M to a corner of the base, calling this point C, we would

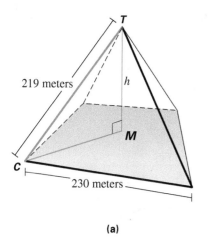

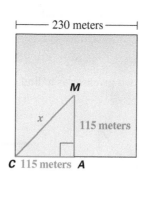

(a)   **(b)**

FIGURE 10.44 (a) The Great Pyramid. (b) The base of the pyramid; M, is the center of the base, C is the corner of the base, and A is the midpoint of a side of the base.

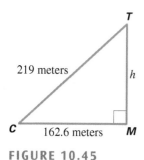

FIGURE 10.45

KEY POINT

We use simple formulas to compute the circumference and area of circles.

form a right triangle $\triangle TMC$, as we see in Figure 10.44(a). Our goal now is to find the length of line segment TM.

We will do the solution in two stages.

Stage 1: We will find the length of line segment CM. We draw the base of the pyramid in Figure 10.44(b), showing segment CM. Because each edge of the base is 230 meters long, MA and CA are both 115 meters long. We can then apply the Pythagorean theorem to triangle $\triangle MAC$ as follows:

$$(\text{length of } CM)^2 = (\text{length of } CA)^2 + (\text{length of } AM)^2,$$

or

$$x^2 = 115^2 + 115^2 = 13{,}225 + 13{,}225 = 26{,}450.$$

Thus, $x = \sqrt{26{,}450} = 115\sqrt{2} \approx 162.6$.

Stage 2: Now that we have found the length of CM, we can find the length of TM in the right triangle $\triangle TMC$ shown in Figure 10.45. Using the Pythagorean theorem again, we get

$$(\text{length of } TC)^2 = (\text{length of } CM)^2 + (\text{length of } TM)^2.$$

Substituting for the various lengths in $\triangle TMC$ gives the equation

$$219^2 = (115\sqrt{2})^2 + h^2,$$

or

$$h^2 = 219^2 - (115\sqrt{2})^2 = 47{,}961 - 26{,}450 = 21{,}511.$$

Taking the square root of both sides, we find that $h \approx 146.7$ meters.

Now try Exercises 57 and 58. ✷

Circles

As with polygons, we often need to calculate the circumference and area of circles. The derivation of these formulas is not as intuitive as those for the polygons we have been discussing, so we will state them without proof. The number π, which appears in these formulas, is the Greek letter pi. It stands for the measure of the circumference of a circle divided by the length of its diameter. We will use 3.14 to approximate pi.

HISTORICAL HIGHLIGHT ✺ ✺ ✺

Hypatia

Throughout the history of mathematics, fewer women than men are mentioned for their contributions because traditionally women were discouraged from studying mathematics. One notable exception is Hypatia, who was born in Greece in 370 AD. Her father, who was a professor of mathematics at the University of Alexandria, gave her a classical education, which included mathematics. She lectured on both philosophy and mathematics at Alexandria and wrote major papers on geometry, including the work of Euclid. She also did work in philosophy and astronomy and is believed to have invented several astronomical devices.

Unfortunately, her work in science caused her problems with the Christian church, and moreover, as a Greek she was seen as a pagan. In 415, a mob attacked and brutally murdered her, which caused other scholars to flee Alexandria. This tragic event marked the end of the golden age of Greek mathematics and, some believe, the beginning of the Dark Ages in Europe.

> **CIRCUMFERENCE AND AREA OF A CIRCLE** A circle with radius r has circumference $C = 2\pi r$ and area $A = \pi r^2$.

These formulas tell us that a circle with radius 10 feet has a circumference of $C = 2\pi r = 2\pi(10) \approx 62.8$ feet and area $A = \pi r^2 = \pi(10)^2 \approx 314$ square feet.

EXAMPLE 6 *Laying Out a Basketball Court* *

A man is designing a basketball court for his children. The court is in the form of a segment of a circle, as shown in Figure 10.46. There will be a fence at the rounded end of the court, and he will paint the court with a concrete sealer.

a) How much fencing is required?

b) What is the area of the surface of the court?

SOLUTION: Since a circle contains 360°, the court is one-sixth of the interior of a circle with a radius of 20 feet.

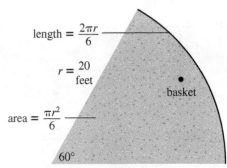

FIGURE 10.46 Basketball court.

a) The circumference of a circle with a 20-foot radius is $2\pi r = 2\pi(20) = 40\pi \approx 125.6$ feet. The fencing we need will be one-sixth of this, or approximately 20.93 feet. The man should buy about 21 feet of fencing.

b) The area of a circle with a 20-foot radius is $\pi(20)^2 = 400\pi \approx 1,256$ square feet. One-sixth of this is about 209.3 square feet.

Now try Exercises 59 and 60. ✳ **11**

Quiz Yourself **11**

Find the circumference and area of a circle that has radius 8.

Exercises 10.3

Looking Back[†]

These exercises follow the general outline of the topics presented in this section and will give you a good overview of the material that you have just studied.

1. In Figure 10.35, what relationship were we showing between the area of a parallelogram and the area of a rectangle?

2. What was the point that we made in Figure 10.36?

3. How does Figure 10.39 help you remember the formula for the area of a trapezoid?

4. Who was Hypatia?

Sharpening Your Skills

*In Exercises 5–16, find the area of each figure.***

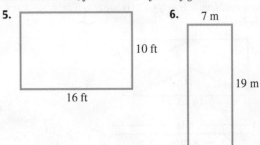

5. 16 ft × 10 ft

6. 7 m × 19 m

---

*Thanks to my friend Dr. Frank Siekman, of the KU music department, for asking me this question several years ago.

[†]Before doing these exercises, you may find it useful to review the note *How to Succeed at Mathematics* on page xix.

**Throughout this exercise set, approximate π by 3.14.

7.

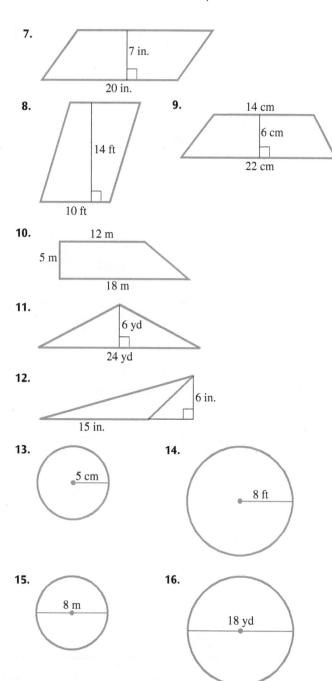

7 in.

20 in.

8.

14 ft

10 ft

9.

14 cm

6 cm

22 cm

10.

12 m

5 m

18 m

11.

6 yd

24 yd

12.

6 in.

15 in.

13.

5 cm

14.

8 ft

15.

8 m

16.

18 yd

In Exercises 17–22, find the area of the shaded regions. Recall that to solve a new problem, it is helpful to relate it to a problem that you have seen before.

17.

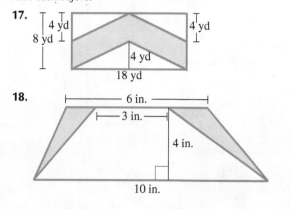

4 yd

8 yd

4 yd

4 yd

18 yd

18.

6 in.

3 in.

4 in.

10 in.

19.

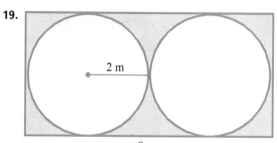

2 m

8 m

20.

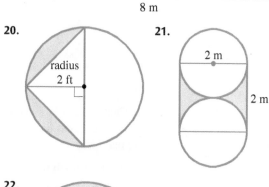

radius
2 ft

21.

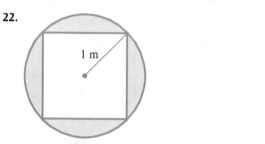

2 m

2 m

22.

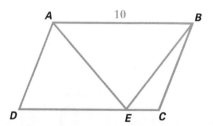

1 m

Use the following figure to answer Exercises 23 and 24. Assume that the area of the parallelogram ABCD is 60 square inches and the area of triangle BEC is 6 square inches.

A   10   B

D   E   C

23. What is the area of triangle *ADE*?

24. What is the area of the trapezoid *ABCE*?

Use the following figure to answer Exercises 25 and 26. Assume that the area of triangle BAE is 30 square yards, the area of the trapezoid ABDF is 66 square yards, and the area of triangle BDC is twice the area of triangle AEF.

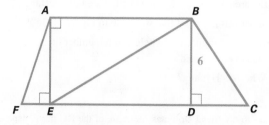

A   B

6

F E   D   C

25. Find the area of triangle *BDC*.

26. Find the area of trapezoid *ABCF*.

A geoboard is a board with rows of nails spaced 1 inch apart in both the vertical and horizontal directions. In Exercises 27–30, we stretched a rubber band around some of the nails. Find the area of the enclosed figures.

27.
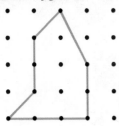

28.

29.
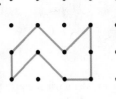

30.

In Exercises 31–34, use Heron's formula to find the area of each triangle.

31.
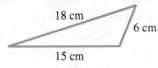

32.
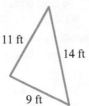

33.
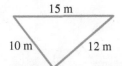

34.
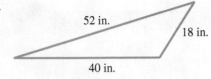

In Exercises 35 and 36, find the height h for each triangle.

35.
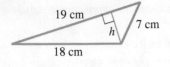

36.
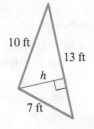

In Exercises 37–40, find the length of side x for each triangle.

37.
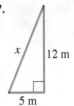

38.
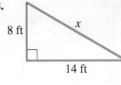

39.

40.
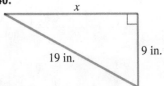

In Exercises 41 and 42, find the area of each triangle.

41.
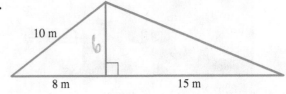

42.
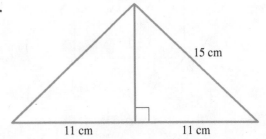

Applying What You've Learned

In Exercises 43–46, state whether perimeter or area would be the more appropriate quantity to measure.

43. You are covering an archeological plot with a tarpaulin.

44. Napoleon wants to buy fencing for a paddock to graze llamas.

45. You are putting a decorative stencil at the top of the walls in your bedroom.

46. You are surfacing your rooftop Japanese garden with slate tiles.

47. Finding distances on a baseball diamond. The bases on a baseball diamond are 90 feet apart. What is the distance from home plate to second base? (All angles in the diamond are right angles.)

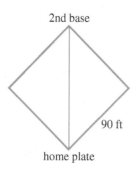

2nd base

90 ft

home plate

48. Finding the area of home plate. In baseball, home plate is shaped as shown ($m \angle FDE = 90°$).

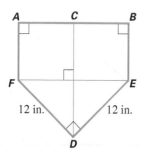

A   C   B

F   E

12 in.   12 in.

D

a. What is the length of line segment AB?

b. If we assume that line segment CD has the same length as segment AB, what is the area of home plate?

49. Find the length of line segment AB in the given figure.

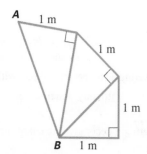

A   1 m

1 m

1 m

B   1 m

50. Continuing the pattern in Exercise 49, construct a line segment having length $\sqrt{6}$.

51. Making a stained glass window. A stained glass window in a museum is in the shape of a rectangle with a semicircle on top. The height of the rectangular part of the window is twice the base. If the base of the window measures 6 feet, what is the area of the window?

⊢— 6 ft —⊣

52. Making a stained glass window. Consider a window like the one in Exercise 51. Assume that the semicircular top has a radius of 2 feet. We want the rectangular part of the window to have the same area as the semicircular top. What should the dimensions of the rectangle be?

53. Comparing pizzas. At Cifaretto's Italian Ristorante, the medium pizza has a diameter of 12 inches and sells for $5.99. The large pizza has a diameter of 16 inches and sells for $8.99. Which pizza is the better buy? Explain.

54. Making a flower bed. A gardener has enough tiger lilies to fill a circular flower bed having an area of 50 square feet. Find the radius of the flower bed to the nearest foot.

55. Measuring a running track. A running track, 4 meters wide, has the dimensions shown in the following diagram. The ends of the track are semicircles with diameter 20 meters. What is the surface area of the track?

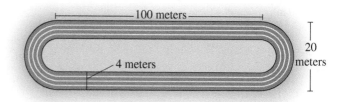

100 meters

4 meters

20 meters

56. Measuring a running track. In Exercise 55, if the 100-meter dimension is increased to 120 meters, the 20-meter dimension is increased to 40 meters, and the width of the track is increased to 6 meters, what is the surface area of the track?

Exercises 57 and 58 are based upon the information given about the Great Pyramid in Example 5.

57. What is the slant height of the pyramid—that is, the distance from its tip to the midpoint of one of its sides?

58. What is the area of one face of the pyramid?

59. Redo Example 6, but now assume that the sides of the basketball court are 18 feet long and the angle measures 72°.

60. Redo Example 6. However, now the tip of the court has been removed, as shown in the figure.

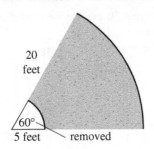

Communicating Mathematics

61. In this section, we derived formulas for the areas of the following figures. Arrange the terms in the order in which we did the derivation: triangle, trapezoid, rectangle, parallelogram.

62. The formula for the area of a trapezoid is $\frac{1}{2} \times (b_1 + b_2) \times h$. What is the meaning of each symbol in this formula?

63. In Example 5, why did we need to find the length of the line segment CM?

64. In Example 6, how did we determine the length of the fencing?

Using Technology to Investigate Mathematics

65. See your instructor for TI-83 programs to compute the areas of various geometric figures. Use them to verify some of the computations in this section.

66. There are many Web sites that have geometry calculators you can use to reproduce the calculations in this section. Run some of these programs and report on your findings. You might search on "triangles, circles, applets" or "geometry calculators" to find such pages.

For Extra Credit

67. A modern art museum has sides shaped like trapezoids with identical equilateral triangular windows with dimensions shown in the accompanying figure. What is the area of one side of the museum, excluding the area of the windows?

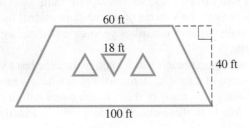

68. One side of an air traffic control tower, with dimensions given, is shown in the accompanying figure. Assume that all polygons are trapezoids. What is the area of the side, excluding the two congruent windows?

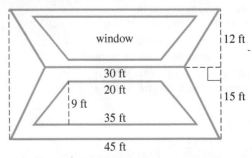

69. True or false? If we double the radius of a circle, the area also doubles.

70. True or false? If we double the radius of a circle, the circumference also doubles.

71. In the figure below, W, X, Y, and Z are the midpoints of the line segments on which they lie. How does the area of $WXYZ$ compare with the area of rectangle $ABCD$? Explain how you got your answer.

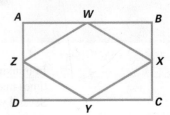

72. If W and Y were not the midpoints of the line segments on which they lie, would it change your answer in Exercise 71? Explain your answer.

73. You have 200 feet of fencing and want to enclose a rectangular area. What shape will enclose the most area? You might solve this problem by experimenting with different lengths and widths until you can make a reasonable guess.

74. Bernie is shaping round and square posts. In figure (a), he is cutting a circular post from a piece of wood with a square cross section. In figure (b), he is cutting a square post from a piece of wood with a circular cross section. In which situation is there the smaller *percentage* of waste? (*Hint:* Answer this question by making up numerical examples.)

(a)   (b)

75. *Extreme Makeover Home Edition* wants to create a housing development with lots clustered in circles and an open area in the center of the circle, as shown in the diagram. The side of a lot is 180 feet and the central common area is 11,304 square feet. Each lot in the cluster is the same size. What is the area of each lot? (We are using 3.14 for π)

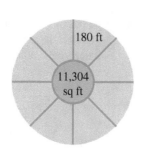

76. Ty Pennington in Exercise 75 wants to put a fence entirely around the lot, except for the curved section away from the common area. How much fencing is required?

In Exercises 77 and 78, express the shaded areas in terms of the radius r *of the circle.*

77.

78.

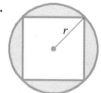

10.4 Volume and Surface Area

Objectives

1. Understand the idea of volume of basic three-dimensional objects.
2. Be able to apply the volume and surface area formulas for cylinders.
3. Understand the relationship between the volume and surface area formulas for cylinders, spheres, and cones.

In thinking about what to use for an opener for this section, I was reflecting on the many times that people have asked me to use mathematics to solve a real problem in their lives.* Several years ago, a colleague in the psychology department asked me to help her determine if her oil deliveryman was cheating her. In order to solve her problem, I needed to know the basic formulas for computing volumes that you will learn in this section.

We will now extend the ideas of two-dimensional Euclidean geometry to three dimensions. Instead of squares and rectangles, we will discuss boxlike figures called *parallelepipeds*; instead of circles we will talk about cylinders, spheres, and cones; and instead of measuring perimeters and areas, we will calculate the volumes and surface areas of three-dimensional geometric figures.

Many applications require a knowledge of three-dimensional geometry. When designing a skyscraper, an architect needs to know the volume of concrete to pour for a foundation. A manufacturer must be able to compute the amount of materials required to fabricate a cylindrical water tank. A state highway department engineer may want to know how much road salt is contained in a conical storage shed.

KEY POINT

The volume of a rectangular parallelepiped is the product of its length, width, and height.

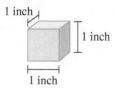

FIGURE 10.47

A cube whose volume is 1 cubic inch.

Volume

When we measure length in one dimension, we use units such as inches, feet, centimeters, and meters. In measuring area in two dimensions, we use square units such as square inches and square centimeters. We measure the **volume** of a three-dimensional figure using *cubic units.* Even though we will study three-dimensional geometric objects, *we will still measure surface area in square units.*

Figure 10.47 shows a cube whose edges are each 1 inch long, so the cube has a volume of 1 cubic inch. In determining the volume of a three-dimensional figure whose measurements are given in inches, we are really asking how many of these 1-inch cubes will fit inside the figure. Because it might be impossible to fit these cubes inside the figure exactly, we can

---

*In Example 6 of Section 10.3, a friend asked me for help in laying out a strangely shaped basketball court for his son. The star problem in Example 3 of Section 10.2 was from a minister asking me to advise his youth group on how to construct a five-pointed star to place on their church steeple during advent.

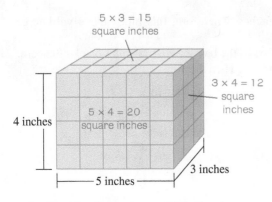

FIGURE 10.48 Rectangular solid sliced into 60 one-inch cubes.

imagine filling 1-cubic-inch containers with water and asking, "How many of these containers of water does it take to fill the figure exactly?"

It is easy to compute the volume of the box-shaped rectangular solid, called a *rectangular parallelepiped*,* shown in Figure 10.48. If we slice along the lines drawn at 1-inch intervals on the solid, we get four layers each containing 15 1-inch cubes. The volume of this solid is given by

$$\text{volume} = \text{length} \times \text{width} \times \text{height} = 5 \times 3 \times 4 = 60 \text{ cubic inches.}$$

It is also easy to find the surface area of the solid in Figure 10.48. Clearly the six sides of the solid have the following areas:

$$\text{areas of top and bottom} = \text{length} \times \text{width} = 5 \times 3 = 15,$$

$$\text{areas of front and back} = \text{length} \times \text{height} = 5 \times 4 = 20, \text{ and}$$

$$\text{areas of two sides} = \text{width} \times \text{height} = 3 \times 4 = 12.$$

The total surface area is therefore $(2 \times 15) + (2 \times 20) + (2 \times 12) = 94$ square inches. Figure 10.48 helps us remember these formulas for volume and surface area. **12**

Quiz Yourself **12**

Find the volume and surface area of a rectangular solid with length 8 centimeters, width 6 centimeters, and height 3 centimeters.

VOLUME AND SURFACE AREA OF A RECTANGULAR SOLID (RECTANGULAR PARALLELEPIPED) If a rectangular solid has length *l*, width *w*, and height *h*, the volume of the solid is $V = lwh$ and the surface area of the solid is

$$S = 2lw + 2lh + 2wh.$$

Another way to look at the way we calculated the area for the rectangular solid above is that we multiplied the area of the base, which is *lw*, times the height, *h*. We can apply this approach to other figures.

**KEY POINT**

For many solids, volume equals base area times height.

VOLUME EQUALS AREA OF BASE TIMES HEIGHT If an object has a flat top and base and *sides perpendicular to the base*, as shown in Figure 10.49, then, if the area of the base is *A* and the height is *h*, the volume will be

$$V = A \cdot h.$$

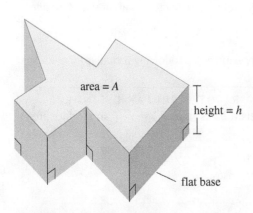

FIGURE 10.49 Volume = area of base times height.

EXAMPLE 1 *Comparing Volumes*

Figure 10.50 shows two blocks of cheese that are selling for the same price. Which block contains the greater volume?

SOLUTION: We calculate the volume of each block by multiplying the area of its base times its height. The area of the base of the trapezoidal block is

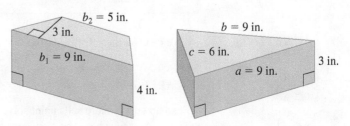

FIGURE 10.50 Which block has greater volume?

---

*A parallelepiped is a solid with six faces, each of which is a parallelogram. In this case, the parallelepiped is rectangular, which means the faces are rectangles.

$\frac{1}{2}(b_1 + b_2) \cdot h = \frac{1}{2}(9 + 5) \cdot 3 = 21$ square inches. Therefore, this block has a volume of $21 \times 4 = 84$ cubic inches.

We use Heron's formula to find the area of the base of the triangular block of cheese. We first must compute $s = \frac{1}{2} \times (9 + 9 + 6) = 12$. Then the area is

$$\sqrt{s(s - a)(s - b)(s - c)} = \sqrt{12(12 - 9)(12 - 9)(12 - 6)} = \sqrt{648} \approx 25.5.$$

Multiplying this area by the height of 3 gives us $25.5 \times 3 = 76.5$ cubic inches. Therefore, the trapezoidal block of cheese has slightly more volume and is the better deal.

Now try Exercises 13 to 18. ❋

✏ **KEY POINT**

Simple diagrams illustrate the formulas for finding the volume and surface area of a cylinder.

Cylinders

We can use this method of multiplying the base area times the height to find the volume of some common three-dimensional solids. A *right circular cylinder* is a solid that is shaped like a soup or tuna fish can (see Figure 10.51). We call these cylinders "right" because the sides are perpendicular to the base. The cylinder's base is a circle with area $A = \pi r^2$. * Thus,

volume of cylinder = area of base × height = $\pi r^2 \cdot h$.

To find the surface area of the cylinder in Figure 10.51(a), imagine that we remove the top and bottom of the cylinder and then cut the side of the cylinder and open it up, as in Figure 10.51(b). If we flatten this curved surface, we get a rectangle with length $2\pi r$ and height h, shown in Figure 10.51(c). Therefore, the surface area of the side of the cylinder is $2\pi rh$. Adding to this the areas of the top and bottom of the cylinder, which are each πr^2, we get the total surface area of the cylinder.

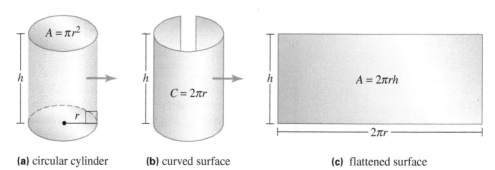

(a) circular cylinder   **(b)** curved surface   **(c)** flattened surface

FIGURE 10.51 (a) Right circular cylinder. (b) Remove top and bottom and cut side of cylinder. (c) Flatten side of cylinder.

The diagrams in Figure 10.51 will help you to remember the following formulas for cylinders.

> **VOLUME AND SURFACE AREA OF A RIGHT CIRCULAR CYLINDER**
> A right circular cylinder with radius r and height h has volume $V = \pi r^2 h$ and surface area $S = 2\pi rh + 2\pi r^2$.

We can use these formulas to compare purchases.

EXAMPLE 2 *Comparing Volumes of Commercial Products*

A Pearl art supply store sells paint solvent in a cylindrical can that has a diameter of 4 inches and a height of 6 inches. The giant economy size can of the same solvent has a diameter twice as large (the height of the can is the same) and costs three times as much as the smaller can.

a) Which can is the better deal?   b) Compare the surface areas of the two cans.

---

*Throughout this section, we again approximate π by 3.14.

SOLUTION:

a) The radius of the smaller can is 2, so its volume is

$$V = \pi r^2 h \approx 3.14 \cdot (2)^2 \cdot 6 = 75.4 \text{ cubic inches.}$$

The radius of the larger can is 4, so its volume is

$$V = \pi r^2 h \approx 3.14 \cdot (4)^2 \cdot 6 = 301.4 \text{ cubic inches.}$$

Because the large can contains *four* times as much solvent but costs only *three* times as much, the larger can is the better deal.

b) The surface area of the smaller can is

$$2\pi rh + 2\pi r^2 = 2\pi(2)(6) + 2\pi(2)^2 \approx 2(3.14) \cdot 2 \cdot 6 + 2(3.14)(2)^2 = 100.5 \text{ square inches.}$$

The surface area of the larger can is

$$2\pi rh + 2\pi r^2 = 2\pi(4)(6) + 2\pi(4)^2 \approx 2(3.14) \cdot 4 \cdot 6 + 2(3.14)(4)^2 = 251.2 \text{ square inches.}$$

Now try Exercises 29 to 32. ✸ **13**

Quiz Yourself **13**

What is the volume and surface area of a right circular cylinder with a radius of 5 centimeters and height of 10 centimeters?

KEY POINT

An efficient container has a small surface area-to-volume ratio.

You may have been surprised in Example 2 that although the larger can contains four times the amount of solvent contained in the smaller can, it takes only two and a half times as much material to make the larger can. Manufacturers are interested in such relationships so they can minimize the amount of materials they need to package a product and, by doing so, reduce their cost. What is the most efficient shape of a container to contain the largest amount of a product? For example, what is the most efficient shape of a soup can?

EXAMPLE 3   *The Most Efficient Shape of a Can*

What are the dimensions of a can that will contain 1 cubic foot of liquid and that will have the smallest amount of surface area?

SOLUTION: We must find the radius, r, and the height, h, of the can. Our intuition tells us that if the radius is small, as in Figure 10.52(a), then the height must be large. On the other hand, if the radius is large, as in Figure 10.52(b), then the height must be small. Our problem then is to find the ideal radius that gives the minimum surface area (Figure 10.52(c)).

Because the volume of the can is to be 1, we can set $\pi r^2 h = 1$. Dividing both sides of this equation by πr^2, we get $h = \frac{1}{\pi r^2}$. Thus, as our intuition tells us, the height depends on the choice of radius. Recall that the formula for finding the surface area of a cylinder is $S = 2\pi rh + 2\pi r^2$. We can substitute $\frac{1}{\pi r^2}$ for h in this equation to get

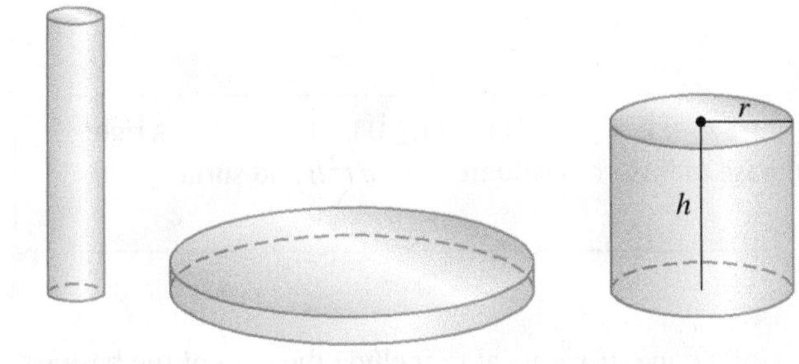

FIGURE 10.52 A can with a small radius requires a large height, whereas a can with a large radius requires a small height.

small radius   large radius   ideal radius
    (a)   (b)   (c)

$$S = 2\pi r \left(\frac{1}{\pi r^2}\right) + 2\pi r^2 = \frac{2\pi r}{\pi r^2} + 2\pi r^2. \qquad (1)$$

Canceling the π and an r from the quotient on the right side of equation (1), we get

$$S = \frac{2}{r} + 2\pi r^2. \qquad (2)$$

The neat thing about equation (2) is that now we have a formula for the surface area of a can (containing 1 cubic foot of liquid) that depends *only on the radius r.* In Table 10.4, we begin with a very small radius, 0.1, which we expect would give us a large surface area. Then as the size of the radius increases, the surface area decreases. Eventually, as the radius becomes too large, the can is becoming too flat, and as Table 10.4 shows, the surface area starts to increase again.

X	Y1
.200	10.251
.300	7.232
.400	6.005
.500	5.570
.600	5.594
.700	5.934
.800	6.519

X=.8

This TI-83 table confirms our calculations in Example 3.

Radius, r	Surface Area, $S = \frac{2}{r} + 2\pi r^2$	
0.1*	20.063	
0.2	10.251	decreasing
0.3	7.232	decreasing
0.4	6.005	decreasing
0.5	5.570	decreasing
0.6	5.594	increasing
0.7	5.934	increasing
0.8	6.519	increasing

Ideal radius is between 0.5 and 0.6.

TABLE 10.4 Surface area first decreases, then increases as r increases.

You can see in Table 10.4 that the ideal radius is somewhere between 0.5 and 0.6. To get a better estimate of the ideal radius, we could use a graphing calculator[†] to calculate the surface area for radii of sizes 0.51, 0.52, 0.53, and so on. If you were to do this, eventually you would find that $r \approx 0.5419$ gives us the smallest surface area for a can with volume 1. (Actually, if you were ever to take a calculus course, you would learn a much more powerful and faster way to find this value for r without doing so many tedious calculations.) ✹

🖉 **KEY POINT**

The formulas for the volume and surface area of cones and spheres are related to the formulas for cylinders.

Cones and Spheres

We will now work with formulas for the volume of two other solid figures: cones and spheres. Figure 10.53 shows a right circular cone with height h and base radius r. We call the cone *circular* because its base is a circle, and we use the adjective *right* because the line segment from its tip to the center of its base forms a right angle with the base.

FIGURE 10.53
Right circular cone.

> **VOLUME AND SURFACE AREA OF A RIGHT CIRCULAR CONE** A right circular cone with height h and base radius r has volume $V = \frac{1}{3}\pi r^2 h$ and surface area $S = \pi r \sqrt{r^2 + h^2}$.

In the formula for the surface area of a cone, if we want to include the area of the base we must add πr^2.

FIGURE 10.54
The cone has a volume $\frac{1}{3}$ that of the cylinder.

🧩 **PROBLEM SOLVING**

The Analogies Principle

We can use what we know about the volume of a cylinder to understand the formula for the volume of a cone. Figure 10.54 shows that a cone with height h and radius r easily fits inside a cylinder with height h and radius r. The cone does not appear to occupy even one-half of the volume of the cylinder, which is $V = \pi r^2 h$. Therefore, it is easy to remember that the volume of the cone is $V = \frac{1}{3}\pi r^2 h$. **

---

*Because the volume is expressed in cubic feet, the radius of the can is measured in feet, so 0.1 is one-tenth of a foot. The surface area is then measured in square feet, so 20.063 is slightly over 20 square feet.

[†]See your instructor for a tutorial that will show you how to use the Table command on a graphing calculator.

**Of course, we cannot tell just by looking at Figure 10.54 that the cone occupies exactly one-third of the cylinder; however, visualizing this diagram may help you remember the formula for the volume of a cone.

EXAMPLE 4   *Finding the Volume and Surface Area of a Cone*

What is the volume and surface area of a cone with a height of 10 meters and a base radius of 8 meters?

SOLUTION: The volume is $V = \frac{1}{3}\pi r^2 h = \frac{1}{3}\pi(8)^2(10) = \frac{640\pi}{3} \approx 669.87$ cubic meters. The surface area is

$$S = \pi r \sqrt{r^2 + h^2} = \pi(8)\sqrt{8^2 + 10^2} = 8\sqrt{164}\,\pi \approx 321.69 \text{ square meters.}$$

Now try Exercises 7 to 10. ✳ **14**

EXAMPLE 5   *The Volume of Conical Storage Buildings*

Many northern states stockpile salt to use for melting road ice. In one such state, the highway department builds sheds in the shape of right circular cones to store the salt. Current sheds have a diameter of 30 feet and a height of 10 feet. The department plans to build larger conical sheds to hold more salt. The larger shed will either have a 10-foot-longer diameter and the same height, or the same diameter and a 10-foot-greater height.

a) Calculate the volume for each of the proposed sheds.
b) Calculate the surface area for each of the proposed sheds.
c) Which design seems to be more economical?

SOLUTION:

a) First, we will compute the volume if we increase the diameter by 10 feet. The radius of the cone will be $\frac{(30 + 10)}{2} = 20$ feet and the height will remain at 10 feet. The volume is therefore $V = \frac{1}{3}\pi r^2 h = \frac{1}{3}\pi(20)^2(10) \approx 4,187$ cubic feet.

   If we increase the height to 20 feet, and keep the radius at 15 feet, the volume will be

$$V = \frac{1}{3}\pi r^2 h = \frac{1}{3}\pi(15)^2(20) \approx 4,710 \text{ cubic feet.}$$

b) The surface area for the shed with radius 20 and height 10 is

$$S = \pi(r)\sqrt{r^2 + h^2} = \pi(20)\sqrt{20^2 + 10^2} \approx 1,404 \text{ square feet.}$$

   A shed with radius 15 and height 20 has a surface area of

$$S = \pi(r)\sqrt{r^2 + h^2} = \pi(15)\sqrt{15^2 + 20^2} \approx 1,178 \text{ square feet.}$$

c) Increasing the height by 10 feet and keeping the diameter at 30 feet gives us more volume and smaller surface area than if we increase the diameter to 40 feet and keep the height at 10 feet. Therefore, increasing the height to 20 feet seems to be the better design. ✳

The last three-dimensional figure we consider is a sphere (Figure 10.55).

> **VOLUME AND SURFACE AREA OF A SPHERE** A sphere with radius r has volume $V = \frac{4}{3}\pi r^3$ and surface area $S = 4\pi r^2$.

Figure 10.56* will help you remember the formula for the volume of a sphere. A sphere with radius r fits exactly inside a cylinder having radius r and height $2r$. The

---

Quiz Yourself **14**

Find the volume and surface area of a right circular cone with a radius of 4 yards and a height of 5 yards.

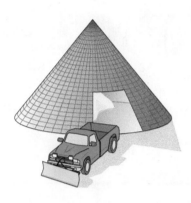

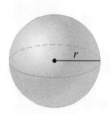

FIGURE 10.55
A sphere with radius r.

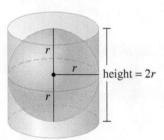

area of base $= \pi r^2$

FIGURE 10.56 A sphere with radius r inside a cylinder with radius r and height $2r$. The cylinder's volume is $\pi r^2 \times 2r = 2\pi r^3$, so the volume of the sphere is less.

---

*Again, we can't tell by just looking at Figure 10.56 that the volume of the sphere is exactly $\frac{4}{3}\pi r^3$, but the diagram may help you remember that the sphere's volume is somewhat less than $2\pi r^3$.

volume of this cylinder is $\pi r^2 \times 2r = 2\pi r^3$. Because the sphere does not completely fill the cylinder, you should remember that the volume of the sphere is *less than* $2\pi r^3$, or $\frac{4}{3}\pi r^3$.

Many containers, such as water tanks, are shaped like spheres.

EXAMPLE 6   *Measuring the Capacity of Water Tanks*

Metrodelphia is replacing existing spherical water tanks with larger spherical water tanks. The water commission insists that to provide for future expansion of the city, the new capacity of the tanks should be at least five times the capacity of the old water tanks. If the city purchases tanks that have a radius that is twice the radius of the old tanks, will these tanks satisfy the water commission?

SOLUTION: Let the radius of the old water tanks be r feet, so the volume of each tank will be $V = \frac{4}{3}\pi r^3$ cubic feet. The new tanks will each have a radius of $2r$ feet, so the volume of the new tanks will be

$$V = \frac{4}{3}\pi(2r)^3 = \frac{4}{3}\pi 8r^3 = 8\left(\frac{4}{3}\pi r^3\right) \text{ cubic feet.}$$

New radius is twice old radius.   original volume

Quiz Yourself **15**

Find the volume of a sphere with a radius of 6 centimeters.

The new volume is eight times the volume of the original tanks. Therefore, the new tanks will exceed the specifications of the water commission. ❁ **15**

Exercises [**10.4**]

Looking Back*

These exercises follow the general outline of the topics presented in this section and will give you a good overview of the material that you have just studied.

1. How are the formulas for computing the volume the same in Figures 10.48 and 10.49?

2. In Example 2, why was the volume of the larger can of solvent four times the volume of the smaller can? Specifically, why did we get the four?

3. What was the point that we were making in Table 10.4?

4. Where did we use the Analogies Principle in this section?

Sharpening Your Skills

In Exercises 5–12, find a) the surface area and b) the volume of each figure. Approximate π by 3.14.

5.

5 cm
6 cm   4 cm

6.   ⊢3 ft⊣
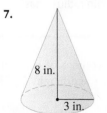
6 ft

7.

8 in.
3 in.

8.

5 yd

9.   ⊢5 ft⊣
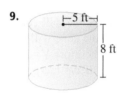
8 ft

10.

18 m
⊢5 m⊣

11.

20 cm

12.
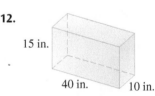
15 in.
40 in.   10 in.

In Exercises 13–18, find the volume of each figure.

13.
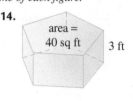
3 ft
area = 25 sq ft

14.
area = 40 sq ft
3 ft

15.
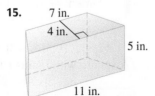
7 in.
4 in.
5 in.
11 in.

16.
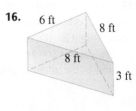
6 ft   8 ft
8 ft   3 ft

---

*Before doing these exercises, you may find it useful to review the note *How to Succeed at Mathematics* on page xix.

17.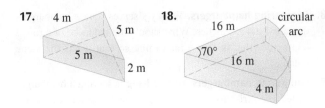

4 m
5 m
5 m
2 m

18.

16 m   circular arc
70°
16 m
4 m

Applying What You've Learned

19. How many cubic inches are in a cubic foot?

20. How many cubic inches are in a cubic yard?

21. Punch bowl. A punch bowl is in the shape of a hemisphere (half of a sphere) with a radius of 9 inches. The cup part of a ladle is also in the shape of a hemisphere with a radius of 2 inches. If the bowl is full, how many full ladles of punch are there in the bowl?

22. Filling glasses. Assume that we are filling cylindrical glasses that have a diameter of 3 inches and a height of 4 inches from the punch bowl in Exercise 21. If the bowl is completely full, how many glasses can we fill?

23. Filling glasses. A cylindrical pitcher with radius 2.5 inches and 8 inches high is filled with a tropical drink. How many glasses shaped like an inverted cone with a height of 1.5 inches and radius 2 inches can be filled from this pitcher?

24. Filling juice containers. The Great American Orange Juice Factory is selling its Caribbean Orange Cocktail in collectible spherical containers. A standard half-gallon container of juice contains 115.5 cubic inches. How many of the spherical containers with a diameter of 3 inches, can be filled from a standard container?

25. Building a Japanese garden. Mariko needs about 16 wheelbarrows full of stone for her Japanese garden. Her wheelbarrow has vertical sides with the given shape and is $2\frac{1}{2}$ feet wide. How many cubic yards of stone should she order?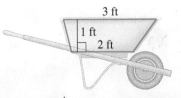

3 ft
1 ft
2 ft

26. Juice barrel. A gallon contains 231 cubic inches. A cylindrical barrel full of juice concentrate has a diameter of 2 feet and is 3 feet high. How many gallons of concentrate are in the barrel?

27. Comparing cakes. One cake is rectangular with a length of 14 inches, a width of 9 inches, and a height of 3 inches. The other cake is a round cake with a radius of 5 inches and a height of 4 inches. Which cake has more volume?

28. Comparing ice cream scoops. Which has more volume: a single scoop of ice cream made with a 3-inch scoop, or two scoops of ice cream made with a $2\frac{1}{2}$-inch scoop? (Assume that both ice cream scoops form perfectly filled spheres of ice cream.)

In Exercises 29–32, we describe a geometric object. Compute the volume you obtain if a) you increase the radius of the object by 2 inches and keep the height the same and b) you increase the height of the object by 2 inches and keep the radius the same.

29. A cylinder with radius 10 inches and height 5 inches. Which causes the volume to increase more: increasing its radius or height? Explain.

30. A cylinder with radius 4 inches and height 8 inches. Which causes the volume to increase more: increasing its radius or height? Explain.

31. A cone with radius 6 inches and height 3 inches. Which causes the volume to increase more: increasing its radius or height? Explain.

32. A cone with radius 5 inches and height 12 inches. Which causes the volume to increase more: increasing its radius or height? Explain.

33. Building an aviary. Luis plans to build a hummingbird aviary with a concrete floor shaped like a regular hexagon. Each side will measure 8 feet, as shown in the diagram, and the floor will be 6 inches deep. How many cubic feet of concrete are needed? Assume that Luis cannot buy a fraction of a cubic foot.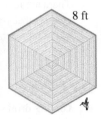

8 ft

(*Hint:* Divide the hexagon into equilateral triangles and use Heron's formula to find the area of the top surface of the aviary.)

34. Constructing a patio. A homeowner is constructing a concrete patio that is 20 feet wide, 30 feet long, and 6 inches thick. Mixed concrete is sold by the cubic yard. How many cubic yards are needed for the project? Assume that the homeowner cannot buy a fraction of a cubic yard of mixed concrete. (*Hint:* You must convert cubic feet into cubic yards.)

35. Diameter of the moon. Earth has a diameter of approximately 7,920 miles and a volume that is roughly 49 times the volume of the moon. Find the diameter of the moon.

36. Diameter of Mars. The volume of Earth is roughly 6.7 times the volume of Mars. Find the diameter of Mars.

Communicating Mathematics

37. How do you "remember how to remember" the volume of a right circular cone?

38. How do you "remember how to remember" the volume of a sphere?

39. If we double the radius of a right circular cone, what effect does that have on the volume? Explain your answer.

40. If we double the radius of a sphere, what effect does that have on the volume? Explain your answer.

41. Assume that three tennis balls fit in a can with no room to spare. Which do you think is larger—the height of the can or the circumference of the can? Explain your answer.

42. A spherical tank has a certain volume. If another spherical tank has twice the volume of the first tank, how do the two radii compare? Explain why this is so.

Using Technology to Investigate Mathematics

43. Following the approach in Example 3, find the radius of a tin can that contains 2 cubic feet of liquid and has the smallest surface area.

44. Repeat Exercise 43, but now the can must contain 8 cubic feet.

45. See your instructor for TI-83 programs that will calculate the volumes and surface areas of the various objects you studied in this chapter. Use them to duplicate some of the computations that we did in this section.

46. There are many Web sites that have interactive geometry calculators that you can use to duplicate the computations that we did in this section. Run some of these programs and report on your findings.

For Extra Credit

47. **Cooling drinks.** Assume that ice cools a liquid proportionally to the amount of surface area of the ice that is in contact with the liquid. Determine whether a large ice cube or a number of smaller ice cubes whose total volume is equal to the larger cube will cool a drink faster. Give specific examples to support your claim.

48. **Comparing hamburgers.** Wendy's serves square hamburgers that are $4 \times 4 \times \frac{1}{4}$ inches. What should the radius be of a round hamburger that is also $\frac{1}{4}$ inch thick so that it has the same volume?

49. **Comparing hamburgers.** Burger King is serving a hamburger called the "tri-burger," which is shaped like an equilateral triangle and is $\frac{1}{4}$ inch thick. What should the length of its side be so that it has the same volume as the hamburgers in Exercise 48?

50. If we cut off the top of a cone by making a horizontal slice, we get a figure called a *frustum* of a cone, as shown in the accompanying figure. Suppose that we cut off the top half of a cone that has radius r and height h. What is the volume of the remaining frustum? (*Hint:* The radius of the top of the frustum is $\frac{r}{2}$.)

51. In Exercise 50, what is the surface area of the side of the frustum?

52. In Example 3, we determined the best shape for a cylinder that contains 1 cubic foot of liquid. Follow that example to determine the shape of a right circular cone with smallest surface area that contains 1 cubic foot. Estimate the radius to within one-tenth of a foot.

10.5 The Metric System and Dimensional Analysis

Objectives

1. Understand the basic units of measurement in the metric system.
2. Make conversions between metric measurements.
3. Use dimensional analysis to make conversions between different measurement systems to solve applied problems.

Would it surprise you if we were to tell you that the United States is an island? We don't mean to say that the United States is entirely surrounded by water, but we are surrounded by a world that uses a very different method for measuring length, volume, weight, and temperature. You are used to measuring length in inches, feet, yards, and miles, whereas the rest of the world uses centimeters, meters, and kilometers.

The Metric System

Unlike the United States, most of the world uses the **metric** system of measurement that is officially known as the **Systèm International d'Unités** or the **SI system**. The U.S. system of measurement is called the **U.S. customary system**.

In order to work in the metric system, you need to understand two things.

1. The basic units that we use to measure length, weight, and volume.

2. The way these different measures of length, volume, and weight relate to each other. As you will see, the relationship between different metric measures is much simpler than the relationship between different customary measures.

In the metric system, length measurement is based on the **meter**, which is slightly more than a yard. If you were to meet a tall man on a train in Argentina, he would be about 2 meters tall. Volume is based on the **liter**, which is a little more than a quart. Instead of buying a half-gallon of iced apple-pear drink in Poland, you would carry home 2 liters from the market. The basic unit of weight in the metric system is the **gram**, which is about the weight of a large paper clip. One thousand grams is called a **kilogram**, which is about 2.2 pounds. If you were visiting Thailand and wanted to make about 2 pounds of chicken breasts with herb-lemongrass crust, you would ask your meat cutter for a kilogram of chicken.

Although measurement in the metric system is based on meters, liters, and grams, we often use variations of these basic units to measure different quantities. For example, we might measure length in centimeters or kilometers, volume in milliliters, or weight in decigrams or kilograms. Table 10.5 explains the meaning of prefixes such as milli-, deka-, kilo-, centi-, and so on.

✎ **KEY POINT**

Units of measure in the metric system are based on powers of 10.

kilo-(k)	hecto-(h)	deka-(da)	base unit	deci-(d)	centi-(c)	milli-(m)
× 1,000	× 100	× 10		× 1/10 or × 0.1	× 1/100 or × 0.01	× 1/1,000 or × 0.001

TABLE 10.5 Some common metric prefixes.

For example, a kilometer is 1,000 meters, a centigram is $\frac{1}{100}$ of a gram or 0.01 gram, and a milliliter is $\frac{1}{1,000}$ of a liter, or 0.001 liter. Conversion of units in the metric system is quite simple. From Table 10.5, we see that 1,000 of something is always a "kilo" and $\frac{1}{100}$ of something is always a "centi." The same pattern of prefixes works the same for length, volume, and weight. In the U.S. customary system, this is certainly not the case. Three feet equal 1 yard, but 4 quarts equal 1 gallon. There are 16 ounces in a pound, but only 2 cups in a pint. There is no consistency or uniformity.

We have listed the abbreviations for the metric prefixes in Table 10.5. Also, we use m for meter, g for gram, and L for liter. For example, to represent kilograms, we could use k for kilo and g for grams, thus we could write 10 kilograms as 10 kg. Similarly, we could write 25 milliliters as 25 mL. ✳ **16**

Quiz Yourself **16**

a) 1 kiloliter is equal to how many liters?

b) 1 gram is equal to how many centigrams?

🧩 **PROBLEM SOLVING**

The Analogies Principle

It helps you to remember the meaning of some metric prefixes if you connect them with some common words. For example, "centi" reminds you of cent, which is one one-hundredth of a dollar. "Milli" might remind you of millennium, which is 1,000 years. "Deci" is found in the word *decimal* and a decimal system is based on powers of 10.

Metric Conversions

If you remember the meaning of the prefixes in Table 10.5, it is easy to convert from one unit to the other in the metric system. For example, in measuring length, a kilometer is 10 times as long as a hectometer and a meter is 100, or 10^2, times as long as a centimeter. A millimeter is $\frac{1}{1,000}$, or 10^{-3}, of a meter.

EXAMPLE 1 *Converting Units of Measurement in the Metric System*

Convert each of the following quantities to the unit of measurement that we specify.

a) 5 dekameters to centimeters   b) 2,300 milliliters to hectoliters

SOLUTION:

a) We can make this conversion as follows:

$$5 \text{ dekameters} = 5 \times (10 \text{ meters}) = 50 \text{ meters,}$$
$$50 \text{ meters} = 50 \times (10 \text{ decimeters}) = 500 \text{ decimeters,}$$
$$500 \text{ decimeters} = 500 \times (10 \text{ centimeters}) = 5,000 \text{ centimeters.}$$

Or, looking at Table 10.5 again, we see that every time we move one column to the right, we require 10 times as many objects. Note that because centimeters are much smaller than dekameters, we need many more centimeters than dekameters.

kilo-	hecto-	deka-	base unit	deci-	centi-	milli-
		1 of these	Equals 10 of these	Equals 100 of these	Equals 1,000 of these	

Moving three places to the right gives us 10^3 as many objects.

You can easily perform this calculation by moving the decimal point in 5.0 dekameters three places to the right to get 5,000 centimeters.

b) A quick way to solve this problem is to realize that because the prefix hecto- is five places to the left of milli- in Table 10.5, all we have to do to make the conversion is move the decimal point in 2,300 milliliters five places to the left to get

or 0.023 hectoliter.

It is good to check if this makes sense to you. Remember that milliliters are much smaller than hectoliters, so therefore it does not require many hectoliters to represent many milliliters.

Now try Exercises 15 to 20. ❋ **17**

Quiz Yourself **17**

a) 5.63 kiloliters is equal to how many deciliters?

b) 4,850 milligrams is equal to how many hectograms?

 *Some Good Advice*

Although it is tempting to simply memorize how to move the decimal point in doing conversions such as those we did in Example 1, it is important to *understand* why you are moving the decimal point and in which direction. If you want to make a number larger, you are multiplying by powers of 10, which means that you move the decimal point to the right. To make the number smaller, you move the decimal point to the left. In checking your answer, remember that it takes many small things to make one large thing, and vice versa.

 KEY POINT

The meter is the basic unit of length in the metric system.

In 1790, the French Academy of Science defined the **meter** to be one ten-millionth of the distance from the North Pole to the equator—a distance of about 39.37 inches. Since that time, scientists have redefined the meter several times, and currently the meter is the distance that light travels in a vacuum in $\frac{1}{299,792,458}$ of a second. A good way to visualize a meter is that it is slightly longer than a yard stick. Figure 10.57 shows the relationship between millimeters $\left(\frac{1}{1,000} \text{ of a meter}\right)$, centimeters $\left(\frac{1}{100} \text{ of a meter}\right)$, and inches.

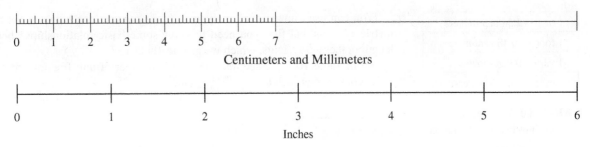

FIGURE 10.57 Comparing millimeters, centimeters, and inches.

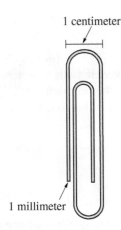

1 centimeter

1 millimeter

From Figure 10.57, you can see that a millimeter is about the thickness of a large paper clip, and the width of the paper clip is roughly one centimeter. One inch is about 2.5 centimeters, and a centimeter is roughly 0.4 inch. We often measure large distances in kilometers (1,000 meters). A kilometer is about 0.6 mile and a mile is approximately 1.6 kilometers.

EXAMPLE 2 *Estimating Metric Lengths*

Match each of the following items with one of these metric measurements: 2 m, 3 cm, 10 m, 16 km.

a) The length of a 30-foot yacht   b) The length of a 10-mile race
c) The length of your bed   d) The thickness of this book

SOLUTION:

a) Thirty feet equals 10 yards, which is about 10 m.

b) One mile is about 1.6 km, so a 10-mile race would be about 16 km long.

c) Your bed is probably a little more than 6 feet long, so it would be approximately 2 m long.

d) If you place the edge of your book on the diagram in Figure 10.57, you will see that the book is around 3 or 4 cm thick. ✳

Dimensional Analysis

Often we need to convert from customary units to metric units, or vice versa. Before we explain how to convert from one system to the other, let us examine how we convert one unit of length to another within our customary system. Recall the relationships among various units of length, which we give in Table 10.6.

To convert one quantity to another, we will use unit fractions. A *unit fraction* is a quotient such as $\frac{3\,feet}{1\,yard}$ or $\frac{1\,foot}{12\,inches}$ that has different units of measurement in the numerator and denominator and whose value is equal to 1. We will show you how to use unit fractions to make conversions in Example 3.

EXAMPLE 3 *Converting Yards to Inches*

Convert 5 yards to inches.

SOLUTION: We want to have an answer that is in inches instead of yards, so we will multiply by the unit fraction $\frac{36\,inches}{1\,yard}$.* Thus,

$$5\ \cancel{yards} \times \frac{36\ inches}{1\ \cancel{yard}} = 5 \times 36\ inches = 180\ inches.\ \text{✳}$$

---

*Notice that because we wanted the final answer in terms of inches, we put "inches" in the numerator.

KEY POINT

We use dimensional analysis to convert from one system to the other.

1 foot = 12 inches
1 yard = 3 feet = 36 inches
1 mile = 5,280 feet

TABLE 10.6 Some relationships among units in the customary system.

1 inch = 2.54 centimeters
1 foot = 30.48 centimeters
1 yard = 0.9144 meter
1 mile = 1.6 kilometers

TABLE 10.7 Some basic relationships between customary and metric units of length.

You can use dimensional analysis to make conversions between the customary and metric systems, but first you need to know some basic relationships* between units of length in the two systems, which we give in Table 10.7.

From Table 10.7, we see that there are a number of unit fractions that we can use to make conversions such as $\frac{1\ inch}{2.54\ centimeters}$ and $\frac{0.9144\ meters}{1\ yard}$.

EXAMPLE 4 *Converting Between the Metric and Customary Systems*

Make each of the following conversions:

a) 5 yards to centimeters   b) 0.3 kilometer to feet

SOLUTION:

a) To make this conversion, we need a unit fraction that will convert yards to meters and then another to convert meters to centimeters.† Multiplying by the unit fraction $\frac{0.9144\ meter}{1\ yard}$ will convert yards to meters, and because 1 meter = 100 *centimeters*, we can use the unit fraction $\frac{100\ centimeters}{1\ meter}$ to finish the conversion. Thus,

$$5\ yards = 5\ \text{yards} \times \underbrace{\frac{0.9144\ meter}{1\ \text{yard}}}_{\text{converts yards to meters}} \times \underbrace{\frac{100\ centimeters}{1\ \text{meter}}}_{\text{converts meters to centimeters}}$$

$$= 5 \times 0.9144 \times 100\ centimeters = 457.2\ centimeters.$$

b) We will solve this problem similarly to the way we solved part a). We need one unit fraction, $\frac{1\ mile}{1.6\ kilometers}$, to convert kilometers to miles and then another, $\frac{5,280\ feet}{1\ mile}$, to convert miles to feet. Therefore,

$$0.3\ kilometer = 0.3\ \text{kilometer} \times \underbrace{\frac{1\ mile}{1.6\ \text{kilometers}}}_{\text{converts kilometers to miles}} \times \underbrace{\frac{5,280\ feet}{1\ \text{mile}}}_{\text{converts miles to feet}}$$

$$= \frac{0.3 \times 5,280}{1.6} = 990\ feet.$$

Now try the Exercises 27 to 40 that deal with length. ❋ **18**

Quiz Yourself **18**

Convert 0.65 kilometers to feet.

✏️ **KEY POINT**

The liter is the basic unit of volume in the metric system.

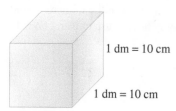

FIGURE 10.58 1 liter = 1 cubic decimeter = 1,000 cubic centimeters.

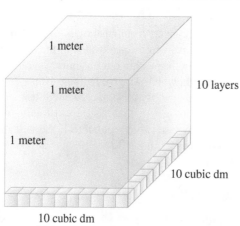

1 kiloliter = 1,000 liters = 1 cubic meter

FIGURE 10.59 Representing a cubic meter in terms of liters.

The **liter** is defined to be 1 cubic decimeter (see Figure 10.58). That is, a liter is the volume of a cube that measures 1 decimeter (or 10 centimeters) on each side. From Figure 10.58, you can see that a liter is 10 × 10 × 10 = 1,000 cubic centimeters.

As we mentioned earlier, a liter is slightly more than a quart. We can use the same prefixes (kilo-, hecto-, deka-, and so on) that we used in measuring length. We use a milliliter, $\frac{1}{1,000}$ of a liter, to measure small quantities, such as a dose of medicine. If you go to a clinic to get a flu shot, you might receive 2 milliliters of vaccine. We measure large volumes in kiloliters (1,000 liters). Figure 10.59 shows that a

---

*You can find more accurate approximations for these relationships in many science books and encyclopedias.
†Of course, we could convert meters to centimeters by moving the decimal point as we did in Example 1. Either approach will give you the same answer.

kiloliter is the same as a cubic meter. Each layer in Figure 10.59 contains $10 \times 10 = 100$ cubic decimeters, and because there are 10 layers, we have 1,000 cubic decimeters. In Canada, you might order 20 cubic meters of cement to build a patio floor. We also use cubic centimeters, cm^3 or cc, to measure dry materials.

EXAMPLE 5 *Estimating Metric Volumes*

Estimate the volume of each of the following items with one of these metric measurements: 3 mL (milliliters), 250 mL (milliliters), 100 L (liters), 500 m³ (cubic meters), 1 dm³ (cubic decimeter).*

a) The gas tank of a car   b) A large pile of gravel at a construction site
c) A glass of soda   d) A quart of orange juice

SOLUTION:

a) 100 liters is about 100 quarts, or 25 gallons, which is the size of the gas tank of a medium-size car.

b) 500 cubic meters is about 500 cubic yards, which is the size of a fairly good-size pile of gravel.

c) A glass of soda would be about $\frac{1}{4}$ of a quart. Because a quart is roughly equal to a liter and a liter is 1,000 milliliters, the glass of soda has a volume of about $\frac{1,000}{4} = 250$ milliliters.

d) A quart is roughly a liter and a liter is 1 cubic decimeter, so the volume of the orange juice is about 1 cubic decimeter. ❋

We make conversions among units of volume in the metric system in exactly the same way we made conversions among units of length.

EXAMPLE 6 *Estimating the Amount of Vaccinations*

The East Side Community Health Clinic has on hand four bottles that each contain 0.35 L of flu vaccine. Each vaccination requires 2 mL of vaccine. How many patients can be treated with the amount of vaccine that the clinic has on hand?

SOLUTION: The total amount of vaccine is $4 \times 0.35 = 1.4$ L. From Table 10.5, we see that to convert liters to millimeters, we can move the decimal point three places to the right. Therefore, the clinic has 1,400 mL of vaccine on hand, so it can give $\frac{1,400}{2} = 700$ vaccinations. ❋

You can use dimensional analysis to make conversions between units of volume in the metric and customary systems, but first you need to know some basic relationships, which we give in Table 10.8.

2 cups = 1 pint	1 cup = 0.2366 liter
2 pints = 1 quart	1 quart = 0.9464 liter
32 fluid ounces = 1 quart	1 cubic foot = 0.03 cubic meter
4 quarts = 1 gallon	1 cubic yard = 0.765 cubic meter

TABLE 10.8 Relationships between units of volume in the metric and customary systems.

You can now use these relationships to define unit fractions to make conversions from one system to the other as we did earlier in this section.

---

*We will denote a liter by L to avoid confusion between lowercase "el" and the numeral 1.

❋ ❋ ❋ HIGHLIGHT

Between the Numbers—But Officer—I Only Had . . .

In most states, you are considered legally drunk and unfit to drive if your blood alcohol content (BAC) is above 0.08. Now what exactly does that mean? The 0.08 stands for 0.08 gram per 100 milliliters of blood.

To put this in context, two beers contain about 30 grams of alcohol and an average-sized man has about 5 liters, or 5,000 milliliters of blood. So dividing 30 by 5,000, we get $\frac{30}{5,000} = 0.006$ gram of alcohol per milliliter in your blood. So in 100 milliliters, there would be $100 \times 0.006 = 0.6$ gram of alcohol. Actually, if this amount of alcohol were absorbed immediately, it would kill you—fatalities often occur with a BAC between 0.4 and 0.5. But, because the alcohol is absorbed over a period of time and the liver also works to eliminate the alcohol, we would not expect two beers to be fatal.

You can find BAC calculators on the Internet that will estimate your blood alcohol content based on your weight, what you are drinking, and so on. When I did this, I was thinking about the custom that some college students have of taking 21 drinks on their 21st birthday. When I tried to calculate my BAC if I had 21 drinks in 6 hours, the calculator responded by saying, "This is not a reasonable number of drinks, enter another number." So I entered 10 drinks for a 6 hour period and the estimated BAC was 0.22, or about three times the legal limit. If we were to double this to 20 drinks, it is not unreasonable to expect a BAC above 0.4, which is in the potentially fatal range.

EXAMPLE 7 *Calculating the Volume of a Car's Gas Tank*

Assume that an American car's gas tank has a capacity of 23 gallons. Supposing that you were driving this same car in France, how many liters of gasoline would you need to fill the tank?

SOLUTION: Looking at the shaded boxes in Table 10.8, we see that we can first use the unit fraction $\frac{4\ quarts}{1\ gallon}$ to convert gallons to quarts and then use the unit fraction $\frac{0.9464\ liter}{1\ quart}$ to convert quarts to liters. Thus,

$$23\ gallons = 23\ \overset{\text{converts gallons to quarts}}{gallons} \times \frac{4\ quarts}{1\ gallon} \times \overset{\text{converts quarts to liters}}{\frac{0.9464\ liter}{1\ quart}}$$
$$= 23 \times 4 \times 0.9464 = 87.07\ liters.$$

So you would need to purchase 87.07 L of gasoline.

Now try Exercises 27 to 40 that deal with volume. ❋

KEY POINT

The gram is the basic unit of mass (weight) in the metric system.

The last type of measurement we will consider is mass, which, for simplicity's sake, you might think of as weight. Strictly speaking, mass and weight are not the same thing. The mass of an object depends on its molecular makeup and does not change. The weight of an object, however, depends on the gravitational pull on that object. Gravity is stronger on a large planet and weaker on a small planet. Because the moon's gravity is only $\frac{1}{6}$ of Earth's gravity, an elephant that weighs 2,400 pounds on Earth would weigh only 400 pounds on the moon. However, the mass of the elephant would be the same on both Earth and the moon.

The basic unit of mass in the metric system is the **gram**, which is defined to be the mass of 1 cubic centimeter (1 milliliter) of water at a certain specified temperature and pressure. A liter (roughly 1 quart) is 1,000 mL, so a liter of water has a mass of 1,000 g or 1 kg. It is common in the metric system to measure the mass of a large object in kilograms; 1 kilogram is approximately 2.2 pounds. So, if you were having a barbecue in Spain and wanted to broil about 8 or 9 quarter-pounders, you would go to the market and buy 1 kg of ground beef.

The pattern of prefixes, and abbreviations, and also the rules for making conversions are the same for mass as they were for length and volume.

EXAMPLE 8   *Estimating Mass in the Metric System*

Estimate the mass of each of the following items with one of these metric measurements: 1 g, 50 cg, 5 kg, 1,000 kg.

a) A decent-size steak   b) A large bag of sugar

c) A medium-size car   d) A large paper clip

SOLUTION:

a) The steak might weigh a pound or more. A kilogram is 2.2 pounds, so the steak would be about one-half of a kilogram, or 50 cg.

b) Typically, we buy sugar in 10-pound bags; 5 kg would be equal to $5 \times 2.2 = 11$ pounds, so the sugar would weigh a little less than 5 kg.

c) A car might weigh 2,200 pounds, which is 1,000 kg.

d) A paper clip is pretty light, so its weight might be about 1 g. ✸

To make mass conversions between the metric and customary systems, you can use the information in Table 10.9.

16 ounces = 1 pound	1 ounce = 28 grams
2,000 pounds = 1 ton	2.2 pounds = 1 kilogram
	1 metric tonne = 1,000 kilograms
	1.1 tons = 1 metric tonne

TABLE 10.9 Relationships between units of mass in the metric and customary systems.

Again, we can use dimensional analysis to convert units in one system to units in the other.

EXAMPLE 9   *Refurbishing a Church with Italian Marble*

A contractor who is refurbishing a church has ordered slabs of Italian marble that weigh 1.8 metric tonnes each. If he wants to rent a crane to lift the slabs of marble, how much, in pounds, should the cranes be able to lift?

SOLUTION: We will convert metric tonnes to tons and then tons to pounds. The unit fraction $\frac{1.1 \ tons}{1 \ metric \ tonne}$ converts metric tonnes to tons and the unit fraction $\frac{2,000 \ pounds}{1 \ ton}$ will convert tons to pounds. Therefore,

$$1.8 \ metric \ tonnes = 1.8 \ \overline{metric \ tonnes} \times \frac{1.1 \ \overline{tons}}{1 \ \overline{metric \ tonne}} \times \frac{2,000 \ pounds}{1 \ \overline{ton}}$$

$$= 1.8 \times 1.1 \times 2,000 = 3,960 \ pounds$$

Converts metric tonnes to tons / Converts tons to pounds

A crane that can lift 4,000 pounds would just barely do the job.

Now try Exercises 27 to 40 that deal with weight. ✸ **19**

We will use the equivalents between the metric and customary systems found in the table on the left to do the following exercises.

Quiz Yourself **19**

Convert 3.8 kg to ounces.

1 meter = 1.0936 yards
1 mile = 1.609 kilometers
1 pound = 454 grams
1 metric tonne = 1.1 tons
1 liter = 1.0567 quarts*

*Note that we are using this equivalence in the exercises, rather than using the equivalence 1 quart = 0.9464 liter that we stated earlier.

Exercises 10.5

Looking Back*

These exercises follow the general outline of the topics presented in this section and will give you a good overview of the material that you have just studied.

1. How did we use Table 10.5 in solving Example 1, part (a)?
2. How might you remember the meaning of the metric prefixes "centi-," "milli-," and "deci-?"
3. In Example 4, what unit fraction did we use to convert miles to kilometers?
4. What do you deduce from the Highlight regarding blood alcohol content?

Sharpening Your Skills

In Exercises 5–14, match the italicized words in the left column with the metric measurement in the right column that corresponds to it. Before calculating your final answer, it would be wise to first convert the given measurement to basic metric units such as meters, grams, or liters.

5. A *quarter-pound* hamburger   **a.** 0.02159 dam
6. A *gallon* of milk   **b.** 946.3 mL
7. A *15-foot* tall giraffe   **c.** 378.5 cl
8. *Five pounds* of potatoes   **d.** 1.77 dL
9. A *6-inch*-long ruler   **e.** 4,572 mm
10. A *quart* of motor oil   **f.** 0.0061 km
11. A book *eight and one-half inches* wide   **g.** 15.24 cm
12. A *12-ounce* gerbil   **h.** 1,135 dg
13. *Six ounces* of orange juice   **i.** 3.405 hg
14. A *20-foot*-long swimming pool   **j.** 2.27 kg

Make the indicated conversions in Exercises 15–20.

15. 2.4 kiloliters to deciliters
16. 240 centigrams to dekagrams
17. 28 decimeters to millimeters
18. 5.6 hectograms to centigrams
19. 3.5 dekaliters to deciliters
20. 7,600 centimeters to meters

Pick the most appropriate measurement for each of the following items. Explain your answer.

21. The volume of a small juice glass
    a. 125 mL   **b.** 500 mL   **c.** 2.5 L
22. The weight of books in your backpack
    a. 500 g   **b.** 80 hg   **c.** 6 kg
23. The length of your nose
    a. 4 dm   **b.** 3 mm   **c.** 5 cm

24. The volume of a bottle of wine
    a. 0.25 L   **b.** 0.2 kL   **c.** 750 mL
25. The height of a Boston terrier
    a. 100 mm   **b.** 0.06 dam   **c.** 0.6 hm
26. The weight of NFL lineman Orlando Pace
    a. 136 kg   **b.** 13,000 g   **c.** 20 dag

Use dimensional analysis† to make each of the following conversions. You may have to define several unit fractions to make the conversions. Also, because the constants that we give in the table are only approximations, depending on the method with which you do your computations, your answers may differ slightly from ours.

27. 18 meters to feet
28. 27 gallons to liters
29. 3 kilograms to ounces
30. 10,000 milliliters to quarts
31. 2.1 kiloliters to gallons
32. 47 pounds to kilograms
33. 10,000 deciliters to quarts
34. 507,820 milligrams to pounds
35. 176 centimeters to inches
36. 3 yards to millimeters
37. 45,000 kg to tons
38. 0.65 tonne to pounds
39. 2.6 feet to decimeters
40. 10 tons to tonnes

Applying What You've Learned

Rewrite each statement, replacing the metric measure by the corresponding customary measure.

41. Hold your ground. Don't give him 2.54 centimeters.
42. Tex was wearing a 9.5-liter hat.
43. It is first down and 9.14 meters to go.
44. 28 grams of prevention is worth 0.45 kilogram of cure.
45. **Volume of a tank.** A rectangular tank is 5 m wide, 8 m long, and 4 m deep.
    a. What is the volume of the tank in cubic meters?
    b. How many liters of water does the tank contain?
    c. What is the weight of the water in kilograms?
46. **Painting a wall.** If a rectangular wall of a gymnasium that measures 2.5 m by 30.8 m requires 8 L of paint, then how much paint would be needed to cover a wall that measures 3.2 m by 26.4 m?

---

*Before doing these exercises, you may find it useful to review the note *How to Succeed at Mathematics* on page xix.
†In some cases, you may find it quicker not to use dimensional analysis to get your answers.

47. **Converting speed.** In *The Amazing Race*, Rachel is driving a car that shows speed in both miles per hour and kilometers per hour. If she is traveling in Italy at 80 kilometers per hour, what is her speed in miles per hour?

48. **Converting speed.** TK is driving in Switzerland at a speed of 55 miles per hour. What is his speed in kilometers per hour?

49. **Finding the volume of a swimming pool.** Adrian's rectangular swimming pool is 20 ft wide, 40 ft long, and averages 6 ft in depth. How many kiloliters of water are needed to fill the pool?

50. **Buying canned food.** Marco purchased a large can of chili that has a diameter of 10 cm and a height of 14 cm. Determine the volume of the chili in the can.

    a. in liters.   **b.** in ounces.

51. **Purchasing fruit in Europe.** While visiting Poland, Anthony purchased some red plums that cost $2.75 per kilogram. What is the cost of the plums per pound?

52. **Measuring a medication.** Justin is taking the anti-inflammatory drug Niamoxin and the instructions say that the patient must receive 10 mg for each 15 kg of body weight. If Justin weighs 275 lb, what dosage should he receive?

53. **Buying gasoline.** If gasoline costs $2.18 per liter in Gambia (Africa), what is its cost in dollars per gallon?

54. **Buying gasoline.** Europeans pay very heavy taxes on gasoline. When I was writing these exercises, gasoline in Germany cost $8.00 per gallon. What would the cost be in dollars per liter?

55. **Fencing a dog pen.** Serina wants to fence in a rectangular exercise pen for her golden labrador retriever. The pen is 35 ft wide and 62 ft long. The fencing is sold in whole meters. How much fencing should she buy?

56. In Exercise 55, what is the area of Serina's pen in square meters?

57. **Calculating gas mileage.** If a car averages 30 miles per gallon, how many kilometers per liter would that be?

58. **Calculating gas mileage.** If a car averages 15 kilometers per liter, how many miles per gallon would that be?

59. **Buying flooring.** If oak flooring costs $8.00 a square foot, how much is that cost per square meter?

60. **Buying flooring.** If vinyl flooring costs $98.00 a square meter, how much is that per square foot?

In the metric system, temperatures are measured using the Celsius (also called centigrade) thermometer instead of Fahrenheit that we commonly use. On the Celsius scale, water freezes at 0 degrees and boils at 100 degrees. To convert a temperature using one thermometer to a temperature using the other, you can use the following equation:

$$F = \frac{9}{5}C + 32, *$$

where F is the Fahrenheit temperature and C is the Celsius temperature. Use this equation in Exercises 61–68 to convert each temperature to a corresponding measurement in the other system.

61. 149 degrees Fahrenheit
62. 95 degrees Fahrenheit
63. 60 degrees Celsius
64. 85 degrees Celsius
65. 20 degrees Celsius
66. 131 degrees Fahrenheit
67. 113 degrees Fahrenheit
68. 50 degrees Celsius

In Exercises 69–72, use the fact that a hectare (pronounced "HEKtaire") is a square that measures 100 meters on each side.

69. What is the relationship between hectares and square meters?

70. What is the relationship between hectares and square kilometers?

71. Thiep purchased a rectangular piece of land that measures 0.75 km by 1.2 km. How many hectares of land is that?

72. If Ivanka purchased a rectangular piece of land that contains 40 hectares and is 0.65 km long, how long is the other dimension?

Communicating Mathematics

73. What is the fundamental base for expressing measurements in a metric system?

74. In Table 10.5, an item in one column represents how many items in the column to its right?

75. If you were converting hectometers to decimeters, would you have more hectometers or more decimeters? Why?

76. What metric units do you use to measure mass? Volume? Length?

77. In converting milligrams to dekagrams, we would move the decimal point either four places to the right or to the left. Which is it? Explain how you would help a fellow classmate remember which to do.

78. If *a* kiloliters equals *b* dekaliters, which is larger, *a* or *b*? Explain how you arrived at your answer.

79. Explain the advantages that you see in using the metric system over the customary system. Be specific. Give concrete examples.

80. Why are conversions easy to do in the metric system? Give specific examples.

Using Technology to Investigate Mathematics

81. Find a blood alcohol content calculator on the Internet. Experiment with different scenarios and write a brief report on your findings.

82. Find an interactive Web site that converts measurements in the U.S. customary system into the metric system. Reproduce some of the conversions from this section. Write a report on your findings.

For Extra Credit

83. Research the history of the definition of an inch. Explain the results of your research.

---

*This equation converts degrees Celsius to degrees Fahrenheit. You can also use it (plus algebra) to convert Fahrenheit to Celsius, which we recommend that you do. If you really want another equation to convert Fahrenheit to Celsius, you can use the equation $C = \frac{5}{9}(F - 32)$. However, we strongly recommend that you memorize only one equation and use algebra to do the second conversion.

84. Research the history of the definition of a yard. Explain the results of your research.

85. Research the definitions of avoirdupois and troy weight. Use your research to explain why a pound of silver does not weigh the same as a pound of steak.

86. In 1870, Jules Verne wrote his famous novel *20,000 Leagues Under the Sea.* What is a league? If the submarine in Jules Verne's book traveled a distance of 20,000 leagues under water, how far did it travel? Give your answer in feet.

CHAPTER SUMMARY*

SECTION	SUMMARY	EXAMPLE
SECTION 10.1	A **ray** is a half line with its endpoint included. A piece of a line joining two points and including the points is called a **line segment**. **Parallel lines** are lines that lie on the same plane and have no points in common. Two lines that have a single point in common are called **intersecting lines**.	Discussion, p. 451
	An **angle** is formed by two rays that have a common endpoint. An **acute** angle has a measure between 0° and 90°. An angle with a measure of 90° is called a **right** angle. An **obtuse** angle has a measure between 90° and 180°. A **straight** angle has a measure of 180°. Two intersecting lines form two pairs of **vertical angles** having equal measures. Two angles are **complementary** if the sum of their measures is 90°. Two angles that have an angle sum of 180° are called **supplementary** angles. Two lines that intersect forming right angles are called **perpendicular** lines. Parallel lines cut by a **transversal** form several pairs of **equal** angles.	Discussion, pp. 452–454
		Example 1, p. 454
	A **circle** is the set of all points lying on a plane that are located at a fixed distance, called the **radius**, from a given point, called the **center**. A **diameter** of a circle is a line segment passing through the center, with both endpoints lying on the circle. The **circumference** is the distance around the circle.	Discussion, p. 455
		Example 2, p. 455
		Example 3, p. 456
SECTION 10.2	A plane figure is **closed** if we can draw it without lifting the pencil and the starting and ending points are the same. A plane figure is **simple** if we can draw it without lifting the pencil and in drawing it, we never pass through the same point twice, with the possible exception of the starting and ending points. A **polygon** is a simple, closed figure consisting only of line segments, called **edges**, such that no two consecutive edges lie on the same line. If all edges are the same length, the polygon is called **regular**. A polygon is **convex** if for any two points X and Y inside the polygon, the entire line segment XY also lies inside the polygon.	Definitions, p. 460
		Definitions, p. 461
		Definition, p. 461
	The **sum** of the measures of the interior angles of a convex polygon that has n sides is $(n-2) \times 180°$.	Examples 1 and 2, p. 463
	Two polygons are **similar** if their corresponding sides are proportional and their corresponding angles are equal.	Discussion, p. 465
	Non-Euclidean geometries have different properties than Euclidean geometry. The shortest distance between two points is not a straight line segment. Triangles do not have angle sums of 180°.	Highlight, p. 466
SECTION 10.3	If a rectangle has length l and width w, then the **perimeter** of the rectangle is $P = 2l + 2w$ and the **area** is $A = l \cdot w$.	Discussion, p. 471
	The **area of a parallelogram** with height h and base b is $A = h \cdot b$. The **area of a triangle** with height h and base b is $A = \frac{1}{2}h \cdot b$. **Heron's formula** states that for a triangle with sides of lengths a, b, and c, if we define the quantity $s = \frac{1}{2}(a+b+c)$, then the area of the triangle is $A = \sqrt{s(s-a)(s-b)(s-c)}$. A **trapezoid** with lower base b_1 and upper base b_2 and height h has **area** $A = \frac{1}{2}(b_1 + b_2) \times h$.	Discussion, p. 471
		Example 1, p. 472
		Example 2, p. 472
		Example 3, p. 473
	The **Pythagorean theorem** states that in a right triangle with legs of lengths a and b and hypotenuse (the side opposite the right angle) of length c, then $a^2 + b^2 = c^2$.	Example 4, p. 475
		Example 5, pp. 475
	A circle with radius r has **circumference** $C = 2\pi r$ and **area** $A = \pi r^2$.	Example 6, p. 477
SECTION 10.4	If a **rectangular solid** has length l, width w, and height h, then the **volume** of the solid is $V = lwh$ and the **surface area** of the solid is $S = 2lw + 2lh + 2wh$. If an object has a flat top and base and *sides perpendicular to the base*, and if the area of the base is A and the height is h, the volume will be $V = A \cdot h$.	Discussion, p. 483
		Example 1, p. 483
	A **right circular cylinder** with radius r and height h has **volume** $V = \pi r^2 h$ and **surface area** $S = 2\pi rh + 2\pi r^2$.	Example 2, p. 484
	A **right circular cone** with base radius r and height h has **volume** $V = \frac{1}{3}\pi r^2 h$ and **surface area** $S = \pi r\sqrt{r^2 + h^2}$. A **sphere** with radius r has volume $V = \frac{4}{3}\pi r^3$ and **surface area** $S = 4\pi r^2$.	Examples 4 and 5, p. 487
		Example 6, p. 488

*Before studying this chapter's material, it would be useful to reread the note *How to Succeed at Mathematics* on page xix.

SECTION 10.5	In the **metric system**, length measurement is based on the **meter**, which is slightly more than a yard. Volume is based on the **liter**, which is a little more than a quart. The basic unit of weight is the **gram**. A pound is 454 grams.	Discussion, p. 491

The following table explains the **prefixes** that we use in the metric system: Table 10.5, p. 491

kilo- (k)	hecto- (h)	deka- (da)	base unit	deci- (d)	centi- (c)	milli- (m)
$\times 1,000$	$\times 100$	$\times 10$		$\times \dfrac{1}{10}$ or $\times 0.1$	$\times \dfrac{1}{100}$ or $\times 0.01$	$\times \dfrac{1}{1,000}$ or $\times 0.001$

We use the following **equivalents** between the metric and customary systems in doing **dimensional analysis**:   Table, p. 497

1 meter = 1.0936 yards
1 mile = 1.609 kilometers
1 pound = 454 grams
1 metric tonne = 1.1 tons
1 liter = 1.0567 quarts

| SECTION 10.6 | A **rigid** motion is the action of taking a geometric object in the plane and moving it in some fashion to some other place in the plane without changing its shape or size. Every rigid motion is essentially a reflection, a translation, a glide reflection, or a rotation. A **reflection** moves an object so that the ending position is a mirror image of the object in its starting position. A **translation** slides an object along a line segment, called the **translation vector**, in the plane. A **glide reflection** is formed by performing a translation (the glide) followed by a reflection. We perform a **rotation** by first selecting a point, called the **center of rotation**, and then while holding this point fixed, rotating the plane about this point through an angle called the **angle of rotation**. | Discussion, p. 500

Example 1, p. 502

Example 2, p. 503

Discussion, p. 504 |
|---|---|---|
| | A **symmetry** of a geometric object is a rigid motion such that the beginning position and the ending position of the object are exactly the same. | Example 3, p. 505 |
| | A **tessellation** (or tiling) of the plane is a pattern made up entirely of polygons that completely cover the plane with no gaps or overlapping polygons. The only regular polygons **that tessellate the plane** are triangles, squares, and hexagons. | Discussion, p. 506

Example 4, p. 507 |
| SECTION 10.7 | A **fractal** object is **self-similar** in the sense that if we magnify it, we see the same patterns that were present in the original object. The **Koch curve** and the **Sierpinski gasket** are examples of fractals.

The Koch curve has infinite **length**, and the **area** of the Sierpinski gasket is zero. | Discussion, p. 514
Example 1, p. 514
Example 2, p. 515
Example 3, p. 516
Example 4, p. 516 |
| | The **fractal dimension** of an object is a number D that satisfies the equation $n = s^D$, where s is a scaling factor and n is the amount by which the quantity we are measuring changes when we apply the scaling factor to the object. | Example 5, p. 519 |

CHAPTER REVIEW EXERCISES

Section 10.1

1. In the given figure:
   a. Find a pair of acute, alternate exterior angles.
   b. Find a pair of obtuse, alternate interior angles.

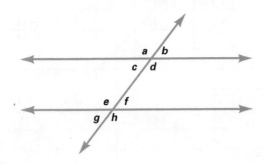

2. Find the measures of angles a, b, and c in the given diagram.

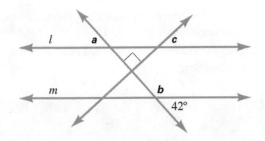

3. Assume that in the given diagram, the circumference is 24 inches and the length of arc DE is 3 inches. Find $m\angle BCD$.

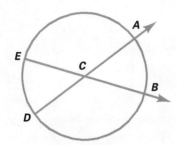

4. Solve for x in the given diagram.

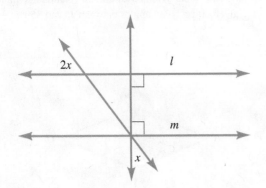

5. What is the shortest distance between two points on a sphere?

Section 10.2

6. What is the measure of an interior angle of a regular 18-sided polygon?

7. The given pair of figures are similar. What information do you know about the figure on the right?

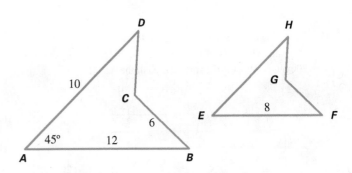

8. Solve for x in the given diagram.

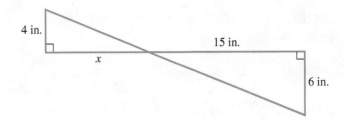

Section 10.3

9. Find the area of each figure.

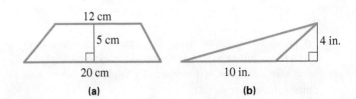

(a)   (b)

10. Find the shaded area of each figure.

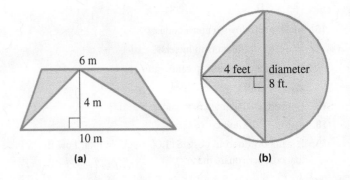

(a)   (b)

11. a. Find the area of the triangle.

   b. Find the height h of the triangle.

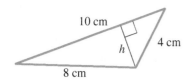

12. A running track, 5 meters wide, has the dimensions shown in the diagram. The ends of the track are semicircles with diameter 20 meters. What is the surface area of the track?

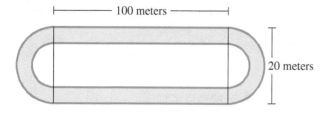

Section 10.4

13. Find the volume of each solid.

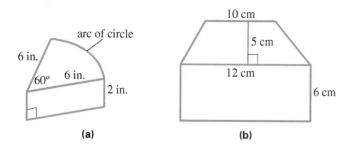

14. A punch bowl shaped like a hemisphere with a radius of 9 inches is full of punch. If we are filling cylindrical glasses that have a diameter of 3 inches and a height of 3 inches, how many glasses can we fill?

15. If we double the radius of a right circular cone, what effect does that have on the volume? Explain your answer.

Section 10.5

16. Make the following conversions:

   a. 3,500 millimeters to meters

   b. 4.315 hectograms to centigrams

   c. 3.86 kiloliters to deciliters

17. Convert 514 decimeters to yards.

18. Convert 2.1 kiloliters to quarts.

19. If bamboo flooring costs $11.00 a square foot, how much is that cost per square meter?

Section 10.6

20. Perform the indicated glide reflection on figure B.

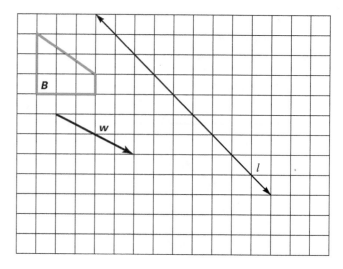

21. a. List all patterns that can be obtained by reflecting pattern (a) about a single line.

   b. List all patterns that can be obtained by rotating pattern (a) about its center.

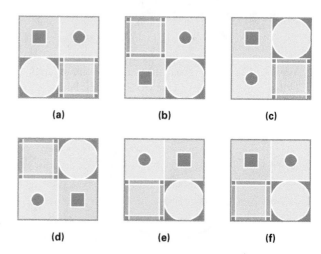

22. Find all reflectional symmetries and all rotational symmetries of the given object using angles between 1° and 359°.

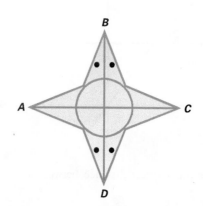

23. Tessellate the plane with the given quadrilateral.

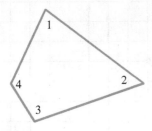

Section 10.7

24. How did we argue that the length of the Koch curve was infinite?

25. What was the area of the Sierpinski gasket?

26. You are given steps 0 and 1 for constructing a fractal. What is the length of the curve in step 8?

step 0   step 1

CHAPTER TEST

1. In the given figure, name each of the following pairs of angles. Assume $l \parallel m$.

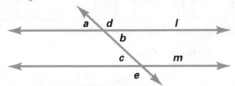

  a. a and b **b.** a and c **c.** d and e **d.** b and c

2. What is the sum of the measure of the interior angles of a regular 12-sided polygon?

3. Find the measure of angles a, b, and c in the given diagram. Assume $l \parallel m$.

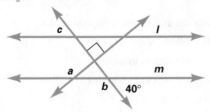

4. A spherical water tank that has a radius of 15 feet is being replaced with a cylindrical tank that also has a radius of 15 feet. How high must the new tank be to contain the same amount of water as the old tank?

5. Find the volume of each solid.

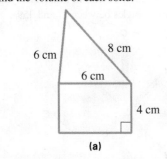

(a)

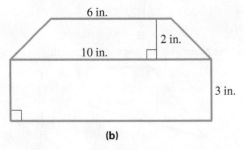

(b)

6. a. List all patterns that can be obtained by reflecting pattern (a) about a single line.

  b. List all patterns that can be obtained by rotating pattern (a) about its center.

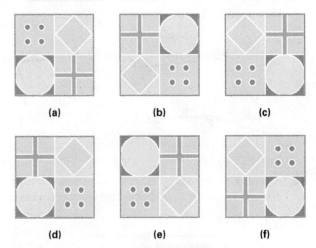

7. Assume that in the given diagram $m\angle BCD = 150°$ and the circumference is 36 inches. What is length of arc DE?

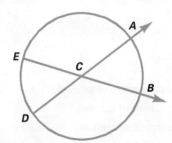

8. What is the length of the Koch curve after five steps?

9. Find the area of each figure.

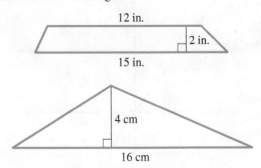

10. Find the shaded area of each figure.

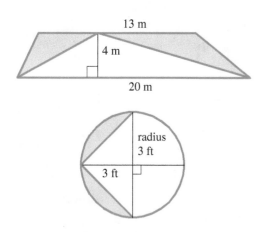

11. The given pair of figures are similar. What information do you know about the figure on the right?

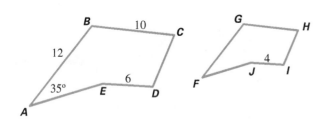

12. A pool is surrounded by a brick walkway as shown in the diagram. The pool is 3 feet deep and the walkway is 4 feet wide.

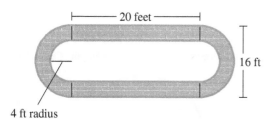

a. Find the surface area of the pool.

b. Find the volume of the pool.

c. Find the area of the walkway.

13. Solve for x in the following diagram:

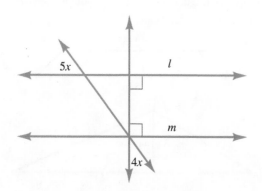

14. Reflect the given figure about the line $x = 1$, and then the line $y = 1$.

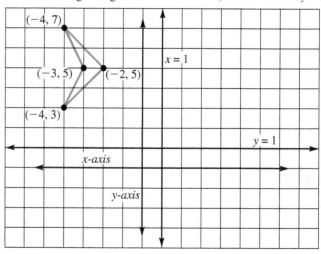

15. a. Find the area of the triangle.

  b. Find the height of the triangle.

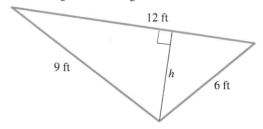

16. What was the area of the Sierpinski gasket?

17. Make the following conversions:

  a. 2,400 centimeters to meters

  b. 3.46 kilograms to milligrams

  c. 2.14 dekaliters to centiliters

18. If we double the radius of a sphere, what effect does that have on the surface area?

19. Convert 18 yards to decimeters.

20. Convert 2,614.35 quarts to kiloliters.

21. Find all reflectional symmetries and all rotational symmetries of the given figure using angles between 1° and 359°.

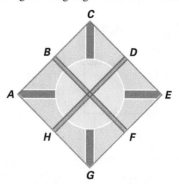

22. Tessellate the plane with the given quadrilateral.

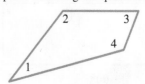

GROUP EXERCISES

1. **a.** Suppose that you have 24 inches of stiff wire to form a rectangle. Experiment by varying length and width to find the dimensions of the rectangle that contains the most area. (*Hint:* You can use the formula for the perimeter of a rectangle to express width in terms of length. Then, instead of doing hand calculations, you can use the table feature of a graphing calculator to calculate areas for you as you vary the length.)

   b. Do the same for triangles.

2. Collect a set of data and present it as a pie graph as we did in the exercise set for Section 1.3. Construct it by hand by finding the central angle of each "slice" of the pie. Then compare your graph with the same graph produced by a product such as Microsoft Word.

3. There are many sites on the Internet that discuss drawings similar to these two that were drawn by the Dutch artist Maurits Cornelis Escher. Escher formed these drawings by first creating a tessellation and then modifying it to create the image.

   a. Identify what tessellations Escher is using in Figures 1 and 2.

   b. Obtain other Escher drawings and analyze them as you did in part (a). A good place to start is www.mcescher.com.

   c. Research a Web site that explains how Escher made his drawings, and then try to make a simple one of your own.

Figure 1

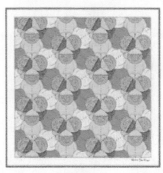

Figure 2

13

Statistics

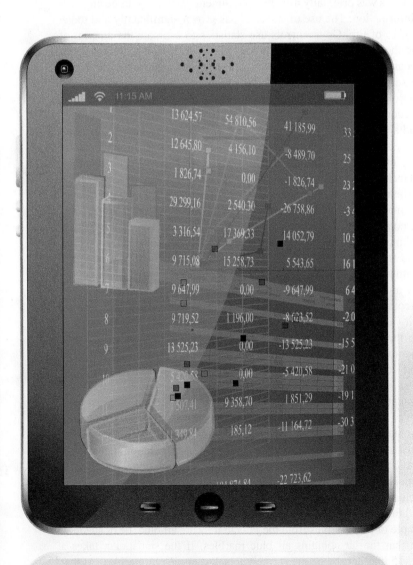

◄ *Numbers are the foundation of all statistical information.*

What You Will Learn

- Sampling techniques
- Misuses of statistics
- Frequency distributions
- Histograms, frequency polygons, stem-and-leaf displays
- Mode, median, mean, and midrange
- Percentiles and quartiles
- Range and standard deviation
- *z*-scores and the normal distribution
- Correlation and regression

Why This is Important

Benjamin Disraeli (1804–1881), once prime minister of the United Kingdom, said that there are three kinds of lies: lies, damned lies, and statistics. Do numbers lie? Numbers are the foundation of all statistical information. The "lie" occurs when, either intentionally or carelessly, a number is used in such a way that leads us to an unjustified or incorrect conclusion. Numbers may not lie, but they can be manipulated and misinterpreted. This chapter will provide information that can help you recognize when statistical information is being manipulated and misinterpreted. It will also help you see the many valuable uses of statistics.

SECTION 13.1   Sampling Techniques

▲ *Statisticians have several different techniques with which they can collect numerical information, such as how many Americans use an e-reader.*

According to Harris Interactive, 20% of Americans use an e-reader, an electronic reading device. It would be very expensive for Harris Interactive to ask every American if he or she uses an e-reader. Instead, to collect this information the polling company may ask a subset of Americans, called a *sample*. If it does not ask every American if he or she uses an e-reader, how do we know that Harris Interactive's results are accurate? In this section, we will discuss different techniques statisticians use to collect numerical information, and how they make accurate conclusions about an entire set of data from the sample collected.

Why This is Important Samples are used to determine a variety of information such as the percentage of college graduates in a city and the average credit card debt of an American family.

The study of statistics was originally used by governments to manage large amounts of numerical information. The use of statistics has grown significantly and today is applied in all walks of life. Governments use statistics to estimate the amount of unemployment and the cost of living. In psychology and education, the statistical theory of tests and measurements has been developed to compare achievements of individuals from diverse places and backgrounds. Newspapers and magazines carry the results of different polls on topics ranging from the president's popularity to the number of cans of soda consumed. Statistics is used in scores of other professions; in fact, it is difficult to find any profession that does not depend on some aspect of statistics.

Before we discuss different techniques used to collect numerical information, we will first introduce a few important definitions. *Statistics* is the art and science of gathering, analyzing, and making inferences (predictions) from numerical information obtained in an experiment. The numerical information so obtained is referred to as *data*. Statistics is divided into two main branches: descriptive and inferential. *Descriptive statistics* is concerned with the collection, organization, and analysis of data. *Inferential statistics* is concerned with making generalizations or predictions from the data collected.

Probability and statistics are closely related. Someone in the field of probability is interested in computing the chance of occurrence of a particular event when all the possible outcomes are known. A statistician's interest lies in drawing conclusions about possible outcomes through observations of only a few particular events.

If a probability expert and a statistician find identical boxes, the probability expert might open the box, observe the contents, replace the cover, and proceed to compute the probability of randomly selecting a specific object from the box. The statistician might select a few items from the box without looking at the contents and make a prediction as to the total contents of the box.

The entire contents of the box constitute the *population*. A population consists of all items or people of interest. The statistician often uses a subset of the population, called a *sample*, to make predictions concerning the population. It is important to understand the difference between a population and a sample. A population includes *all* items of interest. A sample includes *some* of the items in the population.

When a statistician draws a conclusion from a sample, there is always the possibility that the conclusion is incorrect. For example, suppose that a jar contains 90 blue marbles and 10 red marbles, as shown in Fig. 13.1 on page 775. If the statistician selects a random sample of five marbles from the jar and they are all blue, he or she may wrongly conclude that the jar contains all blue marbles. If the statistician takes a larger sample, say, 15 marbles, he or she is likely to select some red marbles. At that

Figure 13.1

MATHEMATICS TODAY

Tune in Tomorrow

The A. C. Nielsen Company, which has been measuring the viewing population of TV shows for more than 50 years, uses a sample of about 9000 metered households in the United States to draw conclusions about more than 110 million American households that have a television. An electronic measurement system, called the People Meter, is placed on each TV in the sample household. Each household member is assigned a personal viewing button on the People Meter to keep track of which channels he or she watches and for how long. Nielsen then computes the rating of the show, using the data obtained from the sample.

You can learn more about the sampling techniques used by A. C. Nielsen at Nielsenmedia.com. A. C. Nielsen is involved in many other areas of statistical testing and measurement.

Why *This is Important* Television programs that have a large audience can charge more for commercial advertising. A. C. Nielsen is only one of a large number of companies that use a sample to make a prediction about an entire population.

point, the statistician may make a prediction about the contents of the jar based on the sample selected. Of course, the most accurate result would occur if every object in the jar, the entire population, were observed. However, in most statistical experiments, observing the entire population is not practical.

Statisticians use samples instead of the entire population for two reasons: (a) it is often impossible to obtain data on an entire population, and (b) sampling is less expensive because collecting the data takes less time and effort. For example, suppose that you wanted to determine the number of each species of all the fish in a lake. To do so would be almost impossible without using a sample. If you did try to obtain this information from the entire population, the cost would be astronomical. Or suppose that you wanted to test soup cans for spoilage. If every can produced by the company was opened and tested, the company wouldn't have any product left to sell. Instead of testing the entire population of soup cans, a sample is selected. The results obtained from the sample of soup cans selected are used to make conclusions about the entire population of soup cans.

Later in this chapter we will discuss statistical measures such as the *mean* and the *standard deviation*. When statisticians calculate the mean and the standard deviation of the entire population, they use different symbols and formulas than when they calculate the mean and standard deviation of a sample. The following chart shows the symbols used to represent the mean and standard deviation of a sample and of a population. Note that the mean and standard deviation of a population are symbolized by Greek letters.

Measure	Sample	Population
Mean	$\bar{x}$ (read "*x* bar")	μ (mu)
Standard deviation	s	σ (sigma)

Unless otherwise indicated, in this book we will always assume that we are working with a sample and so we will use $\bar{x}$ *and* s. If you take a course in statistics, you will use all four symbols and different formulas for a sample and for a population.

Consider the task of determining the political strength of a certain candidate running in a national election. It is not possible for pollsters to ask each of the approximately 213 million eligible voters his or her preference of a candidate. Thus, pollsters must select and use a sample of the population to obtain their information. How large a sample do you think they use to make predictions about an upcoming national election? You might be surprised to learn that pollsters use only about 1600 registered voters in their national sample. How can a pollster using such a small percentage of the population make an accurate prediction?

The answer is that when pollsters select a sample, they use sophisticated statistical techniques to obtain an unbiased sample. An *unbiased sample* is one that is a small replica of the entire population with regard to income, education, gender, race,

Did You Know?

The Birth of Inferential Statistics

PHILOSOPHICAL
TRANSACTIONS:
GIVING SOME
ACCOMPT
OF THE PRESENT
Undertakings , Studies, and Labours
OF THE
INGENIOUS
IN MANY
CONSIDERABLE PARTS
OF THE
WORLD.

Vol I.
For *Anno* 1665, and 1666.

In the *SAVOY,*
Printed by *T. N.* for *John Martyn* at the Bell, a little with-
out *Temple-Bar* , and *James Allestry* in *Duck-Lane* ,
Printers to the *Royal Society.*

John Gaunt, a London merchant, is credited with being the first person to make statistical predictions, or inferences, from a set of data rather than basing the predictions simply on the laws of chance. He studied the vital statistics (births, deaths, marriages) contained in the Bills of Mortality published during the years of the Great Plague. He observed that more males were born than females and that women lived longer than men. From these observations, he made predictions about life expectancies. The keeping of mortality statistics was stimulated considerably by the growth of the insurance industry.

religion, political affiliation, age, and so on. The procedures statisticians use to obtain unbiased samples are quite complex. The following sampling techniques will give you a brief idea of how statisticians obtain unbiased samples.

Random Sampling

If a sample is drawn in such a way that each time an item is selected each item in the population has an equal chance of being drawn, the sample is said to be a *random sample*. When using a random sample, one combination of a specified number of items has the same probability of being selected as any other combination. When all the items in the population are similar with regard to the specific characteristic we are interested in, a random sample can be expected to produce satisfactory results. For example, consider a large container holding 300 tennis balls that are identical except for color. One-third of the balls are yellow, one-third are white, and one-third are green. If the balls can be thoroughly mixed between each draw of a tennis ball so that each ball has an equally likely chance of being selected, randomness is not difficult to achieve. However, if the objects or items are not all the same size, shape, or texture, it might be impossible to obtain a random sample by reaching into a container and selecting an object.

The best procedure for selecting a random sample is to use a random number generator or a table of random numbers. A random number generator is a device, usually a calculator or computer program, that produces a list of random numbers. A random number table is a collection of random digits in which each digit has an equal chance of appearing. To select a random sample, first assign a number to each element in the population. Numbers are usually assigned in order. Then select the number of random numbers needed, which is determined by the sample size. Each numbered element from the population that corresponds to a selected random number becomes part of the sample.

Systematic Sampling

When a sample is obtained by drawing every nth item on a list or production line, the sample is a *systematic sample*. The first item should be determined by using a random number.

It is important that the list from which a systematic sample is chosen includes the entire population being studied. See the *Did You Know?* called "Don't Count Your Votes Until They're Cast" on page 777. Another problem that must be avoided when this method of sampling is used is the constantly recurring characteristic. For example, on an assembly line, every 10th item could be the work of robot X. If only every 10th item is checked for defects, the work of other robots doing the same job may not be checked and may be defective.

Cluster Sampling

A *cluster sample* is sometimes referred to as an *area sample* because it is frequently applied on a geographical basis. Essentially, the sampling consists of a random selection of groups of units. To select a cluster sample, we divide a geographic area into sections. Then we randomly select the sections or clusters. Either each member of the selected cluster is included in the sample or a random sample of the members of each cluster is used. For example, geographically we might randomly select city blocks to use as a sample unit. Then either every member of each selected city block would be used or a random sample from each selected city block would be used. Another example is to select x boxes of screws from a whole order, count the number of defective screws in the x boxes selected, and use this number to determine the expected number of defective screws in the whole order.

Did You Know?

Don't Count Your Votes Until They're Cast

A classic instance of faulty sampling occurred in the 1936 presidential election. On the basis of the responses of 2,300,000 voters, selected from automobile owners and telephone subscribers, the *Literary Digest* confidently predicted that the Republican candidate, Alf Landon, would be elected. As it turned out, Franklin D. Roosevelt, the Democratic candidate, won by a large margin. The erroneous prediction occurred because the voters used in the sample were not representative of the general voting population. In 1936, telephones and automobiles were unaffordable to the average voter.

Stratified Sampling

When a population is divided into parts, called strata, for the purpose of drawing a sample, the procedure is known as *stratified sampling*. Stratified sampling involves dividing the population by characteristics called *stratifying factors* such as gender, race, religion, or income. When a population has varied characteristics, it is desirable to separate the population into classes with similar characteristics and then take a random sample from each stratum (or class). For example, we could separate the population of undergraduate college students into strata called freshmen, sophomores, juniors, and seniors.

The use of stratified sampling requires some knowledge of the population. For example, to obtain a cross section of voters in a city, we must know where various groups are located and the approximate number of voters in each location.

Convenience Sampling

A *convenience sample* uses data that are easily or readily obtained. Occasionally, data that are conveniently obtained may be all that is available. In some cases, some information is better than no information at all. Nevertheless, convenience sampling can be extremely biased. For example, suppose that a town wants to raise taxes to build a new elementary school. The local newspaper wants to obtain the opinion of some of the residents and sends a reporter to a senior citizens center. The first 10 people who exit the building are asked if they are in favor of raising taxes to build a new school. This sample could be biased against raising taxes for the new school. Most senior citizens would not have school-age children and may not be interested in paying increased taxes to build a new school. Although a convenience sample may be very easy to select, one must be very cautious when using the results obtained by this method.

Example 1 *Identifying Sampling Techniques*

Identify the sampling technique used to obtain a sample in the following. Explain your answer.

a) Every 20th soup can coming off an assembly line is checked for defects.

b) A $50 gift certificate is given away at the Annual Bankers Convention. Tickets are placed in a bin, and the tickets are mixed up. Then the winning ticket is selected by a blindfolded person.

c) Children in a large city are classified based on the neighborhood school they attend. A random sample of five schools is selected. All the children from each selected school are included in the sample.

d) The first 50 people entering a zoo are asked if they support an increase in taxes to support a zoo expansion.

e) Viewers of the *USA Network* are classified according to age. Random samples from each age group are selected.

Solution

a) Systematic sampling. The sample is obtained by drawing every nth item. In this example, every 20th item on an assembly line is selected.

b) Random sampling. Every ticket has an equal chance of being selected.

c) Cluster sampling. A random sample of geographic areas is selected.

d) Convenience sampling. The sample is selected by picking data that are easily obtained.

e) Stratified sampling. The viewers are divided into strata based on their age. Then random samples are selected from each strata.

SECTION 13.1 *Exercises*

Warm Up Exercises

In Exercises 1–12, fill in the blank with an appropriate word, phrase, or symbol(s).

1. The art and science of gathering, analyzing, and making inferences (predictions) from numerical information obtained in an experiment is called _____.

2. Making generalizations or predictions from the data collected is called _____ statistics.

3. The collection, organization, and analysis of data is called _____ statistics.

4. All items or people of interest in an experiment is called a(n) _____.

5. A subset of a population used by statisticians to make predictions about a population is called a(n) _____.

6. When a sample is obtained by drawing every *n*th item, the sample is called a(n) _____ sample.

7. If a sample is drawn in such a way that each time an item is selected, each item in the population has an equal chance of being drawn, the sample is called a(n) _____ sample.

8. When a population is divided into parts, called strata, for the purpose of drawing a sample, the procedure is known as _____ sampling.

9. A sample that consists of a random selection of groups or units is called a(n) _____ sample.

10. A sample that uses data that are easily or readily obtained is called a(n) _____ sample.

11. A sample that is a small replica of the entire population is called a(n) _____ sample.

12. An area sample is another name for a(n) _____ sample.

Practice the Skills

Sampling Techniques *In Exercises 13–22, identify the sampling technique used to obtain a sample. Explain your answer.*

13. All registered vehicles in the state of Georgia are classified according to type: subcompact, compact, mid-size, full-size, SUV, and truck. A random sample of vehicles from each category is selected.

14. Every 10th iPod coming off an assembly line is checked for defects.

▲ *See Exercise 14*

15. A state is divided into counties. A random sample of 12 counties is selected. A random sample from each of the 12 selected counties is selected.

16. A door prize is given away at a home improvement seminar. Tickets are placed in a bin, and the tickets are mixed up. Then a ticket is selected by a blindfolded person.

17. Every 17th person in line at a grocery store is asked his or her age.

18. The businesses in Iowa City are grouped according to type: medical, service, retail, manufacturing, financial, construction, restaurant, hotel, tourism, and other. A random sample of 10 businesses from each type is selected.

19. The first 25 adults leaving a grocery store are asked how much money they spend per week on entertainment.

20. The Food and Drug Administration randomly selects five stores from each of four randomly selected sections of a large city and checks food items for freshness. These stores are used as a representative sample of the entire city.

21. Bingo balls in a bin are shaken, and then balls are selected from the bin.

22. The Student Senate at the University of North Carolina is electing a new president. The first 25 people leaving the library are asked for whom they will vote.

Challenge Problems/Group Activities

23. a) *Random Sampling* Select and indicate a topic and population of interest to which a random sampling technique can be applied to obtain data.

    b) Explain how you or your group would obtain a random sample for your population of interest.

    c) Actually obtain the sample by the procedure stated in part (b).

24. *Data from Questionnaire* Some subscribers of *Consumer Reports* respond to an annual questionnaire regarding their satisfaction with new appliances, cars, and other items. The information obtained from these questionnaires is then used as a sample from which frequency of repairs and other ratings are made by the magazine. Are the data obtained from these returned questionnaires representative of the entire population, or are they biased?

Recreational Mathematics

25. Statistically speaking, what is the most dangerous job in the United States?

Internet/Research Activity

26. We have briefly introduced sampling techniques. Using statistics books and Internet Web sites as references, select one type of sampling technique (it may be one that we have not discussed in this section) and write a report on how statisticians obtain that type of sample. Also indicate when that type of sampling technique may be preferred. List two examples of when the sampling technique may be used.

SECTION 13.2   The Misuses of Statistics

▲ *It is important to examine statistical statements about products before accepting the statements as fact.*

Many of us may remember the advertisement stating, "Four out of five dentists recommend sugarless gum for their patients who chew gum." Seeing an advertisement like this one may cause some of us to be a bit skeptical. Should we believe that sugarless chewing gum will not harm our teeth? Or should we investigate a bit further before buying that next pack of chewing gum? In this section, we will learn how to examine statistical statements before accepting them as fact.

Why *This is Important* In order to be an educated consumer, it is important to be able to distinguish between misleading advertisements and actual facts.

Statistics, when used properly, is a valuable tool to society. However, many individuals, businesses, and advertising firms misuse statistics to their own advantage. You should examine statistical statements very carefully before accepting them as fact. You should ask yourself two questions: Was the sample used to gather the statistical data unbiased and of sufficient size? Is the statistical statement ambiguous; that is, can it be interpreted in more than one way?

Let's examine two advertisements. "Four out of five dentists recommend sugarless gum for their patients who chew gum." In this advertisement, we do not know the sample size and the number of times the experiment was performed to obtain the desired results. The advertisement does not mention that possibly only 1 out of 100 dentists recommended gum at all.

In a golf ball commercial, a "type A" ball is hit and a second ball is hit in the same manner. The type A ball travels farther. We are supposed to conclude that the type A is the better ball. The advertisement does not mention the number of times the experiment was previously performed or the results of the earlier experiments. Possible sources of bias include (1) wind speed and direction, (2) that no two swings are identical, and (3) that the ball may land on a rough or smooth surface.

Vague or ambiguous words also lead to statistical misuses or misinterpretations. The word *average* is one such culprit. There are at least four different "averages," some of which are discussed in Section 13.4. Each is calculated differently, and each may have a different value for the same sample. During contract negotiations, it is not uncommon for an employer to state publicly that the average salary of its employees is $45,000, whereas the employees' union states that the average is $40,000. Who is lying? Actually, both sides may be telling the truth. Each side will use the average that best suits its needs to present its case. Advertisers also use the average that most enhances their products. Consumers often misinterpret this average as the one with which they are most familiar.

Another vague word is *largest*. For example, ABC claims that it is the largest department store in the United States. Does that mean largest profit, largest sales, largest building, largest staff, largest acreage, or largest number of outlets?

MATHEMATICS TODAY

Creative Displays

How Employers Make Workers Happy

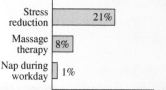

Visual graphics are often used to "dress up" what might otherwise be considered boring statistics. Although visually appealing, such creative displays of numerical data can be misleading. The graph above shows the percentage of employers that offer "perks" such as stress reduction, massage therapy, or a nap during the workday to make workers happy. This graph is misleading because the lengths of the bars are not proportional to one another as they should be to accurately reflect the percent of employers offering each of the named perks. For example, the bar for massage therapy should be eight times as long as the bar for nap during workday instead of being approximately four times as long, as the graph shows.

Why This is Important In order to correctly interpret data from a graph, it is important to be aware that a graph may be misleading.

Still another deceptive technique used in advertising is to state a claim from which the public may draw irrelevant conclusions. For example, a disinfectant manufacturer claims that its product killed 40,760 germs in a laboratory in 5 seconds. "To prevent colds, use disinfectant A." It may well be that the germs killed in the laboratory were not related to any type of cold germ. In another example, company C claims that its paper towels are heavier than its competition's towels. Therefore, they will hold more water. Is weight a measure of absorbency? A rock is heavier than a sponge, yet a sponge is more absorbent.

An insurance advertisement claims that in Duluth, Minnesota, 212 people switched to insurance company Z. One may conclude that this company is offering something special to attract these people. What may have been omitted from the advertisement is that 415 people in Duluth, Minnesota, dropped insurance company Z during the same period.

A foreign car manufacturer claims that 9 of every 10 of a popular-model car it sold in the United States during the previous 10 years were still on the road. From this statement, the public is to conclude that this foreign car is well manufactured and would last for many years. The commercial neglects to state that this model has been selling in the United States for only a few years. The manufacturer could just as well have stated that 9 of every 10 of these cars sold in the United States in the previous 100 years were still on the road.

Charts and graphs can also be misleading or deceptive. In Fig. 13.2, the two graphs show the performance of two stocks over a 6-month period. Based on the graphs, which stock would you purchase? Actually, the two graphs present identical information; the only difference is that the vertical scale of the graph for stock B has been exaggerated.

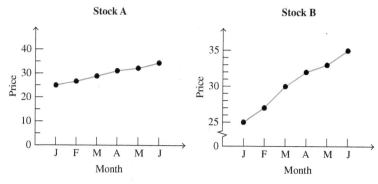

Figure 13.2

The two graphs in Fig. 13.3 show the same change. However, the graph in part (a) appears to show a greater increase than the graph in part (b), again because of a different scale.

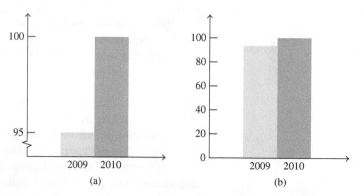

Figure 13.3

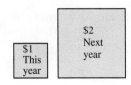

Figure 13.4

Consider a claim that if you invest $1, by next year you will have $2. This type of claim is sometimes misrepresented, as in Fig. 13.4. Actually, your investment has only doubled, but the area of the square on the right is four times that of the square on the left. By expressing the amounts as cubes (Fig. 13.5), you increase the volume eightfold.

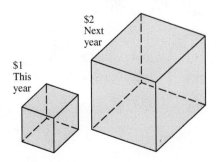

Figure 13.5

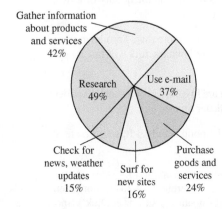

Figure 13.6

The graph in Fig. 13.6 is an example of a circle graph. We will discuss circle graphs in Section 13.3. In a circle graph, the total circle represents 100%. Therefore, the sum of the parts should add up to 100%. This graph is misleading since the sum of its parts is 183%. A graph other than a circle graph should have been used to display the top six reasons Americans say they use the Internet.

Despite the examples presented in this section, you should not be left with the impression that statistics is used solely for the purpose of misleading or cheating the consumer. As stated earlier, there are many important and necessary uses of statistics. Most statistical reports are accurate and useful. You should realize, however, the importance of being an aware consumer.

SECTION 13.2

Exercises

Practice the Skills

Misinterpretations of Statistics *In Exercises 1–14, discuss the statement and tell what possible misuses or misinterpretations may exist.*

1. *Cold Remedy* In a study of patients with cold symptoms, each patient was found to have improved symptoms after taking honey. Therefore, honey cures the common cold.

2. In 2011, Liberty Travel received more requests for travel brochures to Hawaii than to Las Vegas. Therefore, in 2012, Liberty Travel sold more travel packages to Hawaii than to Las Vegas.

3. There are more empty spaces in the parking lot of Mama Mia's Italian restaurant than at Shanghai Chinese restaurant. Therefore, more people prefer Chinese food than Italian food.

4. Healthy Snacks cookies are fat free. So eat as many as you like and you will not gain weight.

5. Most accidents occur on Saturday night. That means that people do not drive carefully on Saturday night.

6. Morgan's is the largest department store in New York. So shop at Morgan's and save money.

7. Eighty percent of all automobile accidents occur within 10 miles of the driver's home. Therefore, it is safer to take long trips.

8. Arizona has the highest death rate for asthma in the United States. Therefore, it is unsafe to go to Arizona if you have asthma.

▲ *Sedona, Arizona*

9. Thirty students said that they would recommend Professor Malone to a friend. Twenty students said that they would recommend Professor Wagner to a friend. Therefore, Professor Malone is a better teacher than Professor Wagner.

10. A steak is more expensive at Dino's Steak House than at Rick's Prime Rib House. Therefore, the quality of a steak at Dino's Steak House is better than the quality of a steak at Rick's Prime Rib House.

11. John Deere lawn tractors cost more than Toro lawn tractors. Therefore, John Deere lawn tractors will last longer than Toro lawn tractors.

12. More men than women are involved in automobile accidents. Therefore, women are better drivers.

13. The average depth of the pond is only 3 ft, so it is safe to go wading.

14. In 2011, more men than women applied for sales positions at Dick's Sporting Goods. Therefore, in 2011, more men than women were hired for sales positions at Dick's Sporting Goods.

15. *Population of Honolulu* The following table shows the population, in thousands, in Honolulu, Hawaii, for selected years.

Year	Population
1980	365.0
1990	365.2
2000	371.7
2010	371.7

Source: U.S Census Bureau

Draw a line graph that makes the increase in the population of Honolulu for the years shown appear to be

a) small.   **b)** large.

16. *Officers in the U.S. Marine Corps* The following table shows the number of officers, in thousands, on active duty in the U.S. Marine Corps for the years 2004–2009.

Year	Number of Officers
2004	19.1
2005	19.1
2006	19.2
2007	19.5
2008	20.1
2009	21.0

Draw a line graph that makes the increase in the number of officers on active duty for the U.S. Marine Corps appear to be

a) small.   **b)** large.

First Marriage In Exercises 17 and 18, use the following table.

Median Age at First Marriage

Male		Female	
Year	Age	Year	Age
2002	26.9	2002	25.3
2004	27.1	2004	25.3
2006	27.5	2006	25.5
2008	27.6	2008	25.9

Source: U.S. Census Bureau

17. **a)** Draw a bar graph that appears to show a small increase in the median age at first marriage for males.

   b) Draw a bar graph that appears to show a large increase in the median age at first marriage for males.

18. **a)** Draw a bar graph that appears to show a small increase in the median age at first marriage for females.

   b) Draw a bar graph that appears to show a large increase in the median age at first marriage for females.

19. *Price of a Movie Ticket* The following graph shows the average price of a movie ticket for the years 2009 and 2010.

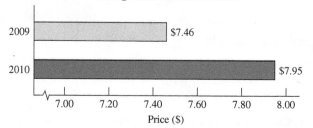

a) Draw a bar graph that shows the entire scale from $0 to $8.00.

b) Does the new graph give a different impression? Explain.

Concept/Writing Exercises

20. Find five advertisements or commercials that may be statistically misleading. Explain why each may be misleading.

21. The following circle graph shows the percentage of commuters who are frustrated by particular driving situations. Is the graph misleading? Explain.

Driving Situations Frustrating to Commuters

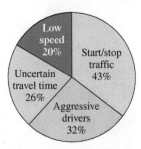

Challenge Problem/Group Activity

22. Consider the following graph, which shows the U.S. population in 2000 and the projected U.S. population in 2050.

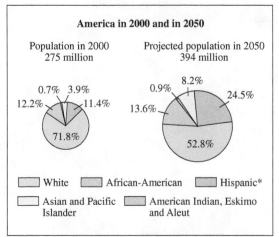

America in 2000 and in 2050

Population in 2000
275 million

Projected population in 2050
394 million

☐ White ☐ African-American ☐ Hispanic*

☐ Asian and Pacific Islander ☐ American Indian, Eskimo and Aleut

Source: U.S. Census Bureau

a) Compute the projected percent increase in population from 2000 to 2050 by using the formula given on page 603.

b) Measure the radius and then compute the area of the circle representing 2000. Use $A = \pi r^2$.

c) Repeat part (b) for the circle representing 2050.

d) Compute the percent increase in the size of the area of the circle from 2000 to 2050.

e) Are the circle graphs misleading?

Recreational Mathematics

23. What mathematical symbol can you place between 1 and 2 to obtain a number greater than 1 but less than 2?

Internet/Research Activity

24. Read the book *How to Lie with Statistics* by Darrell Huff and write a book report on it. Select three illustrations from the book that show how people manipulate statistics.

SECTION 13.3 Frequency Distributions and Statistical Graphs

▲ *Organizing and summarizing data, such as a waitress's daily tips, can make large sets of information more useful.*

Suppose you have a job as a waitress and decide to record the daily amount you make in tips. After keeping a list of your tips each day for several months, you realize that you have a large set of data and want to condense your data into a more manageable form. In this section we will learn a method to organize and summarize data. We will also introduce four types of graphs that can be used to display information in a meaningful way.

Why *This is Important* Organizing and summarizing data and using graphs to display information can make large sets of information more useful.

It is not uncommon for statisticians and others to have to analyze thousands of pieces of data. A *piece of data* is a single response to an experiment. When the amount of data is large, it is usually advantageous to construct a frequency distribution. A *frequency distribution* is a listing of the observed values and the corresponding frequency of occurrence of each value. Example 1 shows how we construct a frequency distribution.

"Statistical thinking will one day be as necessary for efficient citizenship as the ability to read and write."

H. G. Wells

─ Example **1** *Frequency Distribution*

The number of children per family is recorded for 64 families surveyed. Construct a frequency distribution of the following data:

0	1	1	2	2	3	4	5
0	1	1	2	2	3	4	5
0	1	1	2	2	3	4	6
0	1	2	2	2	3	4	6
0	1	2	2	2	3	4	7
0	1	2	2	3	3	4	8
0	1	2	2	3	3	5	8
0	1	2	2	3	3	5	9

Solution Listing the number of children (observed values) and the number of families (frequency) gives the following frequency distribution.

Number of Children (Observed Values)	Number of Families (Frequency)
0	8
1	11
2	18
3	11
4	6
5	4
6	2
7	1
8	2
9	$\dfrac{1}{64}$

Eight families had no children, 11 families had one child, 18 families had two children, and so on. Note that the sum of the frequencies is equal to the original number of pieces of data, 64. ■

Often data are grouped in classes to provide information about the distribution that would be difficult to observe if the data were ungrouped. Graphs called *histograms* and *frequency polygons* can be made of grouped data, as will be explained later in this section. These graphs also provide a great deal of useful information.

When data are grouped in classes, certain rules should be followed.

PROCEDURE   RULES FOR DATA GROUPED BY CLASSES

1. The classes should be the same "width."
2. The classes should not overlap.
3. Each piece of data should belong to only one class.

In addition, it is often suggested that a frequency distribution should be constructed with 5 to 12 classes. If there are too few or too many classes, the distribution may become difficult to interpret. For example, if you use fewer than 5 classes, you risk losing too much information. If you use more than 12 classes, you may gain more detail

RECREATIONAL MATH

Can You Count the F's?

Statistical errors often result from careless observations. To see how such errors can occur, consider the statement below. How many F's do you count in the statement?

FINISHED FILES ARE THE RESULT OF YEARS OF SCIENTIFIC STUDY COMBINED WITH THE EXPERIENCE OF YEARS.

Answer : There are 6 F's.

but you risk losing clarity. Let the spread of the data be a guide in deciding the number of classes to use.

To understand these rules, let's consider a set of observed values that go from a low of 0 to a high of 26. Let's assume that the first class is arbitrarily selected to go from 0 through 4. Thus, any of the data with values of 0, 1, 2, 3, 4 would belong in this class. We say that the *class width* is 5 since there are five integral values that belong to the class. This first class ended with 4, so the second class must start with 5. If this class is to have a width of 5, at what value must it end? The answer is 9 (5, 6, 7, 8, 9). The second class is 5–9. Continuing in the same manner, we obtain the following set of classes.

Classes

Lower class limits $\left\{\begin{array}{l} 0\text{–}4 \\ 5\text{–}9 \\ 10\text{–}14 \\ 15\text{–}19 \\ 20\text{–}24 \\ 25\text{–}29 \end{array}\right\}$ Upper class limits

We need not go beyond the 25–29 class because the largest value we are considering is 26. The classes meet our three criteria: They have the same width, there is no overlap among the classes, and each of the values from a low of 0 to a high of 26 belongs to one and only one class.

The choice of the first class, 0–4, was arbitrary. If we wanted to have more classes or fewer classes, we would make the class widths smaller or larger, respectively.

The numbers 0, 5, 10, 15, 20, 25 are called the *lower class limits*, and the numbers 4, 9, 14, 19, 24, 29 are called the *upper class limits*. Each class has a width of 5. Note that the class width, 5, can be obtained by subtracting the first lower class limit from the second lower class limit: $5 - 0 = 5$. The difference between any two consecutive lower class or upper class limits is also 5.

Example 2 *A Frequency Distribution of Consumer Magazines*

Table 13.1 on page 786 shows the 2008 circulation for the 46 leading U.S. consumer magazines (excluding *AARP Magazine* and *AARP Bulletin*, which are far ahead of the other magazines). The circulation is rounded to the nearest ten thousand. Construct a frequency distribution of the data, letting the first class be 173–237.

Solution Forty-six pieces of data are given in *descending order* from highest to lowest. We are given that the first class is 173–237. The second class must therefore start at 238. To find the class width, we subtract 173 (the lower class limit of the first class) from 238 (the lower class limit of the second class) to obtain a class width of 65. The upper class limit of the second class is found by adding the class width, 65, to the upper class limit of the first class, 237. Therefore, the upper class limit of the second class is $237 + 65 = 302$. Thus,

173–237   first class
238–302   second class

The other classes are found using a similar technique. They are 303–367, 368–432, 433–497, 498–562, 563–627, 628–692, 693–757, 758–822. Since the highest value in the data is 817, there is no need to go any further. Note that each two consecutive lower class limits differ by 65, as does each two consecutive upper class limits. There are 23 pieces of data in the 173–237 class. There are 8 pieces of data in the 238–302 class, 6 in the 303–367 class, 5 in the 368–432 class, 1 in the 433–497 class, 1 in the 498–562 class, 0 in the 563–627 class, 0 in the 628–692 class, 0 in the 693–757 class, and 2 in the 758–822 class. The complete frequency distribution of the 10 classes is given on page 786. The number of magazines totals 46, so we have included each piece of data.

Table 13.1

Magazine	Circulation (ten thousands)
Reader's Digest	817
Better Homes and Gardens	766
National Geographic	506
Good Housekeeping	468
Woman's Day	392
Family Circle	391
AAA Westways	384
Ladies' Home Journal	384
People	369
Game Informer	352
Time	336
Prevention	334
TV Guide	326
Sports Illustrated	322
Taste of Home	320
Cosmopolitan	293
Southern Living	283
AAA	281
Newsweek	270
Playboy	262
AAA Going Places	256
Maxim	252
American Legion Magazine	243
O, The Oprah Magazine	237
Glamour	229
Redbook	221
Guideposts	220
AAA World	213
Parenting	213
Parents	206
ESPN The Magazine	206
Seventeen	203
Martha Stewart Living	203
Smithsonian	203
Real Simple	198
Remedy/Remedy MD	196
Money	191
Us Weekly	190
Family Fun	188
Men's Health	186
Entertainment Weekly	180
Endless Vacation	179
Cooking Light	179
Every Day with Rachael Ray	178
InStyle	176
Country Living	173

Source: *Audit Bureau of Circulations*

Circulation	Number of Magazines (ten thousands)
173–237	23
238–302	8
303–367	6
368–432	5
433–497	1
498–562	1
563–627	0
628–692	0
693–757	0
758–822	2
	46

The *modal class* of a frequency distribution is the class with the greatest frequency. In Example 2, the modal class is 173–237. The *midpoint of a class*, also called the *class mark*, is found by adding the lower and upper class limits and dividing the sum by 2. The midpoint of the first class in Example 2 is

$$\frac{173 + 237}{2} = \frac{410}{2} = 205$$

Note that the difference between successive class marks is the class width. The class mark of the second class can therefore be obtained by adding the class width, 65, to the class mark of the first class, 205. The sum is $205 + 65 = 270$. Note that $\frac{238 + 302}{2} = 270$, which checks with the class mark obtained by adding the class width to the first class mark.

Example 3 *A Frequency Distribution of Family Income*

The following set of data represents the family income (in thousands of dollars, rounded to the nearest hundred) of 15 randomly selected families.

46.5	31.8	45.8	44.7	40.9
65.2	52.4	44.6	53.7	48.8
35.5	40.3	39.8	56.3	50.7

Construct a frequency distribution with a first class of 31.5–37.6.

Solution First rearrange the data from lowest to highest so that the data will be easier to categorize.

31.8	40.3	44.7	48.8	53.7
35.5	40.9	45.8	50.7	56.3
39.8	44.6	46.5	52.4	65.2

The first class goes from 31.5 to 37.6. Since the data are in tenths, the class limits will also be given in tenths. The first class ends with 37.6; therefore, the second class must start with 37.7. The class width of the first class is $37.7 - 31.5$, or 6.2. The upper class limit of the second class must therefore be $37.6 + 6.2$, or 43.8. The frequency distribution is given on page 787.

MATHEMATICS TODAY

Cyberspace Is the Place to Be

Raleigh, North Carolina

Do you remember the days when you were only able to access the Internet from your office, school, or home? With wireless Internet access, we can now connect to the Internet to share information and enjoy entertainment while we are on the go. Today, wireless hotspots, locations offering wireless access to the Internet, show up in diverse places such as coffee shops, parks, gas stations, bowling alleys, airports, and golf courses in addition to more traditional places such as colleges and hotels. According to a survey conducted by *Forbes Magazine* in March 2010, Raleigh, North Carolina, was the most accessible wireless city in the United States. Many Web sites, such as www.wififreespot.com, list worldwide locations that offer free wireless Internet access.

Why This is Important More and more people are using wireless devices every day.

Income ($1000)	Number of Families
31.5–37.6	2
37.7–43.8	3
43.9–50.0	5
50.1–56.2	3
56.3–62.4	1
62.5–68.6	1
	15

Note in Example 3 that the class width is 6.2, the modal class is 43.9–50.0, and the class mark of the first class is $\dfrac{31.5 + 37.6}{2}$, or 34.55.

We have discussed how to organize and summarize data. Now we will introduce graphs that can be used to display information. We will consider four types of graphs: the histogram, the frequency polygon, the stem-and-leaf graph, and the circle graph.

Histograms and Frequency Polygons

Histograms and frequency polygons are statistical graphs used to illustrate frequency distributions. A *histogram* is a graph with observed values on its horizontal scale and frequencies on its vertical scale. A bar is constructed above each observed value (or class when classes are used), indicating the frequency of that value (or class). The horizontal scale need not start at zero, and the calibrations on the horizontal and vertical scales do not have to be the same. The vertical scale must start at zero. To accommodate large frequencies on the vertical scale, it may be necessary to break the scale. Because histograms and other bar graphs are easy to interpret visually, they are used a great deal in newspapers and magazines.

Example 4 *Construct a Histogram*

The frequency distribution developed in Example 1, on page 784, is repeated here. Construct a histogram of this frequency distribution.

Number of Children (Observed Values)	Number of Families (Frequency)
0	8
1	11
2	18
3	11
4	6
5	4
6	2
7	1
8	2
9	1

Solution The vertical scale must extend at least to the number 18 since that is the greatest recorded frequency. The horizontal scale must include the numbers 0–9, the number of children observed. Eight families have no children. We indicate that by constructing a bar above the number 0, centered at 0, on the horizontal scale

Profile in Mathematics

Katherine K. Wallman— Chief U.S. Statistician

Since 1992, Katherine Wallman has served as the chief statistician of the U.S. Office of Management and Budget. In this capacity, she oversees and coordinates U.S. federal statistical policies, standards, and programs; develops and advances long-term improvements in federal statistical activities; and represents the U.S. government in international statistics organizations, including the United Nations and the Organization for Economic Cooperation and Development.

In the United States, there are multiple agencies that actually produce statistics on which the country relies. For example, the Census Bureau provides population data; the Bureau of Economic Analysis provides national accounting data; and the National Center for Health Statistics provides data concerning health and well-being. In her capacity, Katherine Wallman sets standards for a federal statistical establishment that comprises more than 70 agencies spread across every cabinet department.

TIMELY TIP
When constructing a histogram or frequency polygon, be sure to label both scales of the graph.

extended up to 8 on the vertical scale (Fig. 13.7). Eleven families have one child, so we construct a bar extending to 11 above the number 1, centered at 1, on the horizontal scale. We continue this procedure for each observed value. Both the horizontal and vertical scales should be labeled, the bars should be the same width and centered at the observed value, and the histogram should have a title. In a histogram, the bars should always touch.

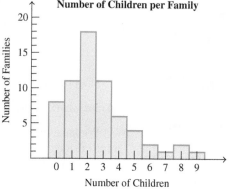

Figure 13.7

Frequency polygons are line graphs with scales the same as those of the histogram; that is, the horizontal scale indicates observed values and the vertical scale indicates frequency. To construct a frequency polygon, place a dot at the corresponding frequency above each of the observed values. Then connect the dots with straight-line segments. When constructing frequency polygons, always put in two additional class marks, one at the lower end and one at the upper end on the horizontal scale (values for these added class marks are not needed on the frequency polygon). Since the frequency at these added class marks is 0, the end points of the frequency polygon will always be on the horizontal scale.

Example 5 *Construct a Frequency Polygon*

Construct a frequency polygon of the frequency distribution in Example 1 on page 784.

Solution Since eight families have no children, place a mark above the 0 at 8 on the vertical scale, as shown in Fig. 13.8. Because there are 11 families with one child, place a mark above the 1 on the horizontal scale at the 11 on the vertical scale, and so on. Connect the dots with straight-line segments and bring the end points of the graph down to the horizontal scale, as shown.

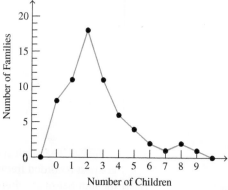

Figure 13.8

Table 13.2

Distance (miles)	Number of Workers
1–7	15
8–14	24
15–21	13
22–28	8
29–35	5
36–42	5

Example 6 *Commuting Distances*

The frequency distribution of the one-way commuting distances for 70 workers is listed in Table 13.2. Construct a histogram and then construct a frequency polygon.

Solution The histogram can be constructed with either class limits or class marks (class midpoints) on the horizontal scale. Frequency polygons are constructed with class marks on the horizontal scale. Since we will construct a frequency polygon on the histogram, we will use class marks. Recall that class marks are found by adding the lower class limit and upper class limit and dividing the sum by 2. For the first class, the class mark is $\frac{1+7}{2}$, or 4. Since the class widths are seven units, the class marks will also differ by seven units (see Fig. 13.9).

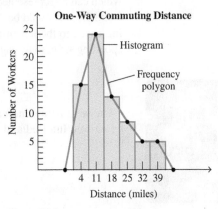

Figure 13.9

Example 7 *Carry-on Luggage Weights*

The histogram in Fig. 13.10 shows the weights of selected pieces of carry-on luggage at an airport. Construct the frequency distribution from the histogram in Fig. 13.10.

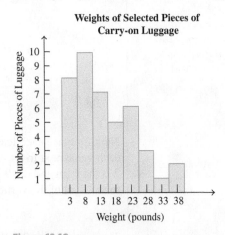

Figure 13.10

Table 13.3

Weight (pounds)	Number of Pieces of Luggage
1–5	8
6–10	10
11–15	7
16–20	5
21–25	6
26–30	3
31–35	1
36–40	2

Solution There are five units between class midpoints, so each class width must also be five units. Since three is the midpoint of the first class, there must be two units below and two units above it. The first class must be 1–5. The second class must therefore be 6–10. The frequency distribution is given in Table 13.3.

Stem-and-Leaf Displays

Frequency distributions and histograms provide very useful tools to organize and summarize data. However, if the data are grouped, we cannot identify specific data values in a frequency distribution and in a histogram. For example, in Example 7, we know that there are eight pieces of luggage in the class of 1 to 5 pounds, but we don't know the specific weights of those eight pieces of luggage.

A *stem-and-leaf display* is a tool that organizes and groups the data while allowing us to see the actual values that make up the data. To construct a stem-and-leaf display each value is represented with two different groups of digits. The left group of digits is called the *stem*. The remaining group of digits on the right is called the *leaf*. There is no rule for the number of digits to be included in the stem. Usually the units digit is the leaf and the remaining digits are the stem. For example, the number 53 would be broken up into 5 and 3. The 5 would be the stem and the 3 would be the leaf. The number 417 would be broken up into 41 and 7. The 41 would be the stem and the 7 would be the leaf. The number 6, which can be represented as 06, would be broken up into 0 and 6. The stem would be the 0 and the leaf would be the 6. With a stem-and-leaf display, the stems are listed, in ascending order, to the left of a vertical line. Then we place each leaf to the right of its corresponding stem, to the right of the vertical line.* Example 8 illustrates this procedure.

▲ *Captain Fairfield Inn Bed and Breakfast*

Example 8   *Stem-and-Leaf Display*

The table below indicates the ages of a sample of 20 guests who stayed at Captain Fairfield Inn Bed and Breakfast. Construct a stem-and-leaf display.

29	31	39	43	56
60	62	59	58	32
47	27	50	28	71
72	44	45	44	68

Solution   By quickly glancing at the data, we can see the ages consist of two-digit numbers. Let's use the first digit, the tens digit, as our stem and the second digit, the units digit, as the leaf. For example, for an age of 62, the stem is 6 and the leaf is 2. Our values are numbers in the 20s, 30s, 40s, 50s, 60s, and 70s. Therefore, the stems will be 2, 3, 4, 5, 6, 7 as shown below.

$$
\begin{array}{c|}
2 & \\
3 & \\
4 & \\
5 & \\
6 & \\
7 & \\
\end{array}
$$

Next we place each leaf on its stem. We will do so by placing the second digit of each value next to its stem, to the right of the vertical line. Our first value is 29. The 2 is the stem and the 9 is the leaf. Therefore, we place a 9 next to the stem of 2 and to the right of the vertical line.

$$2 \mid 9$$

The next value is 31. We will place a leaf of 1 next to the stem of 3.

$$
\begin{array}{c|c}
2 & 9 \\
3 & 1 \\
\end{array}
$$

---

*In stem-and-leaf displays, the leaves are sometimes listed from lowest digit to greatest digit, but that is not necessary.

The next value is 39. Therefore, we will place a leaf of 9 after the leaf of 1 that is next to the stem of 3.

$$
\begin{array}{c|cc}
2 & 9 \\
3 & 1 & 9
\end{array}
$$

We continue this process until we have listed all the leaves on the display. The diagram below shows the stem-and-leaf display for the ages of the guests. In our display, we will also include a legend to indicate the values represented by the stems and leaves. For example, 5|6 represents 56.

5|6 represents 56

$$
\begin{array}{c|ccccc}
\text{Stem} & \text{Leaves} \\
\hline
2 & 9 & 7 & 8 \\
3 & 1 & 9 & 2 \\
4 & 3 & 7 & 4 & 5 & 4 \\
5 & 6 & 9 & 8 & 0 \\
6 & 0 & 2 & 8 \\
7 & 1 & 2
\end{array}
$$

Every piece of the original data can be seen in a stem-and-leaf display. From the above diagram, we can see that five of the guests' ages were in the 40s. Only two guests were older than 70. Note that the stem-and-leaf display gives the same visual impression as a sideways histogram.

Circle Graphs

Circle graphs (also known as pie charts) are often used to compare parts of one or more components of the whole to the whole. The circle graph in Fig. 13.11 shows what moviegoers say is the most annoying distraction during a movie. Since the total circle represents 100%, the sum of the percents of the sectors should be 100%, and it is.

In the next example, we will discuss a circle graph.

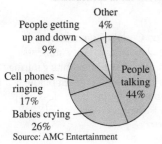

Distractions at the Movies

Other 4%
People getting up and down 9%
Cell phones ringing 17%
Babies crying 26%
People talking 44%
Source: AMC Entertainment

Figure 13.11

Example 9 *Circus Performances*

Eight hundred people who attended a Ringling Bros. and Barnum & Bailey Circus were asked to indicate their favorite performance. The circle graph in Fig. 13.12 shows the percentage of respondents that answered tigers, elephants, acrobats, jugglers, and other. Determine the number of respondents for each category.

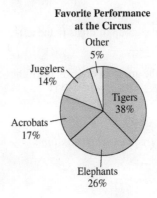

Favorite Performance at the Circus

Other 5%
Jugglers 14%
Acrobats 17%
Tigers 38%
Elephants 26%

Figure 13.12

Solution To determine the number of respondents in a category, we multiply the percentage for each category, written as a decimal number, by the total number of people, 800. The table on page 792 indicates the results.

Performance	Percent of Respondents	Percent Written as a Decimal Number	Number of People
Tigers	38%	0.38	$0.38 \times 800 = 304$
Elephants	26%	0.26	$0.26 \times 800 = 208$
Acrobats	17%	0.17	$0.17 \times 800 = 136$
Jugglers	14%	0.14	$0.14 \times 800 = 112$
Other	5%	0.05	$0.05 \times 800 = 40$
Total			800

As we can see from the table, 304 people indicated that the tigers were their favorite performance, 208 indicated elephants, 136 people indicated the acrobats, 112 people indicated the jugglers, and 40 people indicated some other performance.   ■

SECTION 13.3   *Exercises*

Warm Up Exercises

In Exercises 1–8, fill in the blank with an appropriate word, phrase, or symbol(s).

1. A listing of observed values and the corresponding frequency of occurrence of each value is called a(n) _____ distribution.

2. In a frequency distribution, the class with the greatest frequency is called the _____ class.

3. In a frequency distribution, another name for the midpoint of a class is the class _____.

4. The class width of a frequency distribution with a first class of 9–16 and a second class of 17–24 is _____.

5. A bar graph with observed values on its horizontal scale and frequencies on its vertical scale is called a(n) _____.

6. A line graph with observed values on its horizontal scale and frequencies on its vertical scale is called a frequency _____.

7. In a stem-and-leaf display, the group of digits in the left-hand column is called the _____.

8. In a stem-and-leaf display, the group of digits in the right-hand column is called the _____.

Practice the Skills/Problem Solving

In Exercises 9 and 10, use the frequency distribution to determine

   a) *the total number of observations.*

   b) *the width of each class.*

   c) *the midpoint of the second class.*

   d) *the modal class (or classes).*

   e) *the class limits of the next class if an additional class were to be added.*

9.

Class	Frequency
9–15	4
16–22	7
23–29	1
30–36	0
37–43	3
44–50	5

10.

Class	Frequency
40–49	7
50–59	5
60–69	3
70–79	2
80–89	7
90–99	1

11. *Visits to the Library* Johnson County Community College is planning to expand its library. Forty students were asked how many times they visited the library during the previous semester. Their responses are given below. Construct a frequency distribution, letting each class have a width of 1 (as in Example 1 on page 784).

0	1	1	3	4	5	7	8
0	1	2	3	5	5	7	8
0	1	2	3	5	5	7	9
1	1	2	3	5	6	8	10
1	1	3	4	5	6	8	10

12. *Hot Dog Sales* A hot dog vendor is interested in the number of hot dogs he sells each day at his hot dog cart. The number of hot dogs sold is indicated below for 32 consecutive days. Construct a frequency distribution, letting each class have a width of 1.

15	16	19	20	21	22	24	27
15	18	19	20	21	22	25	27
15	18	19	20	21	23	25	28
16	18	19	21	21	23	26	29

Note that there were no days in which the vendor sold 17 hot dogs. However, it is customary to include a missing value as an observed value and assign to it a frequency of 0.

▲ *See Exercise 12*

Magazine Circulation   *In Exercises 13–16, use the data given in Table 13.1 on page 786 to construct a frequency distribution with a first class (in ten thousands) of*

13. 173–322.

14. 170–316.

15. 173–272.

16. 173–250.

City Population   *In Exercises 17–20, use the following data, which represent the population of the 20 most populous cities in the world in 2010, in millions of people (rounded to the nearest 100,000).*

13.8	12.5	10.1	8.8	7.6
13.8	11.2	9.6	8.4	7.3
13.0	10.6	8.9	7.9	7.2
12.6	10.5	8.9	7.8	7.1

▲ *Shanghai, China, is the world's most populated city.*

Use these data to construct a frequency distribution with a first class of

17. 7.0–7.9.

18. 6.5–7.4.

19. 6.5–7.5.

20. 7.0–7.4.

Residents in Poverty   *In Exercises 21–24, use the data in the table above to the right.*

Percent of U.S. Residents Living in Poverty in 2008, by State

State	Percent	State	Percent
AK	7.9	MT	12.9
AL	14.4	NC	14.7
AR	14.5	ND	10.5
AZ	16.1	NE	10.3
CA	13.6	NH	6.4
CO	10.4	NJ	9.0
CT	8.5	NM	16.6
DE	9.4	NV	10.3
FL	12.8	NY	14.3
GA	14.6	OH	13.2
HI	8.7	OK	13.5
IA	9.2	OR	11.7
ID	11.1	PA	10.7
IL	11.1	RI	11.1
IN	13.1	SC	14.0
KS	12.2	SD	11.2
KY	16.3	TN	14.9
LA	17.1	TX	16.2
MA	11.2	UT	8.6
MD	8.8	VA	9.5
ME	11.4	VT	9.4
MI	11.9	WA	10.3
MN	9.6	WI	10.4
MO	13.1	WV	14.6
MS	20.4	WY	10.5

Source: *Bureau of the Census*

Construct a frequency distribution with a first class of

21. 6.4–8.3.

22. 6.4–9.0.

23. 6.4–7.8.

24. 6.4–8.8.

25. *Jogging Distances*   Twenty members of a health club who jog were asked how many miles they jog per week. The responses are as follows. Construct a stem-and-leaf display. For single digit data, use a stem of 0.

12	15	4	7	12	25	21
33	18	6	8	27	40	22
19	13	23	34	17	16	

26. *College Credits* Eighteen students in a geology class were asked how many college credits they had earned. The responses are as follows. Construct a stem-and-leaf display.

10	15	24	36	48	45
42	53	60	17	24	30
33	45	48	62	54	60

27. *Starting Salaries* Starting salaries (in thousands of dollars) for social workers with a bachelor of science degree and no experience are shown for a random sample of 25 different social workers.

27	28	29	31	33
28	28	29	31	33
28	28	30	32	33
28	29	30	32	34
28	29	30	32	34

a) Construct a frequency distribution. Let each class have a width of one.

b) Construct a histogram.

c) Construct a frequency polygon.

d) Construct a stem-and-leaf display.

28. *Visiting a Symphony* The ages of a random sample of 40 people attending a symphony are

20	26	31	34	39	45	50	62
20	29	31	35	40	47	51	63
23	30	32	35	40	49	51	66
23	30	33	37	40	49	54	69
26	30	34	38	42	49	57	72

a) Construct a frequency distribution with a first class of 20–30.

b) Construct a histogram.

c) Construct a frequency polygon.

d) Construct a stem-and-leaf display.

29. *Concert Tours* The following table shows the 25 top-grossing North American concert tours, in millions of dollars, for the years 1985–2008.

Artist	Total Gross ($ millions)
1. The Rolling Stones (2005)	162
2. U2 (2005)	139
3. The Rolling Stones (2006)	139
4. The Police (2007)	133
5. The Rolling Stones (1994)	121
6. Bruce Springsteen & the E Street Band (2003)	116
7. U2 (2001)	110
8. Madonna (2008)	105
9. Pink Floyd (1994)	104
10. Paul McCartney (2002)	103
11. The Rolling Stones (1989)	98
12. Celine Dion (2008)	94
13. Barbra Streisand (2006)	93
14. The Rolling Stones (1997)	89
15. Tim McGraw/Faith Hill (2006)	89
16. The Rolling Stones (2002)	88
17. Prince (2004)	87
18. 'N Sync (2001)	87
19. Madonna (2006)	86
20. Backstreet Boys (2001)	82
21. Cirque de Soleil: Delirium (2006)	82
22. Celine Dion (2005)	81
23. Celine Dion (2003)	81
24. Celine Dion (2004)	80
25. Tina Turner (2000)	80

Source: Pollstar

a) Construct a frequency distribution with a first class of 80–91.

b) Construct a histogram.

c) Construct a frequency polygon.

30. *U.S. Presidents* The ages of the 44 U.S. presidents at their first inauguration (as of 2011) are

57	57	49	52	50	42	54	55	64
61	61	64	56	47	51	51	56	46
57	54	50	46	55	56	60	61	54
57	68	48	54	55	55	62	52	47
58	51	65	49	54	51	43	69	

a) Construct a frequency distribution with a first class of 42–47.

b) Construct a histogram.

c) Construct a frequency polygon.

31. *Number of Televisions per Home* Use the histogram below to answer the following questions.

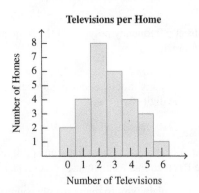

Televisions per Home

a) How many homes were included in the survey?

b) In how many homes were four televisions observed?

c) What is the modal class?

d) How many televisions were observed?

e) Construct a frequency distribution from this histogram.

32. *Car Insurance* Use the histogram below to answer the following questions.

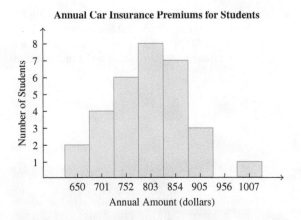

Annual Car Insurance Premiums for Students

a) How many students were surveyed?

b) What are the lower and upper class limits of the first and second classes?

c) How many students have an annual car insurance premium in the class with a class mark of $752?

d) What is the class mark of the modal class?

e) Construct a frequency distribution from this histogram. Use a first class of 625–675.

33. *E-mail Messages* Use the frequency polygon below to answer the following questions.

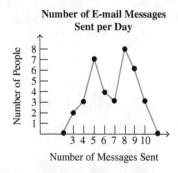

Number of E-mail Messages Sent per Day

a) How many people sent five e-mail messages?

b) How many people sent six or fewer e-mail messages?

c) How many people were included in the survey?

d) Construct a frequency distribution from the frequency polygon.

e) Construct a histogram from the frequency distribution in part (d).

34. *San Diego Zoo* Use the frequency polygon below to answer the following questions.

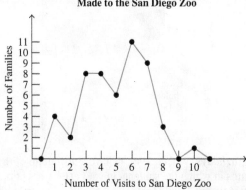

Number of Visits Selected Families Have Made to the San Diego Zoo

a) How many families visited the San Diego Zoo four times?

b) How many families visited the San Diego Zoo at least six times?

c) How many families were surveyed?

d) Construct a frequency distribution from the frequency polygon.

e) Construct a histogram from the frequency distribution in part (d).

35. *College Costs* The cost for Florida residents to attend the University of Florida for the 2010–2011 school year was $14,570. The circle graph on page 796 shows the percentage of that cost for tuition/fees, room, board, and computer costs. Determine the cost, in dollars, for each category.

Cost to Attend the University of Florida for 2010–2011

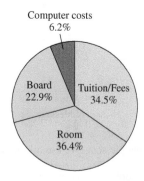

36. *Automobile Accessories* A sample of 600 people were asked which one automobile accessory they would most prefer to have on a family road trip. The following circle graph shows the percentage of respondents that answered GPS, DVD player, extra cup holders, roof rack, and other. Determine the number of respondents for each category.

Automobile Accessories for a Family Road Trip

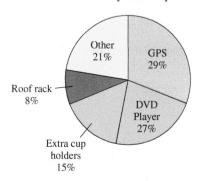

Challenge Problems/Group Activities

37. **a)** *Birthdays* What do you believe a histogram of the months in which the students in your class were born (January is month 1 and December is month 12) would look like? Explain.

b) By asking, determine the month in which the students in your class were born (include yourself).

c) Construct a frequency distribution containing 12 classes.

d) Construct a histogram from the frequency distribution in part (c).

e) Construct a frequency polygon of the frequency distribution in part (c).

38. *Social Security Numbers* Repeat Exercise 37 for the last digit of the students' Social Security numbers. Include classes for the digits 0–9.

Recreational Mathematics

39. **a)** Count the number of F's in the sentence at the bottom of the Recreational Mathematics box on page 785.

b) Can you explain why so many people count the number of F's incorrectly?

40. In what month do people take the least number of daily vitamins?

Internet/Research Activity

41. Over the years many changes have been made in the U.S. Social Security System.

a) Do research and determine the number of people receiving Social Security benefits for the years 1945, 1950, 1955, 1960, …, 2010. Then construct a frequency distribution and histogram of the data.

b) Determine the maximum amount that self-employed individuals had to pay into Social Security (the FICA tax) for the years 1945, 1950, 1955, 1960, …, 2010. Then construct a frequency distribution and a histogram of the data.

SECTION 13.4   Measures of Central Tendency

▲ *An average is used to describe the fuel efficiency of a car.*

Most people have an intuitive idea of what is meant by an "average." The term is used daily in many familiar ways. "This car averages 19 miles per gallon," "The average test grade was 82," and "The average height of adult males is 5 feet 9 inches" are three examples. In this section, we will introduce four different averages and discuss the circumstances in which each average is used.

Why This is Important An average is one of the most common ways to represent a set of data.

Measures of Central Tendency

An *average* is a number that is representative of a group of data. There are at least four different averages: the mean, the median, the mode, and the midrange. Each is calculated differently and may yield different results for the same set of data. Each will result in a number near the center of the data; for this reason, averages are commonly referred to as *measures of central tendency*.

The *arithmetic mean*, or simply the *mean*, is symbolized either by $\bar{x}$ (read "*x* bar") or by the Greek letter mu, μ. The symbol $\bar{x}$ is used when the mean of a *sample* of the population is calculated. The symbol μ is used when the mean of the *entire population* is calculated. Unless otherwise indicated, we will assume that the data featured in this book represent samples; therefore, we will use $\bar{x}$ for the mean.

The Greek letter sigma, Σ, is used to indicate "summation." The notation Σx, read "the sum of *x*," is used to indicate the sum of all the data. For example, if there are five pieces of data—4, 6, 1, 0, 5—then $\Sigma x = 4 + 6 + 1 + 0 + 5 = 16$.

Now we can discuss the procedure for determining the mean of a set of data.

Definition: **Mean**

The **mean,** $\bar{x}$, is the sum of the data divided by the number of pieces of data. The formula for calculating the mean is

$$\bar{x} = \frac{\Sigma x}{n}$$

where Σx represents the sum of all the data and *n* represents the number of pieces of data.

The most common use of the word *average* is the mean.

Example 1   *Determine the Mean*

Determine the mean age of a group of patients at a doctor's office if the ages of the individuals are 28, 19, 49, 35, and 49.

Solution

$$\bar{x} = \frac{\Sigma x}{n} = \frac{28 + 19 + 49 + 35 + 49}{5} = \frac{180}{5} = 36$$

Therefore, the mean, $\bar{x}$, is 36 years.   ∎

The mean represents "the balancing point" of a set of data. For example, if a seesaw were pivoted at the mean and uniform weights were placed at points corresponding to the ages in Example 1, the seesaw would balance. Figure. 13.13 shows the five ages given in Example 1 and the calculated mean.

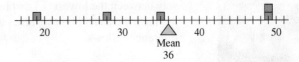

Figure 13.13

A second average is the *median*. To find the median of a set of data, *rank the data from smallest to largest, or largest to smallest, and determine the value in the middle of the set of ranked data*. This value will be the median.

Definition: **Median**

The **median** is the value in the middle of a set of *ranked data*.

TIMELY TIP

Data must be ranked before determining the median. A common error made when determining the median is neglecting to arrange the data in ascending (increasing) or in descending (decreasing) order.

MATHEMATICS TODAY

Buying the American Dream

San Jose, California

O ne of the biggest dreams for most people is to own their own home. Yet depending on where you live, the American dream may be hard to achieve. In 2010, San Jose, California, had the highest median home price for major metropolitan housing markets, $630,000. Saginaw, Michigan, had the lowest median home price for major metropolitan housing markets, $59,700.

Saginaw, Michigan

Source: National Association of Realtors

Example 2 *Determine the Median*

Determine the median of the patients' ages in Example 1 on page 797.

> **Solution** Ranking the data from smallest to largest gives 19, 28, 35, 49, and 49. Since 35 is the value in the middle of this set of ranked data (two pieces of data above it and two pieces below it), 35 years is the median. ■

When there are an even number of pieces of data, the median is halfway between the two middle pieces. In this case, to find the median, add the two middle pieces and divide this sum by 2.

Example 3 *Determine the Median of an Even Number of Pieces of Data*

Determine the median of the following sets of data.

a) 9, 14, 16, 17, 11, 16, 11, 12   b) 7, 8, 8, 8, 9, 10

> **Solution**
>
> a) Ranking the data gives 9, 11, 11, 12, 14, 16, 16, 17. There are eight pieces of data. Therefore, the median will lie halfway between the two middle pieces, the 12 and the 14. The median is $\frac{12+14}{2}$, or $\frac{26}{2}$, or 13.
>
> b) There are six pieces of data, and they are already ranked. Therefore, the median lies halfway between the two middle pieces. Both middle pieces are 8's. The median is $\frac{8+8}{2}$, or $\frac{16}{2}$, or 8. ■

A third average is the *mode*.

> **Definition: Mode**
> The **mode** is the piece of data that occurs most frequently.

Example 4 *Determine the Mode*

Determine the mode of the patients' ages in Example 1 on page 797.

> **Solution** The ages are 28, 19, 49, 35, and 49. The age 49 is the mode because it occurs twice and the other values occur only once. ■

If each piece of data occurs only once, the set of data has no mode. For example, the set of data 1, 2, 3, 4, 5 has no mode. If two values in a set of data occur more often than all the other data, we consider both these values as modes and say that the data are **bimodal*** (which means two modes). For example, the set of data 1, 1, 2, 3, 3, 5 has two modes, 1 and 3.

The last average we will discuss is the midrange. The *midrange* is the value halfway between the lowest (L) and highest (H) values in a set of data. It is found by adding the lowest and highest values and dividing the sum by 2. A formula for finding the midrange follows.

> **Midrange**
> The **midrange** of a set of data can be calculated using the following formula.
>
> $$\text{Midrange} = \frac{\text{lowest value } + \text{ highest value}}{2}$$

---

*Some textbooks say that sets of data such as 1, 1, 2, 3, 3, 5 have no mode.

MATHEMATICS TODAY

When Babies' Eyes Are Smiling

Experimental psychologists formulate hypotheses about human behavior, design experiments to test them, make observations, and draw conclusions from their data. They use statistical concepts at each stage to help ensure that their conclusions are valid. In one experiment, researchers observed that 2-month-old infants who learned to move their heads so as to make a mobile turn began to smile as soon as the mobile turned. Babies in the control group did not smile as often when the mobile moved independently of their head turning. The researchers concluded that it was not the movement of the mobile that made the infant smile; rather, the infants smiled at their own achievement.

Why *This is Important* Statistics is used in many fields of study, including psychology.

Example 5 *Determine the Midrange*

Determine the midrange of the patients' ages given in Example 1 on page 797.

Solution The ages of the patients are 28, 19, 49, 35, and 49. The lowest age is 19, and the highest age is 49.

$$\text{Midrange} = \frac{\text{lowest} + \text{highest}}{2} = \frac{19 + 49}{2} = \frac{68}{2} = 34 \text{ years}$$

The "average" of the ages 28, 19, 49, 35, 49 can be considered any one of the following values: 36 (mean), 35 (median), 49 (mode), or 34 (midrange). Which average do you feel is most representative of the ages? We will discuss this question later in this section.

Example 6 *Measures of Central Tendency*

The salaries of eight selected social workers rounded to the nearest thousand dollars are 40, 25, 28, 35, 42, 60, 60, and 73. For this set of data, determine the (a) mean, (b) median, (c) mode, and (d) midrange. Then (e) list the measures of central tendency from lowest to highest.

Solution

a) $\bar{x} = \dfrac{\Sigma x}{n} = \dfrac{40 + 25 + 28 + 35 + 42 + 60 + 60 + 73}{8} = \dfrac{363}{8} = 45.375$

b) Ranking the data from the smallest to largest gives

$$25, 28, 35, 40, 42, 60, 60, 73$$

Since there are an even number of pieces of data, the median is halfway between 40 and 42. The median $= \dfrac{40 + 42}{2} = \dfrac{82}{2} = 41$.

c) The mode is the piece of data that occurs most frequently. The mode is 60.

d) The midrange $= \dfrac{L + H}{2} = \dfrac{25 + 73}{2} = \dfrac{98}{2} = 49$.

e) The averages from lowest to highest are the median, mean, midrange, and mode. Their values are 41, 45.375, 49, and 60, respectively.

At this point, you should be able to calculate the four measures of central tendency: mean, median, mode, and midrange. Now let's examine the circumstances in which each is used.

The mean is used when each piece of data is to be considered and "weighed" equally. It is the most commonly used average. It is the only average that can be affected by *any* change in the set of data; for this reason, it is the most sensitive of all the measures of central tendency (see Exercise 23).

Occasionally, one or more pieces of data may be much greater or much smaller than the rest of the data. When this situation occurs, these "extreme" values have the effect of increasing or decreasing the mean significantly so that the mean will not be representative of the set of data. Under these circumstances, the median should be used instead of the mean. The median is often used in describing average family incomes because a relatively small number of families have extremely large incomes. These few incomes would inflate the mean income, making it nonrepresentative of the millions of families in the population.

Consider a set of exam scores from a mathematics class: 0, 16, 19, 65, 65, 65, 68, 69, 70, 72, 73, 73, 75, 78, 80, 85, 88, 92. Which average would best represent these grades? The mean is 64.06. The median is 71. Since only 3 of the 18 scores fall below the mean, the mean would not be considered a good representative score. The median of 71 probably would be the better average to use.

MATHEMATICS TODAY

Average Wealth of U.S. Households

Warren Buffet and Bill Gates

In the March 25, 2011, issue of the *St. Petersburg Times* newspaper, an article, with information provided by the Federal Reserve, stated the average net worth (or wealth) of U.S. households had dropped 23% from 2007 to 2009, and the *average net worth* per U.S. household was about $481,000 in 2009.

Upon visiting the Federal Reserve's Web site, we determined the word *average* was referring to the *mean* and included very wealthy people like Bill Gates and Warren Buffet. The Web site also states the *median* U.S. household net worth in 2009 was about $96,000. In your opinion, would you say the average U.S. household net worth in 2009 was $481,000 or $96,000?

Why **This is Important** This example shows that even though the same data are used in the calculations, different averages can vary widely, and so statistics can sometimes be misleading or deceptive.

The mode is the piece of data, if any, that occurs most frequently. Builders planning houses are interested in the most common family size. Retailers ordering shirts are interested in the most common shirt size. An individual purchasing a thermometer might choose one, from those on display, whose temperature reading is the most common reading among those on display. These examples illustrate how the mode may be used.

The midrange is sometimes used as the average when the item being studied is constantly fluctuating. Average daily temperature, used to compare temperatures in different areas, is calculated by adding the lowest and highest temperatures for the day and dividing the sum by 2. The midrange is actually the mean of the high value and the low value of a set of data. Occasionally, the midrange is used to estimate the mean since it is much easier to calculate.

Sometimes an average itself is of little value, and care must be taken in interpreting its meaning. For example, Jim is told that the average depth of Willow Pond is only 3 feet. He is not a good swimmer but decides that it is safe to go out a short distance in this shallow pond. After he is rescued, he exclaims, "I thought this pond was only 3 feet deep." Jim didn't realize that an average does not indicate extreme values or the spread of the values. The spread of data is discussed in Section 13.5.

Measures of Position

Measures of position are used to describe the position of a piece of data in relation to the rest of the data. If you took the Scholastic Aptitude Test (SAT) before applying to college, your score was described as a measure of position rather than a measure of central tendency. *Measures of position* are often used to make comparisons, such as comparing the scores of individuals from different populations, and are generally used when the amount of data is large.

Two measures of position are *percentiles* and *quartiles*. There are 99 percentiles dividing a set of data into 100 equal parts; see Fig. 13.14. For example, suppose that you scored 520 on the math portion of the SAT, and the score of 520 was reported to be in the 78th percentile of high school students. This wording *does not* mean that 78% of your answers were correct; it *does* mean that you outperformed about 78% of all those taking the exam. In general, a score in the nth percentile means that you outperformed about $n\%$ of the population who took the test and that $(100 - n)\%$ of the people taking the test performed better than you did.

Percentiles

1	2	3	4		100	— 100 equal parts
P_1	P_2	P_3	P_4		P_{99}	— Percentile indicators

Figure 13.14

Example 7 *English Achievement Test*

Kara Hopkins took an English achievement test to obtain college credit by exam for freshman English. Her score was at the 81st percentile. Explain what that means.

Solution If a score is at the 81st percentile, it means that about 81% of the scores are below that score. Therefore, Kara scored better than about 81% of the students taking the exam. Also, about 19% of all students taking the exam scored higher than she did. ∎

Quartiles are another measure of position. Quartiles divide data into four equal parts: The first quartile is the value that is higher than about $\frac{1}{4}$, or 25%, of the population. It is the same as the 25th percentile. The second quartile is the value that is higher than about $\frac{1}{2}$ the population and is the same as the 50th percentile, or the median. The third quartile is the value that is higher than about $\frac{3}{4}$ of the population and is the same as the 75th percentile; see Fig. 13.15.

Quartiles

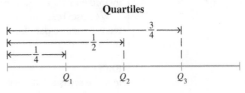

Figure 13.15

PROCEDURE   **TO DETERMINE THE QUARTILES OF A SET OF DATA**

1. List the data from smallest to largest.

2. Determine the median, or the 2nd quartile, of the set of data. If there is an odd number of pieces of data, the median is the middle value. If there is an even number of pieces of data, the median will be halfway between the two middle pieces of data.

3. The first quartile, Q_1, is the median of the lower half of the data; that is, Q_1 is the median of the data less than Q_2.

4. The third quartile, Q_3, is the median of the upper half of the data; that is, Q_3 is the median of the data greater than Q_2.

Example 8 *Finding Quartiles*

Electronics World is concerned about the high turnover of its sales staff. A survey was done to determine how long (in months) the sales staff had been in their current positions. The responses of 27 sales staff follow. Determine Q_1, Q_2, and Q_3.

$$25 \quad 3 \quad 7 \quad 15 \quad 31 \quad 36 \quad 17 \quad 21 \quad 2$$
$$11 \quad 42 \quad 16 \quad 23 \quad 19 \quad 21 \quad 9 \quad 20 \quad 5$$
$$8 \quad 12 \quad 27 \quad 14 \quad 39 \quad 24 \quad 18 \quad 6 \quad 10$$

Solution First we list the data from smallest to largest.

$$2 \quad 3 \quad 5 \quad 6 \quad 7 \quad 8 \quad 9 \quad 10 \quad 11$$
$$12 \quad 14 \quad 15 \quad 16 \quad 17 \quad 18 \quad 19 \quad 20 \quad 21$$
$$21 \quad 23 \quad 24 \quad 25 \quad 27 \quad 31 \quad 36 \quad 39 \quad 42$$

Next we determine the median. Since there are 27 pieces of data, an odd number, the median will be the middle value. The middle value is 17, with 13 pieces of data less than 17 and 13 pieces of data greater than 17. Therefore, the median, Q_2, is 17, shown in red.

To find Q_1, the median of the lower half of the data, we need to find the median of the 13 pieces of data that are less than Q_2. The middle value of the lower half of the data is 9. There are 6 pieces of data less than 9 and 6 pieces of data greater than 9. Therefore, Q_1 is 9, shown in blue.

To find Q_3, the median of the upper half of the data, we need to find the median of the 13 pieces of data that are greater than 17, or Q_2. The middle value of the upper half of the data is 24. There are 6 pieces of data greater than 17 but less than 24 and 6 pieces of data greater than 24. Therefore, Q_3 is 24, shown in blue. ∎

> **TECHNOLOGY TIP**
>
> Several computer software programs and calculators can be used to determine the mean of a set of data. These programs and calculators can also provide other types of statistical information that we will discuss in this chapter. In this *Technology Tip* we will provide the instructions for using a software program called Microsoft Excel as well as information on how to use Texas Instruments TI-83 Plus and TI-84 Plus graphing calculators. In the example, we will use the data from Example 1 on page 797, which represent the ages of patients in a doctor's office.
>
> **EXCEL**
>
> In our discussion, we will use the symbol > to indicate the next item to be selected from the list or menu of items.
>
> Begin by entering the five pieces of data in column A. Press the Enter key after each piece of data is entered. Next select
>
> Insert > Function ... > Statistical > AVERAGE
>
> Then click the $\boxed{\text{OK}}$ box at the bottom. The program will then generate a gray box, where you need to enter the data. In the area to the right of **Number1**, you need to enter the data for which you want to find the mean. Since you have already entered the data in column A, rows 1 to 5, if A1:A5 is not already listed, you can enter A1:A5 in the area to the right of **Number1**. Then, at the bottom of the gray box, *Formula Results* = 36 is displayed. The 36 is the mean of the set of data. If you then press the $\boxed{\text{OK}}$ box, the mean will be displayed in the cell where the cursor was located. If you do not want the mean displayed in a cell, press $\boxed{\text{CANCEL}}$. To find the median or mode you follow a similar procedure, except that instead of selecting AVERAGE you would select MEDIAN or MODE, respectively.
>
> **TI-83 PLUS AND TI-84 PLUS GRAPHING CALCULATORS**
>
> To enter the data, press $\boxed{\text{STAT}}$. Then highlight **1: Edit** and press the $\boxed{\text{ENTER}}$ key. If any data are currently listed in column **L1**, move the cursor to the **L1** and press $\boxed{\text{CLEAR}}$ and then the $\boxed{\text{ENTER}}$ key. This step will eliminate all data from column **L1**. Now enter the data in column **L1**. After you enter each piece of data, press the $\boxed{\text{ENTER}}$ key. After all the data have been entered, press $\boxed{\text{STAT}}$. Then highlight **CALC.** At this point, **1: 1–Var Stats** should be highlighted. Press the $\boxed{\text{ENTER}}$ key twice. You will now see $\bar{x}$ = 36. Thus, the mean is 36. Several other descriptive statistics that we will discuss shortly are also shown. If you scroll down, you will eventually see the values of Q_1, the median, and Q_3.

SECTION 13.4 *Exercises*

Warm Up Exercises

In Exercises 1–10, fill in the blank with an appropriate word, phrase, or symbol(s).

1. A number that is representative of a set of data is called a(n) _____.

2. Averages are referred to as measures of central _____.

3. The average that is found by summing the data and then dividing the sum by the number of pieces of data is called the _____.

4. The value in the middle of a set of ranked data is called the _____.

5. The piece of data that occurs most frequently is called the _____.

6. The value halfway between the lowest and highest values in a set of data is called the _____.

7. The measures of position that divide a set of data into four equal parts are called _____.

8. Data that are listed from the lowest value to the highest value or from the highest value to the lowest value are called _____ data.

9. a) The symbol for the sample mean is _____.

   b) The symbol for the population mean is _____.

10. a) Another name for the 25th percentile is the _____ quartile.

    b) Another name for the 50th percentile is the _____ quartile.

    c) Another name for the 75th percentile is the _____ quartile.

Practice the Skills

In Exercises 11–20, determine the mean, median, mode, and midrange of the set of data. Where appropriate, round your answer to the nearest tenth.

11. 8, 9, 9, 11, 13, 13, 13, 24, 26

12. 7, 9, 10, 10, 10, 12, 12

13. 76, 82, 94, 55, 100, 52, 96

14. 4, 6, 10, 12, 10, 9, 365, 40, 37, 8

15. 1, 3, 5, 7, 9, 11, 13, 15

16. 40, 50, 30, 60, 90, 100, 140

17. 1, 7, 11, 27, 36, 14, 12, 9, 1

18. 1, 1, 1, 1, 4, 4, 4, 4, 6, 8, 10, 12, 15, 21

19. 6, 8, 12, 13, 11, 13, 15, 17

20. 5, 15, 5, 15, 5, 15

21. *Cholesterol Level* The total cholesterol level of 10 patients of Dr. Novak are 176, 202, 285, 153, 200, 182, 248, 132, 214, and 195. Determine the

a) mean.   **b)** median.

c) mode.   **d)** midrange.

22. *Daily Commission* The amount of money Steve Kline collected in sales commission in each of seven days is $48, $67, $51, $25, $102, $61, $80. Determine the mean, median, mode, and midrange.

Problem Solving

23. *Change in the Data* The mean is the "most sensitive" average because it is affected by any change in the data.

a) Determine the mean, median, mode, and midrange for 1, 2, 3, 5, 5, 7, 11.

b) Change the 7 to a 10 in part (a). Determine the mean, median, mode, and midrange.

c) Which averages were affected by changing the 7 to a 10?

d) Which averages will be affected by changing the 11 to a 10 in part (a)?

24. *Life Expectancy* In 2010, the National Center for Health Statistics indicated a record "average life expectancy" of 78.2 years for the total U.S. population. The average life expectancy for men was 75.6 years, and for women it was 80.8 years. Which "average" do you think the National Center for Health is using?

25. *A Grade of B* To get a grade of B, a student must have a mean average of 80 or greater. Jim Condor has a mean average of 79 for 10 quizzes. He approaches his teacher and asks for a B, reasoning that he missed a B by only one point. What is wrong with Jim's reasoning?

26. *Employee Salaries* The salaries of 10 employees of a small company follow.

$29,000	$65,000
26,000	25,000
32,000	28,000
27,000	82,000
27,000	30,000

Determine the

a) mean.   **b)** median.

c) mode.   **d)** midrange.

e) If the employees wanted to demonstrate the need for a raise, which average would they use to show they are being underpaid: the mean or the median? Explain.

f) If the management did not want to give the employees a raise, which average would they use: the mean or the median? Explain.

27. *Ice Cream Consumption* The 10 countries with the highest per person consumption of ice cream in 2008 are listed below.

Country	Consumption (pints per person)
Australia	31.7
USA	26.0
Nauru	25.3
New Zealand	23.4
Canada	22.7
Norway	22.3
Finland	20.9
Sweden	20.4
Iceland	18.5
Italy	18.5

Source: *Euromonitor International*

Determine, to the nearest tenth, the

a) mean.   **b)** median.

c) mode.   **d)** midrange.

28. *Living Expenses* Bob Bennet's monthly living expenses for 1 year are as follows:

$1200	$1050	$1570	$1600
2000	1050	1550	1450
1800	1100	1310	1430

Where appropriate, round your answer to the nearest cent. Determine the

a) mean.   **b)** median.

c) mode.   **d)** midrange.

29. *Internet Retailers* The ten U.S. retailers with the highest Internet sales in 2008 are listed below.

Company	Sales ($ billion)
Amazon.com, Inc.	14.8
Staples, Inc.	5.6
Office Depot, Inc.	4.9
Dell, Inc.	4.2
HP Home & Home Office Store	3.4
OfficeMax, Inc.	3.2
Apple, Inc.	2.7
Sears Holding Corp.	2.6
CDW Corp.	2.4
Newegg.com	1.9

Source: *Internet Retailer*

Determine to the nearest tenth the

a) mean.   **b)** median.

c) mode.   **d)** midrange.

30. *Exam Average* Malcolm Sander's mean average on five exams is 86. Determine the sum of his scores.

31. *Exam Average* Jeremy Urban's mean average on six exams is 92. Determine the sum of his scores.

32. *Creating a Data Set* Construct a set of five pieces of data in which the mode has a lower value than the median and the median has a lower value than the mean.

33. *Creating a Data Set* Construct a set of six pieces of data with a mean, median, and midrange of 75 and where no two pieces of data are the same.

34. *Creating a Data Set* Construct a set of six pieces of data with a mean of 84 and where no two pieces of data are the same.

35. *Water Park* For the 2011 season, 27,000 people visited the Blue Lagoon Water Park. The park was open 120 days for water activities. The highest number of visitors on a single day was 500. The lowest number of visitors on a single day was 50. Determine whether it is possible to find the following with the given information.

a) the mean number of visitors per day

b) the median number of visitors per day

c) the mode number of visitors per day

d) the midrange number of visitors per day

36. *Determine a Necessary Grade* A mean average of 80 or greater for five exams is needed for a final grade of B in a course. Jorge Rivera's first four exam grades are 73, 69, 85, and 80. What grade does Jorge need on the fifth exam to get a B in the course?

37. *Grading Methods* A mean average of 60 on seven exams is needed to pass a course. On her first six exams, Sheryl Ward received grades of 51, 72, 80, 62, 57, and 69.

a) What grade must she receive on her last exam to pass the course?

b) An average of 70 is needed to get a C in the course. Is it possible for Sheryl to get a C? If so, what grade must she receive on the seventh exam?

c) If her lowest grade of the exams already taken is to be dropped, what grade must she receive on her last exam to pass the course?

d) If her lowest grade of the exams already taken is to be dropped, what grade must she receive on her last exam to get a C in the course?

38. Central Tendencies Which of the measures of central tendency *must* be an actual piece of data in the distribution?

39. Creating a Data Set Construct a set of six pieces of data such that if only one piece of data is changed, the mean, median, and mode will all change.

40. Changing One Piece of Data Consider the set of data 1, 1, 1, 2, 2, 2. If one 2 is changed to a 3, which of the following will change: mean, median, mode, midrange?

41. Changing One Piece of Data Is it possible to construct a set of six different pieces of data such that by changing only one piece of data you cause the mean, median, mode, and midrange to change? Explain.

42. Grocery Expenses The Taylors have recorded their weekly grocery expenses for the past 12 weeks and determined that the mean weekly expense was $85.20. Later Mrs. Taylor discovered that 1 week's expense of $74 was incorrectly recorded as $47. What is the correct mean?

43. Percentiles For any set of data, what must be done to the data before percentiles can be determined?

44. Percentiles Josie Waverly scored in the 73rd percentile on the verbal part of her College Board test. What does that mean?

45. Percentiles When a national sample of heights of kindergarten children was taken, Kevin Geis was told that he was in the 35th percentile. Explain what that means.

46. Percentiles A union leader is told that, when all workers' salaries are considered, the first quartile is $22,750. Explain what that means.

47. Quartiles The prices of a gallon of the 21 top-rated interior paints, as rated in the March 2010 issue of *Consumer Reports*, are as follows:

$18 $19 $19 $19 $20 $20 $21
$21 $22 $22 $23 $23 $25 $27
$30 $33 $35 $35 $35 $58 $61

Determine

a) Q_2.   **b)** Q_1.   **c)** Q_3.

48. Quartiles The prices of the 20 top-rated 16-inch laptops, as rated in the June 2010 issue of *Consumer Reports*, are as follows:

$450 $460 $500 $530 $550
$550 $650 $650 $680 $700
$720 $730 $800 $850 $900
$1000 $1200 $1350 $1700 $1900

Determine

a) Q_2.   **b)** Q_1.   **c)** Q_3.

49. The 50th Percentile Give the names of two other statistics that have the same value as the 50th percentile.

50. College Admissions Jonathan Burd took an admission test for the University of California and scored in the 85th percentile. The following year, Jonathan's sister Kendra took a similar admission test for the University of California and scored in the 90th percentile.

a) Is it possible to determine which of the two answered the higher percent of questions correctly on their respective exams?

b) Is it possible to determine which of the two was in a better relative position with regard to their respective populations? Explain.

51. Employee Salaries The following statistics represent weekly salaries at the Midtown Construction Company:

Mean	$600	First quartile	$560
Median	$590	Third quartile	$625
Mode	$580	83rd percentile	$665

a) What is the most common salary?

b) What salary did half the employees' salaries surpass?

c) About what percent of employees' salaries surpassed $625?

d) About what percent of employees' salaries were less than $560?

e) About what percent of employees' salaries surpassed $665?

f) If the company has 100 employees, what is the total weekly salary of all employees?

Challenge Problems/Group Activities

52. The Mean of the Means Consider the following five sets of values.

i) 5 6 7 7 8 9 14

ii) 3 6 8 9

iii) 1 1 1 2 5

iv) 6 8 9 12 15

v) 50 51 55 60 80 100

a) Compute the mean of each of the five sets of data.

b) Compute the mean of the five means in part (a).

c) Find the mean of the 27 pieces of data.

d) Compare your answer in part (b) to your answer in part (c). Are the values the same? Does your answer make sense?

53. *Ruth Versus Mantle* The tables below compare the batting performances for selected years for two well-known former baseball players, Babe Ruth and Mickey Mantle.

Babe Ruth
Boston Red Sox 1914–1919
New York Yankees 1920–1934

Year	At Bats	Hits	Pct.
1925	359	104	
1930	518	186	
1933	459	138	
1916	136	37	
1922	406	128	
Total	1878	593	

Mickey Mantle
New York Yankees 1951–1968

Year	At Bats	Hits	Pct.
1954	543	163	
1957	474	173	
1958	519	158	
1960	527	145	
1962	377	121	
Total	2440	760	

a) For each player, compute the batting average percent (pct.) for each year by dividing the number of hits by the number of at bats. Round to the nearest thousandth. Place the answers in the pct. column.

b) Going across each of the five horizontal lines (for example Ruth, 1925, vs. Mantle, 1954), compare the percents (pct.) and determine which is greater in each case.

c) For each player, compute the mean batting average percent for the 5 given years by dividing the total hits by the total at bats. Which is greater, Ruth's or Mantle's?

d) Based on your answer in part (b), does your answer in part (c) make sense? Explain.

e) Find the mean percent for each player by adding the five pcts. and dividing by 5. Which is greater, Ruth's or Mantle's?

f) Why do the answers obtained in parts (c) and (e) differ? Explain.

g) Who would you say has the better batting average percent for the 5 years selected? Explain.

54. *Employee Salaries* The following table gives the annual salary distribution for employees at Kulzer's Home Improvement.

Annual Salary	Number Receiving Salary
$100,000	1
85,000	2
24,000	6
21,000	4
18,000	5
17,000	7

Using the information provided in the table, determine the

a) mean annual salary.

b) median annual salary.

c) mode annual salary.

d) midrange annual salary.

e) Which is the best measure of central tendency for this set of data? Explain your answer.

Weighted Average Sometimes when we wish to find an average, we may wish to assign more importance, or weight, to some of the pieces of data. To calculate a *weighted average*, we use the formula: weighted average $= \dfrac{\Sigma xw}{\Sigma w}$, where w is the weight of the piece of data, x; Σxw is the sum of the products of each piece of data multiplied by its weight; and Σw is the sum of the weights. For example, suppose that students in a class need to submit a report that counts for 20% of their grade, they need to take a midterm exam that counts for 30% of their grade, and they need to take a final exam that counts for 50% of their grade. Suppose that a student got a 72 on the report, an 85 on the midterm exam, and a 93 on the final exam. To determine this student's weighted average, first find Σxw:

$\Sigma xw = 72(0.20) + 85(0.30) + 93(0.50) = 86.4$.

Next find Σw, the sum of the weights: $\Sigma w = 0.20 + 0.30 + 0.50 = 1.00$. Now determine the weighted average as follows.

$$\text{Weighted average} = \frac{\Sigma xw}{\Sigma w} = \frac{86.4}{1.00} = 86.4$$

Thus, the weighted average is 86.4. Note that Σw does not always have to be 1.00. In Exercises 55 and 56, use the weighted average formula.

55. Course Average Suppose that your final grade for a course is determined by a midterm exam and a final exam. The midterm exam is worth 40% of your grade, and the final exam is worth 60%. If your midterm exam grade is 84 and your final exam grade is 94, calculate your final average.

56. Grade Point Average In a four-point grade system, an A corresponds to 4.0 points, a B corresponds to 3.0 points, a C corresponds to 2.0 points, and a D corresponds to 1.0 points. No points are awarded for an F. Last semester, Tanya Reeves received a B in a four-credit hour course, an A in a three-credit hour course, a C in a three-credit hour course, and an A in another three-credit hour course. Grade point average (GPA) is calculated as a weighted average using the credit hours as weights and the number of points corresponding to the grade as pieces of data. Calculate Tanya's GPA for the previous semester. (Round your answer to the nearest hundredth.)

Recreational Mathematics

57. Your Exam Average a) Calculate the mean, median, mode, and midrange of your exam grades in your mathematics course.

b) Which measure of central tendency best represents your average grade?

c) Which measure of central tendency would you rather use as your average grade?

58. Purchases Matthew Riveria purchased some items at Staples each day for five days. The mode of the number of items Matthew purchased is higher than the median of the number of items he purchased. The median of the number of items Matthew purchased is higher than the mean of the number of items he purchased. He purchased at least two items but no more than seven items each day.

a) How many items did Matthew purchase each day? (*Note:* There is more than one correct answer.)

b) Determine the mean, median, and mode for your answer to part (a).

Internet/Research Activity

59. Two other measures of location that we did not mention in this section are *stanines* and *deciles*. Use statistics books, books on educational testing and measurements, and Internet Web sites to write a report on what stanines and deciles are and when percentiles, quartiles, stanines, and deciles are used.

SECTION 13.5 Measures of Dispersion

▲ *The average life span of a tablet PC battery may not be enough information to make a sound purchasing decision.*

Measures of central tendency by themselves do not always give sufficient information to analyze a situation and make decisions. For example, suppose Apple Computer is considering two companies to produce batteries for its iPads. Testing shows that Company A batteries have a mean life of 10 hours. Company B batteries have a mean life of 9.5 hours. If both manufacturers' batteries cost the same, which one should be purchased? The average battery life may not be the most important factor. If half of Company A batteries last only 5 hours, while half last 15 hours, there is a large variability in the life of the batteries. If all of Company B batteries last between 9.0 and 10.0 hours, the batteries are more consistent and reliable. This example illustrates the importance of knowing something about the *spread*, or *variability*, of the data. In this section we will discuss two measures of variability or dispersion.

Why *This is Important* Knowing the spread, or variability of a set of data helps us make accurate conclusions about the set of data.

M *easures of dispersion* are used to measure the variability of the data, including the *spread of the data*, and how the data varies about the mean. The range and standard deviation* are the measures of dispersion that will be discussed in this section.

Range and Standard Deviation

The *range* is the difference between the highest and lowest values; it indicates the total spread of the data.

> **Range**
>
> The range of a set of data can be calculated using the following formula.
>
> $$\textbf{Range} = \text{highest value} - \text{lowest value}$$

Example 1 *Determine the Range*

The amount of caffeine, in milligrams, of 10 different soft drinks is given below. Determine the range of these data.

$$38, 43, 26, 80, 55, 34, 40, 30, 35, 43$$

Solution   Range = highest value − lowest value = 80 − 26 = 54. The range of the amounts of caffeine is 54 milligrams. ■

The second measure of dispersion we discuss in this section, the *standard deviation*, measures how much the data *differ from the mean*. It is symbolized either by the letter s or by the Greek letter sigma, σ.[†] The s is used when the standard deviation of a *sample* is calculated. The σ is used when the standard deviation of the entire *population* is calculated. *Since we are assuming that all data presented in this section are for samples, we use s to represent the standard deviation* (note, however, that on the height and weight charts on page 814, σ is used).

The larger the variability of the data about the mean, the larger the standard deviation is. Consider the following two sets of data.

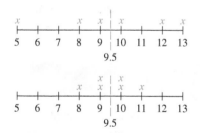

Figure 13.16

$$5, 8, 9, 10, 12, 13 \qquad 8, 9, 9, 10, 10, 11$$

Both have a mean of 9.5. Which set of values on the whole do you believe differs less from the mean of 9.5? Figure 13.16 may make the answer more apparent. The scores in the second set of data are closer to the mean and therefore have a smaller standard deviation. You will soon be able to verify such relationships yourself.

Sometimes only a very small standard deviation is desirable or acceptable. Consider a cereal box that is to contain 8 oz of cereal. If the amount of cereal put into the boxes varies too much—sometimes underfilling, sometimes overfilling—the manufacturer will soon be in trouble with consumer groups and government agencies.

At other times, a larger spread of data is desirable or expected. For example, intelligence quotients (IQs) are expected to exhibit a considerable spread about the

---

Variance, another measure of dispersion, is the square of the standard deviation.

[†]Our alphabet uses both uppercase and lowercase letters, for example, A and a. The Greek alphabet also uses both uppercase and lowercase letters. The symbol Σ is the capital Greek letter sigma, and σ is the lowercase Greek letter sigma.

mean because everyone is different. The following procedure explains how we determine the standard deviation of a set of data.

PROCEDURE   **TO DETERMINE THE STANDARD DEVIATION OF A SET OF DATA**

1. Determine the mean of the set of data.
2. Make a chart having three columns:

    Data   Data − Mean   (Data − Mean)^2

3. List the data vertically under the column marked Data.
4. Subtract the mean from each piece of data and place the difference in the Data − Mean column.
5. Square the values obtained in the Data − Mean column and record these values in the (Data − Mean)^2 column.
6. Determine the sum of the values in the (Data − Mean)^2 column.
7. Divide the sum obtained in Step 6 by $n − 1$, where n is the number of pieces of data.[*]
8. Determine the square root of the number obtained in Step 7. This number is the standard deviation of the set of data.

Example 2 illustrates the procedure to follow to determine the standard deviation of a set of data.

Example 2   *Determine the Standard Deviation*

A veterinarian in an animal hospital recorded the following life spans of selected Labrador retrievers (to the nearest year):

$$7, 9, 11, 15, 18, 12$$

Determine the standard deviation of the life spans.

Solution   First determine the mean:

$$\bar{x} = \frac{\Sigma x}{n} = \frac{7 + 9 + 11 + 15 + 18 + 12}{6} = \frac{72}{6} = 12$$

Next construct a table with three columns, as illustrated in Table 13.4 on page 810, and list the data in the first column (it is often helpful to list the data in ascending or descending order). Complete the second column by subtracting the mean, 12 in this case, from each piece of data in the first column.

The sum of the values in the Data − Mean column should always be zero; if not, you have made an error. (If a rounded value of $\bar{x}$ is used, the sum of the values in the Data − Mean column will not always be exactly zero; however, the sum will be very close to zero.)

---

[*]To determine the standard deviation of a sample, divide the sum of (Data − Mean)^2 column by $n − 1$. To find the standard deviation of a population, divide the sum by n. In this book, we assume that the set of data represents a sample and divide by $n − 1$. The quotient obtained in Step 7 represents a measure of dispersion called the *variance*.

MATHEMATICS TODAY

Statistics and Opera Houses

Sydney Opera House in Sydney, Australia

Architects have developed a mathematical rule based on statistics to help them construct opera houses with exceptional acoustics. The rule was first developed by having conductors rate the overall sound quality in 23 opera houses. Then acoustical engineers measured several acoustical properties in those 23 buildings. By using statistical analysis, the engineers were able to determine which combination of properties produced exceptional sound and which of the acoustic characteristics were most important. This mathematical rule is now used in the development of new opera houses.

Why *This is Important* Statistics is used is many different professions including architecture and engineering.

Table 13.4

Data	Data − Mean	(Data − Mean)^2
7	$7 - 12 = -5$	
9	$9 - 12 = -3$	
11	$11 - 12 = -1$	
12	$12 - 12 = 0$	
15	$15 - 12 = 3$	
18	$18 - 12 = 6$	
	$\;0$	

Next square the values in the second column and place the squares in the third column (Table 13.5).

Table 13.5

Data	Data − Mean	(Data − Mean)^2
7	-5	$(-5)^2 = (-5)(-5) = 25$
9	-3	$(-3)^2 = (-3)(-3) = 9$
11	-1	$(-1)^2 = (-1)(-1) = 1$
12	0	$(0)^2 = (0)(0) = 0$
15	3	$(3)^2 = (3)(3) = 9$
18	6	$(6)^2 = (6)(6) = 36$
	0	80

Add the squares in the third column. In this case, the sum is 80. Divide this sum by one less than the number of pieces of data ($n - 1$). In this case, the number of pieces of data is 6. Therefore, we divide by 5 and get

$$\frac{80}{5} = 16*$$

Finally, take the square root of this number. Since $\sqrt{16} = 4$, the standard deviation, symbolized s, is 4. ■

Now we will develop a formula for determining the standard deviation of a set of data. If we call the individual data x and the mean $\bar{x}$, we could write the three column heads Data, Data − Mean, and (Data − Mean)^2 in Table 13.4 as

$$x \qquad x - \bar{x} \qquad (x - \bar{x})^2$$

Let's follow the procedure we used to obtain the standard deviation in Example 2. We found the sum of the (Data − Mean)^2 column, which is the same as the sum of the $(x - \bar{x})^2$ column. We can represent the sum of the $(x - \bar{x})^2$ column by using the summation notation, $\Sigma(x - \bar{x})^2$. Thus, in Table 13.5, $\Sigma(x - \bar{x})^2 = 80$. We then divided this number by 1 less than the number of pieces of data, $n - 1$. Thus, we have

$$\frac{\Sigma(x - \bar{x})^2}{n - 1}$$

---

*16 is the variance, symbolized s^2, of this set of data.

Finally, we took the square root of this value to obtain the standard deviation.

Standard Deviation

The standard deviation, s, of a set of data can be calculated using the following formula.

$$s = \sqrt{\frac{\Sigma (x - \bar{x})^2}{n - 1}}$$

Example 3 *Determine the Standard Deviation of Stock Prices*

The following are the prices of nine stocks on the New York Stock Exchange. Determine the standard deviation of the prices.

$17, $28, $32, $36, $50, $52, $66, $74, $104

Solution The mean, $\bar{x}$, is

$$\bar{x} = \frac{\Sigma x}{n} = \frac{17 + 28 + 32 + 36 + 50 + 52 + 66 + 74 + 104}{9} = \frac{459}{9} = 51$$

The mean is $51.

Table 13.6

x	$x - \bar{x}$	$(x - \bar{x})^2$
17	−34	1156
28	−23	529
32	−19	361
36	−15	225
50	−1	1
52	1	1
66	15	225
74	23	529
104	53	2809
	0	5836

Table 13.6 shows us that $\Sigma(x - \bar{x})^2 = 5836$. Since there are nine pieces of data, $n - 1 = 9 - 1$, or 8.

$$s = \sqrt{\frac{\Sigma (x - \bar{x})^2}{n - 1}} = \sqrt{\frac{5836}{8}} = \sqrt{729.5} \approx 27.01$$

The standard deviation, to the nearest tenth, is $27.01.

Standard deviation will be used in Section 13.6 to find the percent of data between any two values in a normal curve. Standard deviations are also often used in determining norms for a population (see Exercise 29).

TECHNOLOGY TIP

In this *Technology Tip*, we will explain how to find the standard deviation using Excel as well as with the TI-83 Plus and TI-84 Plus graphing calculators. In our illustration, we will use the data from Example 3 on page 811, which represent the prices of nine stocks on the New York Stock Exchange.

EXCEL
The instructions used to determine the standard deviation are very similar to those used to determine the mean in the *Technology Tip* on page 802 in Section 13.4. Please read that material now. Then enter the nine piece of data in columns A1–A9 and press the Enter key. Now select the following:

Insert > Function ... > Statistical > STDEV

Then click the OK box. The program will then generate a gray box where you need to enter the data. In the area to the right of **Number1** you need to enter the data for which you want to find the standard deviation. Since you have already entered the data in column A, rows 1 to 9, if A1:A9 is not already listed, you can enter A1:A9 in the area to the right of **Number1.** At the bottom of the gray box, *Formula Results* = 27.00925767, which is the standard deviation, is displayed. If you click OK, Excel will place the standard deviation in cell A10.

TI-83 PLUS AND TI-84 PLUS GRAPHING CALCULATORS
To find the standard deviation on Texas Instruments graphing calculators, follow the instructions for finding the mean in the *Technology Tip* on page 802 in Section 13.4. As explained there, press STAT > EDIT > ENTER. Remove existing data by highlighting **L1** and then pressing CLEAR > ENTER. Then enter the nine pieces of data, pressing the Enter key after each entry. Then press STAT > CALC > ENTER > ENTER. The fourth statistic down is S_x = 27.00925767. This value is the standard deviation.

SECTION 13.5   *Exercises*

Warm Up Exercises

In Exercises 1–6, fill in the blank with an appropriate word, phrase, or symbol(s).

1. Measures of dispersion are used to indicate the spread or _____ of the data.

2. The difference between the highest and lowest values in a set of data is called the _____.

3. The measure of dispersion that measures how much the data differ from the mean is called the _____.

4. The symbol, σ, is used to indicate the standard deviation of a(n) _____.

5. The symbol, s, is used to indicate the standard deviation of a(n) _____.

6. The standard deviation of a set of data in which all the data values are the same is _____.

Practice the Skills

In Exercises 7–14, determine the range and standard deviation of the set of data. When appropriate, round standard deviations to the nearest hundredth.

7. 11, 9, 6, 12, 17

8. 15, 15, 19, 21, 13, 13

9. 130, 131, 132, 133, 134, 135, 136

10. 3, 7, 8, 12, 0, 9, 11, 12, 6, 2

11. 4, 8, 9, 11, 13, 15

12. 9, 9, 9, 9, 9, 9, 9

13. 7, 9, 7, 9, 9, 10, 12

14. 60, 58, 62, 67, 48, 51, 72, 70

Problem Solving

15. *Digital Cameras* Determine the range and standard deviation of the following prices of selected digital cameras: $158, $95, $175, $180, $95, $129, $228, $300.

16. *Years Until Retirement* Seven employees at a large company were asked the number of additional years they planned to work before retirement. Their responses were 10, 23, 28, 4, 1, 6, 12. Determine the range and standard deviation of the number of years.

17. *Camping Tents* Determine the range and standard deviation of the following prices of selected camping tents: $109, $60, $80, $60, $210, $250, $60, $100, $115.

18. *Prescription Prices* The amount of money seven people spent on prescription medication in a year are as follows: $600, $100, $850, $350, $250, $140, $300. Determine the range and standard deviation of the amounts.

19. Can you think of any situations in which a large standard deviation may be desirable?

20. Can you think of any situations in which a small standard deviation may be desirable?

21. Without actually doing the calculations, decide which, if either, of the following two sets of data will have the greater standard deviation. Explain why.

    10, 13, 14, 15, 17, 21   16, 17, 17, 18, 18, 19

22. Without actually doing the calculations, decide which, if either, of the following two sets of data will have the greater standard deviation. Explain why.

    2, 4, 6, 8, 10   102, 104, 106, 108, 110

23. By studying the standard deviation formula, explain why the standard deviation of a set of data will always be greater than or equal to 0.

24. Patricia Wolff teaches two statistics classes, one in the morning and the other in the evening. On the midterm exam, the morning class had a mean of 75.2 and a standard deviation of 5.7. The evening class had a mean of 75.2 and a standard deviation of 12.5.

a) How do the means compare?

b) If we compare the set of scores from the first class with those in the second class, how will the distributions of the two sets of scores compare?

25. *Count Your Money* Six people were asked to determine the amount of money they were carrying, to the nearest dollar. The results were

$$\$32, \$60, \$14, \$25, \$5, \$68$$

a) Determine the range and standard deviation of the amounts.

b) Add $10 to each of the six amounts. How do you expect the range and standard deviation of the new set of data to change?

c) Determine the range and standard deviation of the new set of data. Do the results agree with your answer to part (b)? If not, explain why.

26. a) *Adding to or Subtracting from Each Number* Pick any five numbers. Compute the mean and the standard deviation of this distribution.

b) Add 20 to each of the numbers in your original distribution and compute the mean and the standard deviation of this new distribution.

c) Subtract 5 from each number in your original distribution and compute the mean and standard deviation of this new distribution.

d) What conclusions can you draw about changes in the mean and the standard deviation when the same number is added to or subtracted from each piece of data in a distribution?

e) How will the mean and standard deviation of the numbers 8, 9, 10, 11, 12, 13, 14 differ from the mean and standard deviation of the numbers 648, 649, 650, 651, 652, 653, 654? Determine the mean and standard deviation of both sets of numbers.

27. a) *Multiplying Each Number* Pick any five numbers. Compute the mean and standard deviation of this distribution.

b) Multiply each number in your distribution by 3 and compute the mean and the standard deviation of this new distribution.

c) Multiply each number in your original distribution by 9 and compute the mean and the standard deviation of this new distribution.

d) What conclusions can you draw about changes in the mean and the standard deviation when each value in a distribution is multiplied by the same number?

e) The mean and standard deviation of the distribution 1, 3, 4, 4, 5, 7 are 4 and 2, respectively. Use the conclusion drawn in part (d) to determine the mean and standard deviation of the distribution

$$5, 15, 20, 20, 25, 35$$

28. *Waiting in Line* Consider the following illustrations of two bank-customer waiting systems.

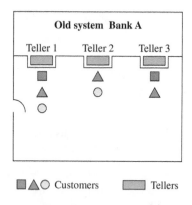

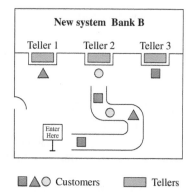

a) How would you expect the mean waiting time in Bank A to compare with the mean waiting time in Bank B?

b) How would you expect the standard deviation of waiting times in Bank A to compare with the standard deviation of waiting times in Bank B?

29. *Height and Weight Distribution* The chart shown on the right uses the symbol σ to represent the standard deviation. Note that 2σ represents the value that is two standard deviations above the mean; -2σ represents the value that is two standard deviations below the mean. The unshaded areas, from two standard deviations below the mean to two standard deviations above the mean, are considered the

normal range. For example, the average (mean) 8-year-old boy has a height of about 50 inches, but any heights between approximately 45 inches and 55 inches are considered normal for 8-year-old boys. Refer to the chart below to answer the following questions.

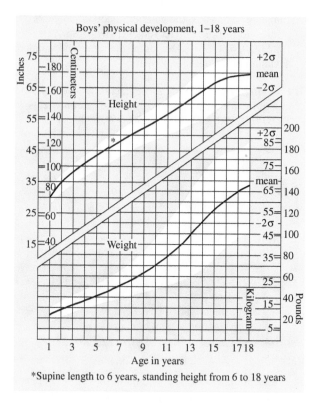

*Supine length to 6 years, standing height from 6 to 18 years

a) What happens to the standard deviation for weights of boys as the age of boys increases? What is the significance of this fact?

b) At age 16, what is the mean weight, in pounds, of boys?

c) What is the approximate standard deviation of boys' weights at age 16?

d) Determine the mean weight and normal range for boys at age 13.

e) Determine the mean height and normal range for boys at age 13.

f) Assuming that this chart was constructed so that approximately 95% of all boys are always in the normal range, determine what percentage of boys are not in the normal range.

Challenge Problems/Group Activities

30. *Athletes' Salaries* The tables on page 815 list the 10 highest-paid athletes in Major League Baseball and in the National Football League.

Major League Baseball (2010 Season)

Player	Salary (millions of dollars)
1. Alex Rodriguez	33.0
2. C. C. Sabathia	24.3
3. Derek Jeter	22.6
4. Mark Teixeira	20.6
5. Johan Santana	20.1
6. Miguel Cabrera	20.0
7. Carlos Beltran	19.4
8. Ryan Howard	19.0
9. Carlos Lee	19.0
10. Alfonso Soriano	19.0

Source: Major League Baseball Players Association

National Football League (2009–2010 season)

Player	Salary (millions of dollars)
1. Philip Rivers	25.6
2. Jay Cutler	22.0
3. Eli Manning	20.5
4. Kurt Warner	19.0
5. Kelvin Hayden	17.5
6. Matt Schaub	17.0
7. Julius Peppers	16.7
8. Chris Long	16.6
9. Greg Jennings	16.3
10. Antonio Smith	15.5

Source: National Football League Players Association

a) Without doing any calculations, which do you believe is greater, the mean salary of the 10 baseball players or the mean salary of the 10 football players?

b) Without doing any calculations, which do you believe is greater, the standard deviation of the salary of the 10 baseball players or the standard deviation of the salary of the 10 football players?

c) Compute the mean salary of the 10 baseball players and the mean salary of the 10 football players and determine whether your answer in part (a) was correct.

d) Compute the standard deviation of the salary of the 10 baseball players and the standard deviation of the salary of the 10 football players and determine whether your answer in part (b) is correct. Round each mean to the nearest tenth to determine the standard deviation.

31. *Oil Change* Jiffy Lube has franchises in two different parts of a city. The number of oil changes made daily, for 25 days, is given below.

East Store					West Store				
33	59	27	30	42	38	46	38	38	30
19	42	25	22	32	38	38	37	39	31
43	27	57	37	52	39	36	40	37	47
40	67	38	44	43	30	34	42	45	29
15	31	49	41	35	31	46	28	45	48

a) Construct a frequency distribution for each store with a first class of 15–20.

b) Draw a histogram for each store.

c) Using the histogram, determine which store appears to have a greater mean, or do the means appear about the same? Explain.

d) Using the histogram, determine which store appears to have the greater standard deviation. Explain.

e) Calculate the mean for each store and determine whether your answer in part (c) was correct.

f) Calculate the standard deviation for each store and determine whether your answer in part (d) was correct.

Recreational Mathematics

32. Calculate the range and standard deviation of your exam grades in this mathematics course. Round the mean to the nearest tenth to calculate the standard deviation.

33. Construct a set of five pieces of data with a mean, median, mode, and midrange of 6 and a standard deviation of 0.

Internet/Research Activity

34. Use a calculator with statistical function keys to find the mean and standard deviation of the salaries of the 10 Major League Baseball players and the 10 National Football League players in Exercise 30.

▲ *Some sets of data, such as exam grades, may form a bell-shaped distribution.*

Suppose your mathematics teacher states that exam scores for the previous exam followed a bell-shaped distribution and that your score was 1.5 standard deviations above the mean. How does your exam grade compare with the exam grades of your classmates? What percentage of students in your class had exam grades below your exam grade? In this section, we will discuss sets of data that form bell-shaped distributions and learn how to determine the percentage of data that fall below a particular piece of data in the set of data.

Why *This is Important* There are many real-life applications, such as IQ scores, heights and weights of males, heights and weights of females, and wearout mileage of automobile tires, that have a bell-shaped distribution.

When examining data using a histogram, we can refer to the overall appearance of the histogram as the *shape* of the distribution of the data. Certain shapes of distributions of data are more common than others. In this section, we will illustrate and discuss a few of the more common ones. In each case, the vertical scale is the frequency and the horizontal scale is the observed values.

In a *rectangular distribution* (Fig. 13.17), all the observed values occur with the same frequency. If a die is rolled many times, we would expect the numbers 1–6 to occur with about the same frequency. The distribution representing the outcomes of the die is rectangular.

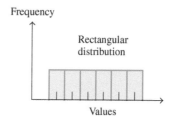

Figure 13.17

In *J-shaped distributions*, the frequency is either constantly increasing (Fig. 13.18(a)) or constantly decreasing (Fig. 13.18(b)). The number of hours studied per week by students may have a distribution like that in Fig. 13.18(b). The bars might represent (from left to right) 0–5 hours, 6–10 hours, 11–15 hours, and so on.

J-shaped Distributions

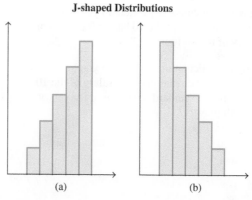

Figure 13.18

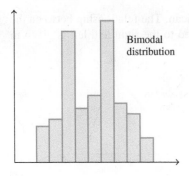

Figure 13.19

A *bimodal distribution* (Fig. 13.19) is one in which two nonadjacent values occur more frequently than any other values in a set of data. For example, if an equal number of men and women were weighed, the distribution of their weights would probably be bimodal, with one mode for the women's weights and the second for the men's weights. For a distribution to be considered bimodal, both modes need not have the same frequency but they must both have a frequency greater than the frequency of each of the other values in the distribution.

The life expectancy of lightbulbs has a bimodal distribution: a small peak very near 0 hours of life, resulting from the bulbs that burned out very quickly because of a manufacturing defect, and a much higher peak representing the nondefective bulbs. A bimodal frequency distribution generally means that you are dealing with two distinct populations, in this case, defective and nondefective lightbulbs.

Another distribution, called a *skewed distribution*, has more of a "tail" on one side than the other. A skewed distribution with a tail on the right (Fig. 13.20(a)) is said to be skewed to the right. If the tail is on the left (Fig. 13.20(b)), the distribution is referred to as skewed to the left.

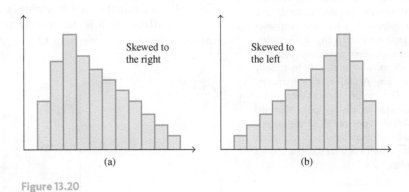

Figure 13.20

The number of children per family might be a distribution skewed to the right. Some families have no children, more families may have one child, the greatest percentage may have two children, fewer may have three children, still fewer may have four children, and so on.

Since few families have high incomes, distributions of family incomes might be skewed to the right.

Smoothing the histograms of the skewed distributions shown in Fig. 13.20 to form curves gives the curves illustrated in Fig. 13.21.

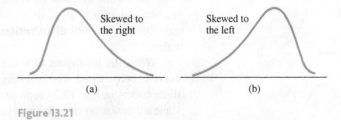

Figure 13.21

In Fig. 13.21(a), the greatest frequency appears on the left side of the curve and the frequency decreases from left to right. Since the mode is the value with the greatest frequency, the mode would appear on the left side of the curve.

Every value in the set of data is considered in determining the mean. The values on the far right side of the curve in Fig. 13.21(a) would tend to increase the value of the mean. Thus, the value of the mean would be farther to the right than the mode.

Did You Know?

What Conclusions Can You Draw?

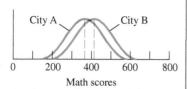

Based on the figure, which shows the distribution of scores on the mathematics part of the SAT test for two different cities, can we say that any given person selected at random from city B has outperformed any given person selected at random from city A? Both distributions appear normal, and the mean of city A is slightly smaller than the mean of city B. Consider, however, two randomly selected students who took this test: Sally from city A and Kendra from city B. The graph shows that many students in city A outperformed students from city B, so we cannot conclude that Sally scored higher than Kendra or that Kendra scored higher than Sally.

The median would be between the mode and the mean. The relationship between the mean, median, and mode for curves that are skewed to the right and left is given in Fig. 13.22.

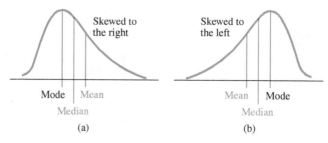

Figure 13.22

Normal Distributions

Each of these distributions is useful in describing sets of data. However, the most important distribution is the *normal* or *Gaussian distribution*, named for German mathematician Carl Friedrich Gauss. The histogram of a normal distribution is illustrated in Fig. 13.23.

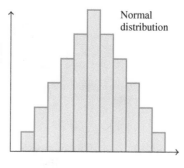

Figure 13.23

The normal distribution is important because many sets of data are normally distributed or closely resemble a normal distribution. Such distributions include intelligence quotients, heights and weights of males, heights and weights of females, lengths of full-grown boa constrictors, weights of watermelons, wearout mileage of automobile brakes, and life spans of refrigerators, to name just a few.

The normal distribution is symmetric about the mean. If you were to fold the histogram of a normal distribution down the middle, the left side would fit the right side exactly. **In a normal distribution, the mean, median, and mode all have the same value.**

When the histogram of a normal distribution is smoothed to form a curve, the curve is bell-shaped. The bell may be high and narrow or short and wide. Each of the three curves in Fig. 13.24 represents a normal curve. Curve 13.24(a) has the smallest standard deviation (spread from the mean); curve 13.24(c) has the largest.

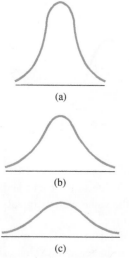

Figure 13.24

Properties of a Normal Distribution
- The graph of a normal distribution is called a normal curve.
- The normal curve is bell-shaped and symmetric about the mean.
- The mean, median, and mode of a normal distribution all have the same value and all occur at the center of the distribution.

Profile In Mathematics

David Blackwell (1919–2010)

David H. Blackwell, (1919–2010), professor of statistics, was the author of more than 90 publications on statistics, probability, game theory, set theory, dynamic programming, and information theory. Blackwell, past president of the American Statistical Society, was the first African-American elected to the National Academy of Sciences. When he received his Ph.D. in mathematics from the University of Illinois in 1941, he was only the sixth African-American to receive a doctorate in mathematics in the United States.

Blackwell taught both at the Institute for Advanced Study at Princeton University and at Howard University.

In 1954, he joined the Department of Statistics at the University of California, Berkeley. Blackwell, who taught a wide variety of mathematics courses, said, "Basically, I'm not interested in doing research and I never have been. I'm interested in understanding, which is quite a different thing."

Since the curve representing the normal distribution is symmetric, 50% of the data always falls above (to the right of) the mean and 50% of the data falls below (to the left of) the mean. In addition, every normal distribution has approximately 68% of the data between the value that is one standard deviation below the mean, and the value that is one standard deviation above the mean, see Fig. 13.25. Approximately 95% of the data falls between the value that is two standard deviations below the mean and the value that is two standard deviations above the mean. Approximately 99.7% of the data falls between the value that is three standard deviations below the mean, and the value that is three standard deviations above the mean. These three percentages, 68%, 95%, and 99.7%, are used in what is referred to as the *empirical rule.*

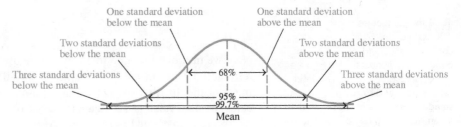

Figure 13.25

Thus, if a normal distribution has a mean of 100 and a standard deviation of 10, then approximately 68% of all the data falls between $100 - 10$ and $100 + 10$, or between 90 and 110. Approximately 95% of the data falls between $100 - 20$ and $100 + 20$, or between 80 and 120, and approximately 99.7% of the data falls between $100 - 30$, and $100 + 30$, or between 70 and 130.

The empirical rule is summarized as follows.

Empirical Rule

In any normal distribution.

- Approximately 68% of all the data lies within one standard deviation of the mean (in both directions).
- Approximately 95% of all the data lies within two standard deviations of the mean (in both directions).
- Approximately 99.7% of all the data lies within three standard deviations of the mean (in both directions).

Example 1 *Applying the Empirical Rule*

The cholesterol levels for females are normally distributed. In a random sample of 500 females, determine the approximate number of females in the sample who are expected to have a cholesterol level

a) within one standard deviation of the mean.

b) within two standard deviations of the mean.

Solution

a) By the empirical rule, about 68% of females have a cholesterol level within one standard deviation of the mean. Since there are 500 females in the sample, the number of females expected to have a cholesterol level within one standard deviation of the mean is

$$68\% \times 500 = 0.68 \times 500 = 340$$

MATHEMATICS TODAY

Six Sigma

Many companies use a process called Six Sigma, a quality-control strategy, to help the company improve quality and reduce errors. Six Sigma refers to an interval in a normal distribution from six standard deviations below the mean to six standard deviations above the mean. As 99.9997% of a normal distribution is within six standard deviations of the mean, Six Sigma means the company's goal is to produce error-free products 99.9997% of the time. Companies such as General Electric (GE), Whirlpool, and Motorola have all reported success after implementing Six Sigma. GE estimates that by using Six Sigma, it was able to save approximately $30 billion during the first 6 years of implementation. Thousands of companies worldwide now use Six Sigma.

Why *This is Important* Many companies use statistics to improve quality control and reduce costs.

Therefore, about 340 females are expected to have a cholesterol level within one standard deviation of the mean.

b) By the empirical rule, about 95% of females have a cholesterol level within two standard deviations the mean. Since there are 500 females in the sample, the number of females expected to have a cholesterol level within two standard deviations of the mean is

$$95\% \times 500 = 0.95 \times 500 = 475$$

Therefore, about 475 females are expected to have a cholesterol level within two standard deviations of the mean. ∎

z-Scores

Now we turn our attention to z-scores. We use *z-scores* (or *standard scores*) to determine how far, in terms of standard deviations, a given data value is from the mean of the distribution. For example, a data value that has a z-score of 1.5 indicates the data value is 1.5 standard deviations above the mean. The standard score or z-score is calculated as follows.

> ### z-Scores or Standard Scores
> The formula for finding **z-scores** or standard scores is
> $$z = \frac{\text{value of the piece of data} - \text{mean}}{\text{standard deviation}}$$

In this book, the notation z_x represents the z-score, or standard score, of the value x. For example, if a normal distribution has a mean of 86 with a standard deviation of 12, a score of 110 has a standard score or z-score of

$$z_{110} = \frac{110 - 86}{12} = \frac{24}{12} = 2$$

Therefore, a value of 110 in this distribution has a z-score of 2 and is two standard deviations above the mean.

Data below the mean will always have negative z-scores; data above the mean will always have positive z-scores. The mean will always have a z-score of 0.

Example 2   *Finding z-Scores*

A normal distribution has a mean of 80 and a standard deviation of 10. Determine z-scores for the following values.

a) 90   b) 95   c) 80   d) 64

Solution

a)
$$z = \frac{\text{value} - \text{mean}}{\text{standard deviation}}$$

$$z_{90} = \frac{90 - 80}{10} = \frac{10}{10} = 1$$

A value of 90 has a z-score of 1. Therefore, a value of 90 is one standard deviation above the mean.

b)
$$z_{95} = \frac{95 - 80}{10} = \frac{15}{10} = 1.5$$

A value of 95 has a z-score of 1.5, and is 1.5 standard deviations above the mean.

c)
$$z_{80} = \frac{80 - 80}{10} = \frac{0}{10} = 0$$

The mean always has a z-score of 0.

d)
$$z_{64} = \frac{64 - 80}{10} = \frac{-16}{10} = -1.6$$

A value of 64 has a z-score of -1.6, and is 1.6 standard deviations below the mean. ∎

If we are given any normal distribution with a known mean and standard deviation, it is possible through the use of Table 13.7 on pages 822 and 823 (the z-table) to determine the percent of data between any two given values. The total area under any normal curve is 1.00. Table 13.7 will be used to determine the cumulative area under the normal curve that lies to the *left of a specified z-score*. We will use Table 13.7(a) when we wish to determine area to the left of a *negative z-score*, and we will use Table 13.7(b) when we wish to determine area to the left of a *positive z-score*.

Example 3 illustrates the procedure to follow when using Table 13.7 to determine the area under the normal curve. When you are determining the area under the normal curve, it is often helpful to draw a picture and shade the area to be determined.

Example 3 *Determining the Area Under the Normal Curve*

Determine the area under the normal curve
a) to the left of $z = -1.00$.
b) to the left of $z = 1.19$.
c) to the right of $z = 1.19$.
d) between $z = -1.62$ and $z = 2.57$.

Solution

a) To determine the area under the normal curve to the left of $z = -1.00$, as illustrated in Fig. 13.26, we use Table 13.7(a) since we are looking for an area to the left of a negative z-score. In the upper-left corner of the table, we see the letter z. The column under z gives the units and the tenths value for z. To locate the hundredths value of z, we use the column headings to the right of z. In this case, the hundredths value of $z = -1.00$ is 0, so we use the first column labeled .00. To determine the area to the left of $z = -1.00$, we use the row labeled -1.0 and move to the column labeled .00. The table entry, .1587, is circled in blue. Therefore, the total area to the left of $z = -1.00$ is 0.1587

b) To determine the area under the normal curve to the left of $z = 1.19$ (Fig. 13.27), we use Table 13.7(b) since we are looking for an area to the left of a positive z-score. We first look for 1.1 in the column under z. Since the hundredths value

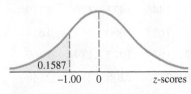

0.1587

−1.00 0   z-scores

Figure 13.26

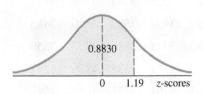

0.8830

0   1.19   z-scores

Figure 13.27

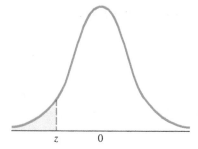

Table entry for z is the area to the left of z.

Table 13.7 Areas of a Standard Normal Distribution

(a) Table of Areas to the Left of z When z is Negative

z	.00	.01	.02	.03	.04	.05	.06	.07	.08	.09
−3.4	.0003	.0003	.0003	.0003	.0003	.0003	.0003	.0003	.0003	.0002
−3.3	.0005	.0005	.0005	.0004	.0004	.0004	.0004	.0004	.0004	.0003
−3.2	.0007	.0007	.0006	.0006	.0006	.0006	.0006	.0005	.0005	.0005
−3.1	.0010	.0009	.0009	.0009	.0008	.0008	.0008	.0008	.0007	.0007
−3.0	.0013	.0013	.0013	.0012	.0012	.0011	.0011	.0011	.0010	.0010
−2.9	.0019	.0018	.0018	.0017	.0016	.0016	.0015	.0015	.0014	.0014
−2.8	.0026	.0025	.0024	.0023	.0023	.0022	.0021	.0021	.0020	.0019
−2.7	.0035	.0034	.0033	.0032	.0031	.0030	.0029	.0028	.0027	.0026
−2.6	.0047	.0045	.0044	.0043	.0041	.0040	.0039	.0038	.0037	.0036
−2.5	.0062	.0060	.0059	.0057	.0055	.0054	.0052	.0051	.0049	.0048
−2.4	.0082	.0080	.0078	.0075	.0073	.0071	.0069	.0068	.0066	.0064
−2.3	.0107	.0104	.0102	.0099	.0096	.0094	.0091	.0089	.0087	.0084
−2.2	.0139	.0136	.0132	.0129	.0125	.0122	.0119	.0116	.0113	.0110
−2.1	.0179	.0174	.0170	.0166	.0162	.0158	.0154	.0150	.0146	.0143
−2.0	.0228	.0222	.0217	.0212	.0207	.0202	.0197	.0192	.0188	.0183
−1.9	.0287	.0281	.0274	.0268	.0262	.0256	.0250	.0244	.0239	.0233
−1.8	.0359	.0351	.0344	.0336	.0329	.0322	.0314	.0307	.0301	.0294
−1.7	.0446	.0436	.0427	.0418	.0409	.0401	.0392	.0384	.0375	.0367
−1.6	.0548	.0537	.0526	.0516	.0505	.0495	.0485	.0475	.0465	.0455
−1.5	.0668	.0655	.0643	.0630	.0618	.0606	.0594	.0582	.0571	.0559
−1.4	.0808	.0793	.0778	.0764	.0749	.0735	.0721	.0708	.0694	.0681
−1.3	.0968	.0951	.0934	.0918	.0901	.0885	.0869	.0853	.0838	.0823
−1.2	.1151	.1131	.1112	.1093	.1075	.1056	.1038	.1020	.1003	.0985
−1.1	.1357	.1335	.1314	.1292	.1271	.1251	.1230	.1210	.1190	.1170
−1.0	.1587	.1562	.1539	.1515	.1492	.1469	.1446	.1423	.1401	.1379
−0.9	.1841	.1814	.1788	.1762	.1736	.1711	.1685	.1660	.1635	.1611
−0.8	.2119	.2090	.2061	.2033	.2005	.1977	.1949	.1922	.1894	.1867
−0.7	.2420	.2389	.2358	.2327	.2296	.2266	.2236	.2206	.2177	.2148
−0.6	.2743	.2709	.2676	.2643	.2611	.2578	.2546	.2514	.2483	.2451
−0.5	.3085	.3050	.3015	.2981	.2947	.2912	.2877	.2843	.2810	.2776
−0.4	.3446	.3409	.3372	.3336	.3300	.3264	.3228	.3192	.3156	.3121
−0.3	.3821	.3783	.3745	.3707	.3669	.3632	.3594	.3557	.3520	.3483
−0.2	.4207	.4168	.4129	.4090	.4052	.4013	.3974	.3936	.3897	.3859
−0.1	.4602	.4562	.4522	.4483	.4443	.4404	.4364	.4325	.4286	.4247
−0.0	.5000	.4960	.4920	.4880	.4840	.4801	.4761	.4721	.4681	.4641

For z-scores less than −3.49, use 0.000 to approximate the area.

Table 13.7 Areas of a Standard Normal Distribution (*continued*)

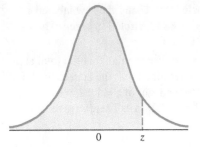

Table entry for *z* is the area to the left of *z*.

(b) Table of Areas to the Left of *z* When *z* is Positive

z	.00	.01	.02	.03	.04	.05	.06	.07	.08	.09
0.0	.5000	.5040	.5080	.5120	.5160	.5199	.5239	.5279	.5319	.5359
0.1	.5398	.5438	.5478	.5517	.5557	.5596	.5636	.5675	.5714	.5753
0.2	.5793	.5832	.5871	.5910	.5948	.5987	.6026	.6064	.6103	.6141
0.3	.6179	.6217	.6255	.6293	.6331	.6368	.6406	.6443	.6480	.6517
0.4	.6554	.6591	.6628	.6664	.6700	.6736	.6772	.6808	.6844	.6879
0.5	.6915	.6950	.6985	.7019	.7054	.7088	.7123	.7157	.7190	.7224
0.6	.7257	.7291	.7324	.7357	.7389	.7422	.7454	.7486	.7517	.7549
0.7	.7580	.7611	.7642	.7673	.7704	.7734	.7764	.7794	.7823	.7852
0.8	.7881	.7910	.7939	.7967	.7995	.8023	.8051	.8078	.8106	.8133
0.9	.8159	.8186	.8212	.8238	.8264	.8289	.8315	.8340	.8365	.8389
1.0	.8413	.8438	.8461	.8485	.8508	.8531	.8554	.8577	.8599	.8621
1.1	.8643	.8665	.8686	.8708	.8729	.8749	.8770	.8790	.8810	.8830
1.2	.8849	.8869	.8888	.8907	.8925	.8944	.8962	.8980	.8997	.9015
1.3	.9032	.9049	.9066	.9082	.9099	.9115	.9131	.9147	.9162	.9177
1.4	.9192	.9207	.9222	.9236	.9251	.9265	.9279	.9292	.9306	.9319
1.5	.9332	.9345	.9357	.9370	.9382	.9394	.9406	.9418	.9429	.9441
1.6	.9452	.9463	.9474	.9484	.9495	.9505	.9515	.9525	.9535	.9545
1.7	.9554	.9564	.9573	.9582	.9591	.9599	.9608	.9616	.9625	.9633
1.8	.9641	.9649	.9656	.9664	.9671	.9678	.9686	.9693	.9699	.9706
1.9	.9713	.9719	.9726	.9732	.9738	.9744	.9750	.9756	.9761	.9767
2.0	.9772	.9778	.9783	.9788	.9793	.9798	.9803	.9808	.9812	.9817
2.1	.9821	.9826	.9830	.9834	.9838	.9842	.9846	.9850	.9854	.9857
2.2	.9861	.9864	.9868	.9871	.9875	.9878	.9881	.9884	.9887	.9890
2.3	.9893	.9896	.9898	.9901	.9904	.9906	.9909	.9911	.9913	.9916
2.4	.9918	.9920	.9922	.9925	.9927	.9929	.9931	.9932	.9934	.9936
2.5	.9938	.9940	.9941	.9943	.9945	.9946	.9948	.9949	.9951	.9952
2.6	.9953	.9955	.9956	.9957	.9959	.9960	.9961	.9962	.9963	.9964
2.7	.9965	.9966	.9967	.9968	.9969	.9970	.9971	.9972	.9973	.9974
2.8	.9974	.9975	.9976	.9977	.9977	.9978	.9979	.9979	.9980	.9981
2.9	.9981	.9982	.9982	.9983	.9984	.9984	.9985	.9985	.9986	.9986
3.0	.9987	.9987	.9987	.9988	.9988	.9989	.9989	.9989	.9990	.9990
3.1	.9990	.9991	.9991	.9991	.9992	.9992	.9992	.9992	.9993	.9993
3.2	.9993	.9993	.9994	.9994	.9994	.9994	.9994	.9995	.9995	.9995
3.3	.9995	.9995	.9995	.9996	.9996	.9996	.9996	.9996	.9996	.9997
3.4	.9997	.9997	.9997	.9997	.9997	.9997	.9997	.9997	.9997	.9998

For *z*-scores greater than 3.49, use 1.000 to approximate the area.

of $z = 1.19$ is 9, we move to the column labeled .09. Using the row labeled 1.1 and the column labeled 0.09, the table entry is .8830, circled in green. Therefore, the total area to the left of $z = 1.19$ is 0.8830.

c) To determine the area to the right of $z = 1.19$, we use the fact that the total area under the normal curve is 1. In part (b), we determined that the area to the left of $z = 1.19$ was 0.8830. To determine the area to the right of $z = 1.19$, we can subtract the area to the left of $z = 1.19$ from 1 (Fig. 13.28(a)). Therefore, the area to the right of $z = 1.19$ is $1 - 0.8830$, or 0.1170.

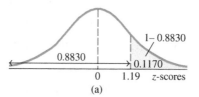 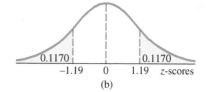

Figure 13.28

Another way to determine the area to the right of $z = 1.19$ is to use the fact that the normal curve is symmetric about the mean. Thus, the area to the left of a negative z-score is equal to the area to the right of a positive z-score. Therefore, the area to the left of $z = -1.19$ is equal to the area to the right of $z = 1.19$ (Fig. 13.28(b)). Using Table 13.7(a), we see that the area to the left of $z = -1.19$ is .1170. This value is circled in red in the table. Therefore, the area to the right of $z = 1.19$ is also .1170. This answer agrees with our answer obtained by subtracting the area to the left of $z = 1.19$ from 1.

d) To determine the area between two z-scores, we subtract the smaller area from the larger area (Fig. 13.29). Using Table 13.7(b), we see that the area to the left of $z = 2.57$ is .9949 (Fig. 13.29(a)). Using Table 13.7(a), we see that the area to the left of $z = -1.62$ is .0526 (Fig. 13.29(b)). Thus, the area between $z = -1.62$ and $z = 2.57$ is $0.9949 - 0.0526$, or 0.9423 (Fig. 13.29(c)).

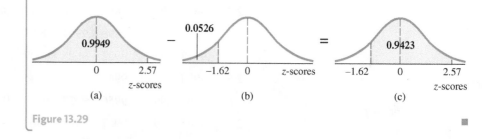

Figure 13.29

To change the area under the normal curve to a percent, multiply the area by 100%. In Example 3(a), we determined the area to the left of $z = -1.00$ to be 0.1587. To change this area to a percent, multiply 0.1587 by 100%.

$$0.1587 = 0.1587 \times 100\% = 15.87\%$$

Therefore 15.87% of the normal curve is less than a score that is one standard deviation below the mean.

Below, we summarize the procedure to determine the percent of data for any interval under the normal curve.

PROCEDURE   **TO DETERMINE THE PERCENT OF DATA BETWEEN ANY TWO VALUES IN A NORMAL DISTRIBUTION**

1. Draw a diagram of the normal curve, indicating the area or percent to be determined.

2. Use the formula $z = \dfrac{\text{value of the piece of data } - \text{ mean}}{\text{standard deviation}}$ to convert the given values to z-scores. Indicate these z-scores on the diagram.

3. Look up the areas that correspond to the specified z-scores in Table 13.7.
   a) When determining the area to the left of a negative z-score, use Table 13.7(a).

   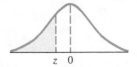

   b) When determining the area to the left of a positive z-score, use Table 13.7(b).

   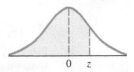

   c) When determining the area to the right of a z-score, subtract the percent of data to the left of the specified z-score from 100%.

   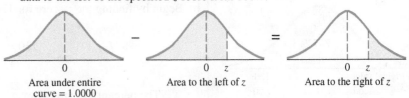

   Area under entire   Area to the left of z Area to the right of z
   curve = 1.0000

   Or, use the symmetry of a normal distribution.

   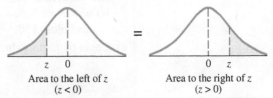

   Area to the left of z Area to the right of z
   $(z < 0)$ $(z > 0)$

   d) When determining the area between two z-scores, subtract the smaller area from the larger area.

   In the figure below, we let z_1 represent the smaller z-score and z_2 represent the larger z-score.

   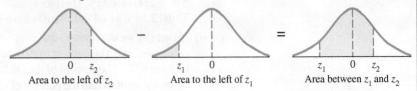

   Area to the left of z_2 Area to the left of z_1 Area between z_1 and z_2

4. Change the areas you determined in Step 3 to percents as explained on page 824.

Example 4 *IQ Scores*

Intelligence quotients (IQ scores) are normally distributed with a mean of 100 and a standard deviation of 15. Determine the percent of individuals with IQ scores

a) below 115.

b) below 130.

c) below 70.

d) between 70 and 115.

e) between 115 and 130.

f) above 122.5.

Solution

a) We want to determine the area under the normal curve below the value of 115, as illustrated in Fig. 13.30(a). Converting 115 to a z-score yields a z-score of 1.00.

$$z_{115} = \frac{115 - 100}{15} = \frac{15}{15} = 1.00$$

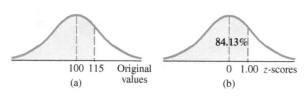

(a)   (b)

Figure 13.30

The percent of individuals with IQ scores below 115 is the same as the percent of data below a z-score of 1.00 (Fig. 13.30(b)). Since our z-score is positive, we use Table 13.7(b). From Table 13.7(b), we determine that the area to the left of a z-score of 1.00 is .8413. Therefore, 84.13% of all the IQ scores are below a z-score of 1.00. Thus, 84.13% of individuals have IQ scores below 115.

b) Begin by finding the z-score for 130.

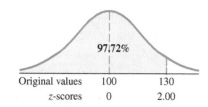

Figure 13.31

$$z_{130} = \frac{130 - 100}{15} = \frac{30}{15} = 2.00$$

The percent of data below a z-score of 130 is the same as the percent of data below a z-score of 2.00 (Fig. 13.31). Using Table 13.7(b), we determine that the area to the left of a z-score of 2.00 is .9772. Therefore, 97.72% of the IQ scores are below a z-score of 2.00. Thus, 97.72% of all individuals have IQ scores below 130.

c) Begin by finding the z-score for 70.

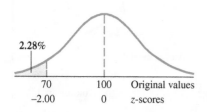

Figure 13.32

$$z_{70} = \frac{70 - 100}{15} = \frac{-30}{15} = -2.00$$

The percent of data below a score of 70 is the same as the percent of data below a z-score of −2.00 (Fig. 13.32). Since our z-score is negative, we use Table 13.7(a). Using the table, we determine that the area to the left of $z = -2.00$ is .0228. Therefore, 2.28% of the data is below a z-score of −2.00. Thus, 2.28% of all individuals have IQ scores below 70.

d) In part (a), we determined that $z_{115} = 1.00$, and in part (c), we determined that $z_{70} = -2.00$. The percent of data below a z-score of 1.00 is 84.13% (Fig. 13.33(a) on page 827). The percent of data below a z-score of −2.00 is 2.28% (Fig. 13.33(b)). Since we want to find the percent of data between two z-scores, we subtract the smaller percent from the larger percent: 84.13% − 2.28% = 81.85% (Fig. 13.33(c)). Thus, 81.85% of all individuals have IQ scores between 70 and 115.

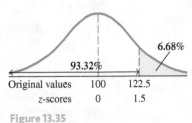

Figure 13.33

e) In part (a), we determined that $z_{115} = 1.00$, and in part (b), we determined $z_{130} = 2.00$. The percent of data below a z-score of 1.00 is 84.13%. The percent of data below a z-score of 2.00 is 97.72%. Since we want to find the percent of data between two z-scores, we subtract the smaller percent from the larger percent: 97.72% − 84.13% = 13.59% (Fig. 13.34). Thus, 13.59% of all individuals have IQ scores between 115 and 130.

f) Begin by determining a z-score for 122.5.

$$z_{122.5} = \frac{122.5 - 100}{15} = \frac{22.5}{15} = 1.50$$

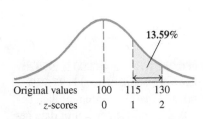

Figure 13.34

The percent of IQ scores above 122.5 is the same as the percent of data above $z = 1.50$ (Fig. 13.35). To determine the percent of data above $z = 1.50$, we can determine the percent of data below $z = 1.50$ and subtract this percent from 100%. In Table 13.7(b), we see that the area to the left of $z = 1.50$ is .9332. Therefore, 93.32% of the IQ scores are below $z = 1.50$. The percent of IQ scores above $z = 1.50$ are 100% − 93.32%, or 6.68%. Thus, 6.68% of all IQ scores are greater than 122.5.

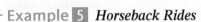

Figure 13.35

Example 5 *Horseback Rides*

Assume that the length of time for a horseback ride on the trail at Triple R Ranch is normally distributed with a mean of 3.2 hours and a standard deviation of 0.4 hour.

a) What percent of horseback rides last at least 3.2 hours?

b) What percent of horseback rides last less than 2.8 hours?

c) What percent of horseback rides are at least 3.7 hours?

d) What percent of horseback rides are between 2.8 hours and 4.0 hours?

e) In a random sample of 500 horseback rides at Triple R Ranch, how many are at least 3.7 hours?

Solution

a) In a normal distribution, half the data are always above the mean. Since 3.2 hours is the mean, half, or 50%, of the horseback rides last at least 3.2 hours.

b) Convert 2.8 hours to a z-score.

$$z_{2.8} = \frac{2.8 - 3.2}{0.4} = -1.00$$

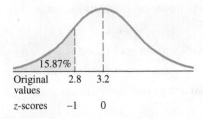

Figure 13.36

Use Table 13.7(a) to find the area of the normal curve that lies below a z-score of −1.00. The area to the left of $z = -1.00$ is 0.1587. Therefore, the percent of horseback rides that last less than 2.8 hours is 15.87% (Fig. 13.36).

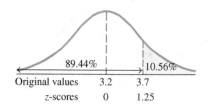

Figure 13.37

TIMELY TIP

Following is a summary of some important items presented in this section.

- The normal curve is symmetric about the mean.
- The area under the normal curve cannot be negative.
- A negative z-score indicates that the corresponding value in the original distribution is less than the mean.
- A positive z-score indicates that the corresponding value in the original distribution is greater than the mean.
- A z-score of 0 indicates that the corresponding value in the original distribution is the mean.
- Table 13.7 provides the area to the left of a specified z-score.
- When using Table 13.7 to determine the area to the left of a specified z-score, locate the units value and tenths value of your specified z-score under the column labeled z. Then move to the column containing the hundredths value of your specified z-score to obtain the area.

c) At least 3.7 hours means greater than or equal to 3.7 hours. Therefore, we are seeking to find the percent of data to the right of 3.7 hours. Convert 3.7 hours to a z-score.

$$z_{3.7} = \frac{3.7 - 3.2}{0.4} = 1.25$$

From Table 13.7(b), we determine that the area to the left of $z = 1.25$ is .8944. Therefore, 89.44% of the data are below $z = 1.25$. The percent of data above $z = 1.25$ (or to the right of $z = 1.25$) is $100\% - 89.44\%$, or 10.56% (Fig. 13.37). Thus, 10.56% of horseback rides last at least 3.7 hours.

d) Convert 4.0 to a z-score.

$$z_{4.0} = \frac{4.0 - 3.2}{0.4} = 2.00$$

From Table 13.7(b), we determine that the area to the left of $z = 2.00$ is .9772 (Fig.13.38(a)). Therefore the percent of data below a z-score of 2.00 is 97.72%. From part (b), we determined that $z_{28} = -1.00$ and that the percent of data below a z-score of -1.00 is 15.87% (Fig. 13.38(b)). To find the percent of data between a z-score of -1.00 and a z-score of 2.00, we subtract the smaller percent from the larger percent. Thus, the percent of horseback rides that last between 2.8 hours and 4.0 hours is $97.72\% - 15.87\%$, or 81.85% (Fig. 13.38(c)).

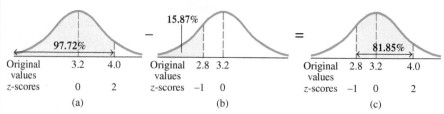

Figure 13.38

e) In part (c), we determined that 10.56% of all horseback rides last at least 3.7 hours. We now multiply 0.1056 times the number in the random sample, 500, to determine the number of horseback rides that last at least 3.7 hours. There are $0.1056 \times 500 = 52.8$, or approximately 53, horseback rides that last at least 3.7 hours. ∎

SECTION 13.6   *Exercises*

Warm Up Exercises

In Exercises 1–12, fill in the blank with an appropriate word, phrase, or symbol(s).

1. A distribution in which all the values have the same frequency is called a(n) _____ distribution.

2. A distribution in which the frequency is either constantly increasing or constantly decreasing is called a(n) _____ distribution.

3. A distribution that has a "tail" on its right is skewed to the _____.

4. A distribution that has a "tail" on its left is skewed to the _____.

5. A distribution in which two nonadjacent values occur more frequently than any other values in a set of data is called a(n) _____ distribution.

6. A normal distribution is a(n) _____ shaped distribution.

7. A measure of how far, in terms of standard deviations, a given data value is from the mean is called a z-score or a(n) _____ score.

8. The mean of a set of data will always have a z-score of _____.

9. A piece of data that has a negative z-score is _____ the mean.

10. A piece of data that has a positive *z*-score is _____ the mean.

11. According to the empirical rule, in a normal distribution,

  a) approximately _____ % of the data lie within plus or minus 1 standard deviation of the mean,

  b) approximately _____ % of the data lie within plus or minus 2 standard deviations of the mean, and

  c) approximately _____ % of the data lie within plus or minus 3 standard deviations of the mean.

12. In a normal distribution, the mean, median, and mode all have the same _____ .

In Exercises 13–16, give an example of the type of distribution.

13. Rectangular   **14.** Skewed

15. J-shaped   **16.** Bimodal

For the distributions in Exercises 17–20, state whether you think the distribution would be normal, J-shaped, bimodal, rectangular, skewed left, or skewed right.

17. The wearout mileage of automobile tires

18. The numbers resulting from tossing a die many times

19. The number of people per household in the United States

20. The heights of a sample of high school seniors, where there are an equal number of males and females

Practice the Skills

In Exercises 21–32, use Table 13.7 on pages 822 and 823 to find the specified area.

21. Above the mean   **22.** Below the mean

23. Between two standard deviations below the mean and one standard deviation above the mean

24. Between 1.10 and 1.60 standard deviations above the mean

25. To the right of $z = 1.53$ **26.** To the left of $z = 1.62$

27. To the left of $z = -1.78$ **28.** To the right of $z = -1.78$

29. Between $z = -1.32$ and $z = -1.64$

30. To the left of $z = 1.84$

31. To the left of $z = -2.13$

32. To the left of $z = -0.92$

In Exercises 33–42, use Table 13.7 on pages 822 and 823 to determine the percent of data specified.

33. Less than $z = 0.71$ **34.** Less than $z = -0.82$

35. Between $z = -1.34$ and $z = 2.24$

36. Between $z = -2.18$ and $z = -1.90$

37. Greater than $z = -1.90$

38. Greater than $z = 2.66$

39. Less than $z = 1.96$

40. Between $z = -1.53$ and $z = -1.82$

41. Between $z = 0.72$ and $z = 2.14$

42. Between $z = -2.15$ and $z = 3.31$

Problem Solving

Heights of Girls *In Exercises 43 and 44, assume that the heights of 7-year-old girls are normally distributed. The heights of 8 girls are given in z-scores below.*

Emily	0.9	Jenny	0.0	Heather	−1.3	Shenice	0.0
Sarah	1.7	Sadaf	−0.2	Carol	0.8	Kim	−1.2

43. a) Which of these girls are taller than the mean?

  b) Which of these girls are at the mean?

  c) Which of these girls are shorter than the mean?

44. a) Which girl is the tallest?

  b) Which girl is the shortest?

Police Officer's Salaries In Exercises 45–48, assume the annual salaries of police officers are normally distributed with a mean of $50,000 and a standard deviation of $7000.

45. Determine the percent of police officers with an annual salary of at least $50,000.

46. Determine the percent of police officers with an annual salary between $43,000 and $64,000.

47. Determine the percent of police officers with an annual salary of at least $58,750.

48. In a random sample of 500 police officers, how many have an annual salary of at least $58,750.

SAT Scores In Exercises 49–54, assume that the mathematics scores on the SAT are normally distributed with a mean of 500 and a standard deviation of 100.

49. What percent of students who took the test have a mathematics score below 550?

50. What percent of students who took the test have a mathematics score above 650?

51. What percent of students who took the test have a mathematics score between 550 and 650?

52. What percent of students who took the test have a mathematics score below 300?

53. What percent of students who took the test have a mathematics score between 400 and 525?

54. What percent of students who took the test have a mathematics score above 380?

Vending Machine In Exercises 55–58, a vending machine is designed to dispense a mean of 7.6 oz of coffee into an 8-oz cup. If the standard deviation of the amount of coffee dispensed is 0.4 oz and the amount is normally distributed, find the percent of times the machine will

55. dispense from 7.4 oz to 7.7 oz.

56. dispense less than 7.0 oz.

57. dispense less than 7.7 oz.

58. result in the cup overflowing (therefore dispense more than 8 oz).

▲ *See Exercises 55–58*

Automobile Speed In Exercises 59–64, assume that the speed of automobiles on an expressway during rush hour is normally distributed with a mean of 62 mph and a standard deviation of 5 mph.

59. What percent of cars are traveling faster than 62 mph?

60. What percent of cars are traveling between 58 mph and 66 mph?

61. What percent of cars are traveling slower than 56 mph?

62. What percent of cars are traveling faster than 70 mph?

63. If 200 cars are selected at random, how many will be traveling slower than 56 mph?

64. If 200 cars are selected at random, how many will be traveling faster than 70 mph?

Corn Flakes In Exercises 65–68, assume that the amount of corn flakes in a box is normally distributed with a mean of 16 oz and a standard deviation of 0.1 oz.

65. Determine the percent of boxes that will contain between 15.83 oz and 16.32 oz of corn flakes.

66. Determine the percent of boxes that will contain more than 16.16 oz of corn flakes.

67. If the manufacturer produces 300,000 boxes, how many of them will contain less than 15.83 oz of corn flakes?

68. If the manufacturer produces 300,000 boxes, how many of them will contain more than 16.16 oz of corn flakes?

Cost of Day Care In Exercises 69–74, assume the annual day care cost per child is normally distributed with a mean of $8000 and a standard deviation of $1500.

69. What percent of day care costs are more than $7250 annually?

70. What percent of day care costs are between $6500 and $8750 annually?

71. What percent of day care costs are more than $11,750 annually?

72. What percent of day care costs are less than $11,750 annually?

73. In a random sample of 120 families, how many pay more than $7250 annually for day care per child?

74. In a random sample of 120 families, how many pay between $6500 and $8750 annually for day care per child?

75. *Weight Loss* A weight-loss clinic guarantees that its new customers will lose at least 5 lb by the end of their first month of participation or their money will be refunded. If the weight loss of customers at the end of their first month is normally distributed, with a mean of 6.7 lb and a standard deviation of 0.81 lb, determine the percent of customers who will be able to claim a refund.

76. *Battery Warranty* The warranty on a car battery is 36 months. If the breakdown times of this battery are normally distributed with a mean of 46 months and a standard deviation of 8 months, determine the percent of batteries that can be expected to require repair or replacement under warranty.

77. *Coffee Machine* A vending machine that dispenses coffee does not appear to be working correctly. The machine rarely gives the proper amount of coffee. Some of the time the cup is underfilled, and some of the time the cup overflows. Does this variation indicate that the mean number of ounces dispensed has to be adjusted, or does it indicate that the standard deviation of the amount of coffee dispensed by the machine is too large?

78. *Grading on a Normal Curve* Mr. Sanderson marks his class on a normal curve. Those with *z*-scores above 1.8 will receive an A, those between 1.8 and 1.1 will receive a B, those between 1.1 and −1.2 will receive a C, those between −1.2 and −1.9 will receive a D, and those under −1.9 will receive an F. Determine the percent of grades that will be A, B, C, D, and F.

79. Consider the following normal curve, representing a normal distribution, with points *A*, *B*, and *C*. One of these points corresponds to the mean, one point corresponds to the mean plus one standard deviation and one point corresponds to the mean minus two standard deviations.

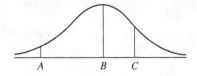

a) Which point corresponds to the mean?

b) Which point corresponds to the mean plus one standard deviation?

c) Which point corresponds to the mean minus two standard deviations?

80. Consider the following two normal curves.

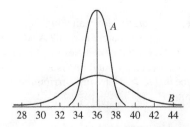

a) Do these distributions have the same mean? If so, what is the mean?

b) One of these curves corresponds to a normal distribution with a standard deviation of 1. The other curve corresponds to a normal distribution with a standard deviation of 3. Which curve, *A* or *B*, has a standard deviation of 3?

Concept/Writing Exercises

81. In a distribution that is skewed to the right, which has the greatest value: the mean, median, or mode? Which has the smallest value? Explain.

82. In a distribution skewed to the left, which has the greatest value: the mean, median, or mode? Which has the smallest value? Explain.

83. List three populations other than those given in the text that may be normally distributed.

84. List three populations other than those given in the text that may not be normally distributed.

Challenge Problems/Group Activities

85. *Salesperson Promotion* The owner at Kim's Home Interiors is reviewing the sales records of two managers who are up for promotion, Katie and Stella, who work in different stores. At Katie's store, the mean sales have been $23,200 per month, with a standard deviation of $2170. At Stella's store, the mean sales have been $25,600 per month, with a standard deviation of $2300. Last month, Katie's store

sales were $28,408 and Stella's store sales were $29,510. At both stores, the distribution of monthly sales is normal.

a) Convert last month's sales for Katie's store and for Stella's store to *z*-scores.

b) If one of the two were to be promoted based solely on the increase in sales last month, who should be promoted? Explain.

86. *Chebyshev's Theorem* How can you determine whether a distribution is approximately normal? A statistical theorem called *Chebyshev's theorem* states that the *minimum percent* of data between plus and minus *K* standard deviations from the mean $(K > 1)$ in *any distribution* can be found by the formula

$$\text{Minimum percent} = 1 - \frac{1}{K^2}$$

Thus, for example, between ± 2 standard deviations from the mean there will always be a minimum of 75% of data. This minimum percent applies to any distribution. For $K = 2$,

$$\text{Minimum percent} = 1 - \frac{1}{2^2}$$

$$= 1 - \frac{1}{4} = \frac{3}{4}, \quad \text{or} \quad 75\%$$

Likewise, between ± 3 standard deviations from the mean there will always be a minimum of 89% of the data. For $K = 3$,

$$\text{Minimum percent} = 1 - \frac{1}{3^2}$$

$$= 1 - \frac{1}{9} = \frac{8}{9}, \quad \text{or} \quad 89\%$$

The following table lists the minimum percent of data in *any distribution* and the actual percent of data in *the normal distribution* between ± 1.1, ± 1.5, ± 2.0, and ± 2.5 standard deviations from the mean. The minimum percents of data in any distribution were calculated by using Chebyshev's theorem. The actual percents of data for the normal distribution were calculated by using the area given in the standard normal, or *z*, table.

	K = 1.1	K = 1.5	K = 2	K = 2.5
Minimum (for any distribution)	17.4%	55.6%	75%	84%
Normal distribution	72.9%	86.6%	95.4%	98.8%
Given distribution				

The third row of the chart has been left blank for you to fill in the percents when you reach part (e).

Consider the following 30 pieces of data obtained from a quiz.

1, 1, 1, 1, 2, 2, 2, 2, 3, 3, 4, 4, 4, 5, 6,

6, 6, 7, 7, 7, 7, 8, 8, 8, 8, 9, 9, 9, 10, 10

a) Determine the mean of the set of scores.

b) Determine the standard deviation of the set of scores.

c) Determine the values that correspond to 1.1, 1.5, 2, and 2.5 standard deviations above the mean.
    Then determine the values that correspond to 1.1, 1.5, 2, and 2.5 standard deviations below the mean.

d) By observing the 30 pieces of data, determine the actual percent of quiz scores between

   ± 1.1 standard deviations from the mean.

   ± 1.5 standard deviations from the mean.

   ± 2 standard deviations from the mean.

   ± 2.5 standard deviations from the mean.

e) Place the percents found in part (d) in the third row of the chart.

f) Compare the percents in the third row of the chart with the minimum percents in the first row and the normal percents in the second row, and then make a judgment as to whether this set of 30 scores is approximately normally distributed.

87. *Test Scores* Obtain a set of test scores from your instructor.

a) Determine the mean, median, mode, and midrange of the test scores.

b) Determine the range and standard deviation of the set of scores. (You may round the mean to the nearest tenth when finding the standard deviation.)

c) Construct a frequency distribution of the set of scores. Select your first class so that there will be between 5 and 12 classes.

d) Construct a histogram and frequency polygon of the frequency distribution in part (c).

e) Does the histogram in part (d) appear to represent a normal distribution? Explain.

f) Use the procedure explained in Exercise 86 to determine whether the set of scores approximates a normal distribution. Explain.

88. Determine a value of *z* such that $z \geq 0$ and 47.5% of the standard normal curve lies between 0 and the *z*-value.

89. Determine a value of *z* such that $z \leq 0$ and 38.1% of the standard normal curve lies between 0 and the *z*-value.

Recreational Mathematics

90. Ask your instructor for the class mean and class standard deviation for one of the exams taken by your class. For that exam, calculate the z-score for your exam grade. How many standard deviations is your exam grade away from the mean?

91. If the mean score on a math quiz is 12.0 and 77% of the students in your class scored between 9.6 and 14.4, determine the standard deviation of the quiz scores.

Internet/Research Activity

92. In this project, you actually become the statistician.

a) Select a project of interest to you in which data must be collected.

b) Write a proposal and submit it to your instructor for approval. In the proposal, discuss the aims of your project and how you plan to gather the data to make your sample unbiased.

c) After your proposal has been approved, gather 50 pieces of data by the method you proposed.

d) Rank the data from smallest to largest.

e) Compute the mean, median, mode, and midrange.

f) Determine the range and standard deviation of the data. You may round the mean to the nearest tenth when computing the standard deviation.

g) Construct a frequency distribution, histogram, frequency polygon, and stem-and-leaf display of your data. Select your first class so that there will be between 5 and 12 classes. Be sure to label your histogram and frequency polygon.

h) Does your distribution appear to be normal? Explain your answer. Does it appear to be another type of distribution discussed? Explain.

i) Determine whether your distribution is approximately normal by using the technique discussed in Exercise 86.

CHAPTER 13   *Summary*

Important Facts and Concepts	Examples and Discussion
Section 13.1 *Sampling Techniques* Random sampling Systematic sampling Cluster sampling Stratified sampling Convenience sampling	Example 1, page 777
Section 13.2 Misuses of statistics	Discussion pages 779–781
Section 13.3 Frequency Distribution	Examples 1–2, pages 784–786
Rules for Data Grouped by Classes 1. The classes should be the same width. 2. The classes should not overlap. 3. Each piece of data should belong to only one class.	Discussion, page 784; Examples 1–3, pages 784–787
Statistical Graphs Histogram Frequency polygon Stem-and-leaf display Circle graph	Examples 4, 6, 7, pages 787–789 Examples 5–6, pages 788–789 Examples 8, pages 790–791 Examples 9, pages 791–792
Section 13.4 *Measures of Central Tendency* The **mean** is the sum of the data divided by the number of pieces of data: $\bar{x} = \dfrac{\Sigma x}{n}$.	Example 1, page 797
The **median** is the value in the middle of a set of ranked data.	Examples 2–3, 6, pages 798–799
The **mode** is the piece of data that occurs most frequently (if there is one).	Examples 4, 6, pages 798–799
The **midrange** is the value halfway between the lowest and highest values: midrange $= \dfrac{L + H}{2}$.	Examples 5, 6, page 799
Percentiles and **Quartiles** are measures of position.	Examples 7–8, pages 800–801

Section 13.5
Measures of Dispersion

The **range** is the difference between the highest value and lowest value in a set of data.

The **standard deviation,** s, is a measure of the spread of a set of data about the mean: $s = \sqrt{\dfrac{\Sigma(x - \bar{x})^2}{n - 1}}$.

Discussion pages 808–812;
Example 1, page 808

Examples 2–3, pages 809–811

Section 13.6
z–SCORES

$$z = \dfrac{\text{value of the piece of data} - \text{mean}}{\text{standard deviation}}$$

Discussion pages 820–828;
Examples 2–5, pages 820–828

Section 13.7
Linear Correlation And Regression

Linear correlation coefficient, r, is

$$r = \dfrac{n(\Sigma xy) - (\Sigma x)(\Sigma y)}{\sqrt{n(\Sigma x^2) - (\Sigma x)^2}\ \sqrt{n(\Sigma y^2) - (\Sigma y)^2}}$$

Discussion pages 833–835;
Examples 1–2, pages 835–838

Equation of the Line of the Best Fit

$y = mx + b$, where

$$m = \dfrac{n(\Sigma xy) - (\Sigma x)(\Sigma y)}{n(\Sigma x^2) - (\Sigma x)^2}$$

$$b = \dfrac{\Sigma y - m(\Sigma x)}{n}$$

Discussion pages 839–840;
Examples 3–4, pages 839–841

CHAPTER 13 Review Exercises

13.1

1. a) What is a population?

b) What is a sample?

2. What is a random sample?

13.2

In Exercises 3 and 4, tell what possible misuses or misinterpretations may exist in the statements.

3. The Stay Healthy Candy Bar indicates on its label that it has no cholesterol. Therefore, it is safe to eat as many of these candy bars as you want.

4. More copies of *Time* magazine are sold than are copies of *Money* magazine. Therefore, *Time* is a more profitable magazine than *Money*.

5. U.S. Households with Cable Television In 2008, 99.7 million households in the United States subscribed to cable television. In 2009, 103.0 million households in the United States subscribed to cable television. Draw a graph that appears to show a

a) small increase in the number of households subscribing to cable television from 2008 to 2009.

b) large increase in the number of households subscribing to cable television from 2008 to 2009.

13.3

6. Consider the following set of data.

35	37	38	41	43
36	37	38	41	43
36	37	39	41	43
36	37	39	41	44
37	37	39	42	45

a) Construct a frequency distribution letting each class have a width of 1.

b) Construct a histogram.

c) Construct a frequency polygon.

7. *Average Monthly High Temperature* Consider the following average monthly high temperature in July for 40 selected U.S. cities.

```
71  79  58  73  80  75  84  77
82  72  80  70  75  66  73  72
80  66  74  68  81  84  75  67
91  76  82  79  63  69  68  79
71  76  80  83  73  87  82  71
```

a) Construct a frequency distribution. Let the first class be 58–62.

b) Construct a histogram of the frequency distribution.

c) Construct a frequency polygon of the frequency distribution.

d) Construct a stem-and-leaf display.

13.4, 13.5

In Exercises 8–13, for the following test scores 67, 74, 79, 83, 84, 93, determine the

8. mean.

9. median.

10. mode.

11. midrange.

12. range.

13. standard deviation.

In Exercises 14–19, for the set of data 4, 5, 12, 14, 19, 7, 12, 23, 7, 17, 15, 21, determine the

14. mean.

15. median.

16. mode.

17. midrange.

18. range.

19. standard deviation.

13.6

Police Response Time In Exercises 20–24, assume that police response time to emergency calls is normally distributed with a mean of 9 minutes and a standard deviation of 2 minutes. Determine the percent of emergency calls with a police response time

20. between 7 and 11 minutes.

21. between 5 and 13 minutes.

22. less than 12.2 minutes.

23. more than 12.2 minutes.

24. more than 7.8 minutes.

Pizza Delivery In Exercises 25–28, assume that the amount of time to prepare and deliver a pizza from Pepe's Pizza

is normally distributed with a mean of 20 minutes and standard deviation of 5 minutes. Determine the percent of pizzas that were prepared and delivered

25. between 20 and 25 minutes.   **26.** in less than 18 minutes.

27. between 22 and 28 minutes.

28. If Pepe's Pizza advertises that the pizza is free if it takes more than 30 min to deliver, what percent of the pizza will be free?

13.7

29. *Hiking* The following table shows the number of hiking permits issued for a specific trail at Yellowstone National Park for selected years and the corresponding number of bears sighted by the hikers on that trail.

Hiking permits	765	926	1145	842	1485	1702
Bears	119	127	150	119	153	156

a) Construct a scatter diagram with hiking permits on the horizontal axis.

b) Use the scatter diagram in part (a) to determine whether you believe that a correlation exists between the number of hiking permits issued and the number of bears sighted by hikers. If so, is it a positive or negative correlation?

c) Calculate the correlation coefficient between the number of hiking permits issued and the number of bears sighted by hikers.

d) Determine whether a correlation exists at $\alpha = 0.05$.

e) Determine the equation of the line of best fit between the number of hiking permits issued and the number of bears sighted by hikers. Round both the slope and y-intercept to the nearest hundredth.

f) Assuming that this trend continues, use the equation of the line of best fit to estimate the number of bears sighted if 1500 hiking permits were issued.

30. *Daily Sales* Ace Hardware recorded the number of a particular item sold per week for 6 weeks and the corresponding weekly price, in dollars, of the item as shown in the table below.

Price ($)	0.75	1.00	1.25	1.50	1.75	2.00
Number sold	200	160	140	120	110	95

a) Construct a scatter diagram with price on the horizontal axis.

b) Use the scatter diagram in part (a) to determine whether you believe that a correlation exists between the price of the item and number sold. If so, it is a positive or a negative correlation?

c) Determine the correlation coefficient between the price and the number sold.

d) Determine whether a correlation exists at $\alpha = 0.05$.

e) Determine the equation of the line of best fit for the price and the number sold.

f) Use the equation in part (e) to estimate the number sold if the price is $1.60.

13.4–13.6

Men's Weight In Exercises 31–38, use the following data obtained from a study of the weights of adult men.

Mean	192 lb	First quartile	178 lb
Median	185 lb	Third quartile	232 lb
Mode	180 lb	86th percentile	239 lb
Standard deviation	23 lb		

31. What is the most common weight?

32. What weight did half of those surveyed exceed?

33. About what percent of those surveyed weighed more than 232 lb?

34. About what percent of those surveyed weighed less than 178 lb?

35. About what percent of those surveyed weighed more than 239 lb?

36. If 100 men were surveyed, what is the total weight of all men?

37. What weight represents two standard deviations above the mean?

38. What weight represents 1.8 standard deviations below the mean?

13.2–13.6

Presidential Children The following list shows the names of the 43 U.S. presidents and the number of children in their families.

Washington	0	B. Harrison	3
J. Adams	5	McKinley	2
Jefferson	6	T. Roosevelt	6
Madison	0	Taft	3
Monroe	2	Wilson	3
J. Q. Adams	4	Harding	0
Jackson	0	Coolidge	2
Van Buren	4	Hoover	2
W. H. Harrison	10	F. D. Roosevelt	6
Tyler	14	Truman	1
Polk	0	Eisenhower	2
Taylor	6	Kennedy	3
Fillmore	2	L. B. Johnson	2
Pierce	3	Nixon	2
Buchanan	0	Ford	4
Lincoln	4	Carter	4
A. Johnson	5	Reagan	4
Grant	4	G. Bush	6
Hayes	8	Clinton	1
Garfield	7	G. W. Bush	2
Arthur	3	Obama	2
Cleveland	5		

In Exercises 39–50, use the data to determine the following.

39. Mean   **40.** Mode

41. Median   **42.** Midrange

43. Range

44. Standard deviation (round the mean to the nearest tenth)

45. Construct a frequency distribution; let the first class be 0–1.

46. Construct a histogram of the frequency distribution.

47. Construct a frequency polygon of the frequency distribution.

48. Does this distribution appear to be normal? Explain.

49. Do you think the number of children per family in the United States is a normal distribution? Explain.

50. Is this set of data representative of the U.S. population? Explain.

CHAPTER 13 *Test*

In Exercises 1–6, for the set of data 27, 43, 43, 45, 52, determine the

1. mean.

2. median.

3. mode.

4. midrange.

5. range.

6. standard deviation.

In Exercises 7–9, use the set of data

26	28	35	46	49	56
26	30	36	46	49	58
26	32	40	47	50	58
26	32	44	47	52	62
27	35	46	47	54	66

to construct the following.

7. a frequency distribution; let the first class be 25–30

8. a histogram of the frequency distribution

9. a frequency polygon of the frequency distribution

Statistics on Salaries In Exercises 10–16, use the following data on weekly salaries at Donovan's Construction Company.

Mean	$740	First quartile	$690
Median	$710	Third quartile	$745
Mode	$735	79th percentile	$752
Standard deviation	$40		

10. What is the most common salary?

11. What salary did half the employees exceed?

12. About what percent of employees' salaries exceeded $690?

13. About what percent of employees' salaries was less than $752?

14. If the company has 100 employees, what is the total weekly salary of all employees?

15. What salary represents one standard deviation above the mean?

Anthropology In Exercises 16–19, assume that anthropologists have determined that the akidolestes, a small primitive mammal believed to have lived with the dinosaurs, had a head circumference that was normally distributed with a mean of 42 cm and a standard deviation of 5 cm.

16. What percent of head circumferences were between 36 and 53 cm?

17. What percent of head circumferences were greater than 35.75 cm?

18. What percent of head circumferences were greater than 48.25 cm?

19. What percent of head circumferences were less than 50 cm?

20. *Minimum Wage* The following table shows the hourly minimum wage in the U.S. for the years 2006–2010, where the column labeled Year refers to the number of years since 2006.

Year	Minimum Wage
0	$5.15
1	$5.85
2	$6.55
3	$7.25
4	$7.25

Source: *Bureau of Labor Statistics*

a) Construct a scatter diagram placing the year on the horizontal axis.

b) Use the scatter diagram in part (a) to determine whether you believe a correlation exists between the year and the minimum wage.

c) Determine the correlation coefficient between the year and the minimum wage.

d) Determine whether a correlation exists at $\alpha = 0.05$.

e) Determine the equation of the line of best fit between the year and the minimum wage. Round both the slope and y-intercept to the nearest hundredth.

f) Use the equation in part (e) to predict the minimum wage in 2014.

GROUP PROJECTS

Watching TV

1. Do you think that men or women, aged 17–20, watch more hours of TV weekly, or do you think that they watch the same number of hours?

   a) Write a procedure to use to determine the answer to that question. In your procedure, use a sample of 30 men and 30 women. State how you will obtain an unbiased sample.

   b) Collect 30 pieces of data from men aged 17–20 and 30 pieces of data from women aged 17–20. Round answers to the nearest 0.5 hr. Follow the procedure developed in part (a) to obtain your unbiased sample.

   c) Compute the mean for your two groups of data to the nearest tenth.

   d) Using the means obtained in part (c), answer the question asked at the beginning of the problem.

   e) Is it possible that your conclusion in part (d) is wrong? Explain.

   f) Compute the standard deviation for each group to the nearest tenth. How do the standard deviations compare?

   g) Do you believe that the distribution of data from either or both groups resembles a normal distribution? Explain.

   h) Add the two groups of data to get one group of 60 pieces of data. If these 60 pieces of data are added and divided by 60, will you obtain the same mean as when you add the two means from part (c) and divide the sum by 2? Explain.

   i) Compute the mean of the 60 pieces of data by using both methods mentioned in part (h). Are they the same? If so, why? If not, why not?

   j) Do you believe that this group of 60 pieces of data represents a normal distribution? Explain.

Bivariate Data Experiment

2. a) Have your group select a category of bivariate data that it thinks has a strong negative correlation. Indicate the variable that you will designate as the independent variable and the variable that you will designate as the dependent variable. Explain why your group believes that the bivariate data have a strong negative correlation.

   b) Collect at least 10 pieces of bivariate data that can be used to determine the correlation coefficient. Explain how your group chose these data.

   c) Plot a scatter diagram.

   d) Calculate the correlation coefficient.

   e) Is there a negative correlation at $\alpha = 0.05$? Explain your answer.

   f) Calculate the equation of the line of best fit.

   g) Explain how the equation in part (f) may be used.

Probability **14**

What Are the Chances?

*T*he 2008 presidential race . . . being hit by lightning . . . the Super Bowl . . . drilling for oil in the Arctic National Wildlife Refuge . . . car insurance . . . Las Vegas . . . . You might ask why we would start a chapter with these seemingly unrelated topics. The common thread that runs through all of these topics is the theme of this chapter—probability.

Whenever you hear a prediction as to who will win an election, the likelihood of finding oil, bets being placed on the Super Bowl, or deciding how much insurance you should carry on your car, you are dealing with uncertainty. But the good thing is there are well-known mathematical rules that enable us to make reasonable predictions out of uncertain situations. *(continued)*

By applying the rules of probability you will see how to determine if a flu drug is effective and to calculate how much profit an insurance company can expect to earn on its policies. You will find that playing roulette is a 10 times better gamble than playing the daily number and that the odds of being killed by lightning are thousands of times greater than the odds of winning a large state lottery. Later in the chapter, we will show you an example of how it is possible that a person who tests positive on a drug test has a surprisingly high likelihood of being innocent. ●

14.1 The Basics of Probability Theory

Objectives

1. Calculate probabilities by counting outcomes in a sample space.
2. Use counting formulas to compute probabilities.
3. Understand how probability theory is used in genetics.
4. Understand the relationship between probability and odds.

Have you ever been camping in the rain? If not, try to imagine it. You are sitting in a tent with the rain flaps down, with nothing to do—the weather report was wrong and you wish that you had picked another weekend for this experience. As we all know, predicting weather is not an exact science. The weather is an example of a random phenomenon. **Random phenomena** are occurrences that vary from day-to-day and case-to-case. In addition to the weather, rolling dice in Monopoly, drilling for oil, and driving your car are all examples of random phenomena.

Although we never know exactly how a random phenomenon will turn out, we can often calculate a number called a **probability** that it will occur in a certain way. We will now begin to introduce some basic probability terminology.

Sample Spaces and Events

✏️ **KEY POINT**

Knowing the sample space helps us compute probabilities.

Our first step in calculating the probability of a random phenomenon is to determine the sample space of an experiment.

> **DEFINITIONS** An **experiment** is any observation of a random phenomenon. The different possible results of the experiment are called **outcomes**. The set of all possible outcomes for an experiment is called a **sample space**.

If we observe the results of flipping a single coin, we have an example of an experiment. In the Oscar-winning film *No Country for Old Men*, Anton flips a coin to bet on a person's life. The possible outcomes are head and tail, so a sample space for the experiment would be the set {head, tail}.

EXAMPLE 1   *Finding Sample Spaces*

Determine a sample space for each experiment.

a) We select an iPhone from a production line and determine whether it is defective.

b) Three children are born to a family and we note the birth order with respect to gender.

c) We select one card from a standard 52-card deck,* and then without returning the card to the deck, we select a second card. We will assume the order in which we select the cards is important.

d) We roll two dice and observe the pair of numbers showing on the top faces.

---

*See Figure 13.1 in Chapter 13 for a picture of a standard 52-card deck.

SOLUTION: In each case, we find the sample space by collecting the outcomes of the experiment into a set.

a) This sample space is {defective, nondefective}.

b) In this experiment, we want to know not only how many boys and girls are born but also the birth order. For example, a boy followed by two girls is not the same as two girls followed by a boy. The tree diagram* in Figure 14.1 helps us find the sample space.

   There are two ways that the first child can be born, followed by two ways for the second child, and finally two ways for the third. If we abbreviate "boy" by "b" and "girl" by "g," following the branches of the tree diagram gives us the following sample space:

$$\{bbb, bbg, bgb, bgg, gbb, gbg, ggb, ggg\}.$$

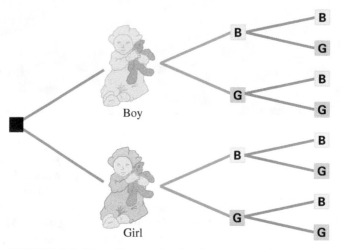

FIGURE 14.1 Tree diagram showing the genders of three children.

c) This sample space is too large to list; however, we can use the *fundamental counting principle* from Section 13.2 to count its members. Because we can choose the first card in 52 ways and the second card in 51 ways (we are not replacing the first card), we can select the two cards in $52 \times 51 = 2,652$ ways.

d) As we did in Example 4 of Section 13.1, we will think of the first die as being red and the second die as being green. As you can see, the pairs $(1, 3)$ and $(3, 1)$ are not the same. With this in mind, the sample space for this experiment consists of the following 36 pairs.

$$\{(1, 1), \quad (1, 2), \quad (1, 3), \quad (1, 4), \quad (1, 5), \quad (1, 6),$$
$$(2, 1), \quad (2, 2), \quad (2, 3), \quad (2, 4), \quad (2, 5), \quad (2, 6),$$
$$(3, 1), \quad (3, 2), \quad (3, 3), \quad (3, 4), \quad (3, 5), \quad (3, 6),$$
$$(4, 1), \quad (4, 2), \quad (4, 3), \quad (4, 4), \quad (4, 5), \quad (4, 6),$$
$$(5, 1), \quad (5, 2), \quad (5, 3), \quad (5, 4), \quad (5, 5), \quad (5, 6),$$
$$(6, 1), \quad (6, 2), \quad (6, 3), \quad (6, 4), \quad (6, 5), \quad (6, 6)\}$$

✎ *KEY POINT*

An event is a subset of a sample space.

Imagine that you are playing Monopoly and are on the verge of going bankrupt. If you roll a total of seven, you will lose the game and you want to know the probability that this will happen. At this point, you are only concerned with the *set* of pairs (1, 6), (2, 5), (3, 4), (4, 3), (5, 2), and (6, 1). This focus on particular *subsets* of the sample space is a recurring theme in probability theory.

DEFINITION In probability theory, an **event** is a subset of the sample space.

───────

*We introduced tree diagrams in Chapter 13.

Keep in mind that *any* subset of the sample space is an event, including such extreme subsets as the empty set, one-element sets, and the whole sample space.

 some Good Advice

Although we usually describe events verbally, you should remember that *an event is always a subset of the sample space.* You can use the verbal description to identify the set of outcomes that make up the event.

Example 2 illustrates some events from the sample spaces in Example 1.

EXAMPLE 2   *Describing Events as Subsets*

Write each event as a subset of the sample space.

a) A head occurs when we flip a single coin.
b) Two girls and one boy are born to a family.
c) A total of five occurs when we roll a pair of dice.

SOLUTION:

a) The set {head} is the event.
b) Noting that the boy can be the first, second, or third child, the event is {bgg, gbg, ggb}.
c) The following set shows how we can roll a total of five on two dice: {(1, 4), (2, 3), (3, 2), (4, 1)}.

Now try Exercises 7 to 14. ✳ **1**

We will use the notions of outcome, sample space, and event to compute probabilities. Intuitively, you may expect that when rolling a fair die, each number has the same chance, namely $\frac{1}{6}$, of showing. In predicting weather, a forecaster may state that there is a 30% chance of rain tomorrow. You may believe that you have a 50–50 chance (that is, a 50% chance) of getting a job offer in your field. In each of these examples, we have assigned a number between 0 and 1 to represent the likelihood that the outcome will occur. You can interpret probability intuitively as in the diagram below at left.

> **DEFINITIONS** The **probability of an outcome** in a sample space is a number between 0 and 1 inclusive. The sum of the probabilities of all the outcomes in the sample space must be 1. The **probability of an event** E, written $P(E)$,[†] is defined as the sum of the probabilities of the outcomes that make up E.

One way to determine probabilities is to use *empirical information*. That is, we make observations and assign probabilities based on those observations.

> **EMPIRICAL ASSIGNMENT OF PROBABILITIES** If E is an event and we perform an experiment several times, then we estimate the probability of E as follows:
>
> $$P(E) = \frac{\text{the number of times } E \text{ occurs}}{\text{the number of times the experiment is performed}}.$$
>
> This ratio is sometimes called the *relative frequency* of E.

Left margin column:

 Quiz Yourself **1** *

Write each event as a set of outcomes.

a) A total of six occurs when we roll two dice.

b) In a family with three children, there are more boys than girls.

KEY POINT

The probability of an event is the sum of the probabilities of the outcomes in that event.

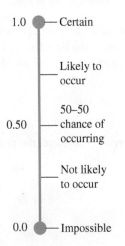

1.0 ●—Certain

Likely to occur

50–50
0.50 —chance of occurring

Not likely to occur

0.0 ●—Impossible

Intuitive meaning of probability.

[†]Do not confuse $P(E)$, which is the notation for the probability of an event, with $P(n, r)$, which is the notation for the number of permutations of *n* objects taken *r* at a time (see Section 13.3).

Side Effects	Number of Times
None	72
Mild	25
Severe	3

TABLE 14.1 Summary of side effects of the flu vaccine.

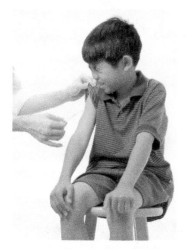

Quiz Yourself ❷

Use Table 14.1 to find the probability that a patient receiving the flu vaccine will experience no side effects.

EXAMPLE 3 Using Empirical Information to Assign Probabilities

A pharmaceutical company is testing a new flu vaccine. The experiment is to inject a patient with the vaccine and observe the occurrence of side effects. Assume that we perform this experiment 100 times and obtain the information in Table 14.1.

Based on Table 14.1, if a physician injects a patient with this vaccine, what is the probability that the patient will develop severe side effects?

SOLUTION: In this case, we base our probability assignment of the event that severe side effects occur on observations. We use the formula for the relative frequency of an event as follows:

$$P(\text{severe side effects}) = \frac{\text{the number of times severe side effects occurred}}{\text{the number of times the experiment was performed}}$$

$$= \frac{3}{100} = 0.03$$

Thus, from this empirical information, we can expect a 3% chance that there will be severe side effects from this vaccine.

Now try Exercises 29 to 32. ✳ ❷

EXAMPLE 4 Investigating Marital Data

Table 14.2* summarizes the marital status of men and women in the United States in 2006. All numbers represent number of thousands. If we randomly pick a male, what is the probability that he is divorced?

We are only interested in males. ———

	Now Married (except separated)	Widowed	Divorced	Separated	Never Married
Males	60,955	2,908	10,818	2,210	39,435
Females	59,173	12,226	14,182	3,179	33,377

TABLE 14.2 Marital status of men and women (in thousands) in the United States in 2006.

SOLUTION: It is important to recognize that not all entries in Table 14.2 are relevant to the question that you were asked. We are only interested in males, so the line that we have highlighted in the table contains all the information that we need to solve the problem. Therefore, we consider our sample space to be the

$$60,955 + 2,908 + 10,818 + 2,210 + 39,435 = 116,326$$

males.

The event, call it D, is the set of 10,818 men who are divorced. Therefore, the probability that we would select a divorced male is

$$P(D) = \frac{n(D)}{n(S)} = \frac{10,818}{116,326} \approx 0.093.$$

Now try Exercises 41, 42, and 47 to 50. ✳ ❸

Quiz Yourself ❸

Using Table 14.2, if we select a widowed person, what is the probability that the person is a woman?

 **KEY POINT**

We can use counting formulas to compute probabilities.

Counting and Probability

Another way we can determine probabilities is to use *theoretical information*, such as the counting formulas we discussed in Chapter 13.

---

*U.S. Bureau of the Census.

In order to understand the difference between using theoretical and empirical information, compare these two experiments:

Experiment one—Without looking, draw a ball from a box, note its color, and return the ball to the box. If you repeat this experiment 100 times and get 60 red balls and 40 blue balls, based on this *empirical information*, you would expect that the probability of getting a red ball on your next draw to be $\frac{60}{100} = 0.60$.

Experiment two—Draw a 5-card hand from a standard 52-card deck. As you will soon see, you can use *theoretical information*, namely, combination formulas from Chapter 13, to calculate the probability that *all* cards will be hearts.

EXAMPLE 5   *Using Counting Formulas to Calculate Probabilities*

Assign probabilities to the outcomes in the following sample spaces.

a) We flip three fair coins. What is the probability of each outcome in this sample space?

b) We draw a 5-card hand randomly from a standard 52-card deck. What is the probability that we draw one particular hand?

SOLUTION:

a) This sample space has eight outcomes, as we show in Figure 14.2. Because the coins are fair, we expect that heads and tails are equally likely to occur. Therefore, it is reasonable to assign a probability of $\frac{1}{8}$ to each outcome in this sample space.

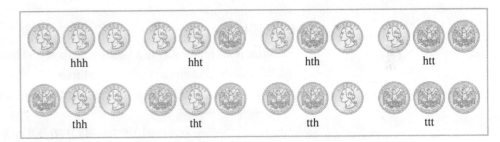

FIGURE 14.2 Eight theoretically possible outcomes for flipping three coins.

Quiz Yourself ④

If we were to flip four coins, how many outcomes would there be in the sample space?

b) In Chapter 13, we found that there are $C(52, 5) = 2,598,960$ different ways to choose 5 cards from a deck of 52. Because we are drawing the cards randomly, each hand has the same chance of being drawn. Therefore, the probability of drawing any one hand is $\frac{1}{2,598,960}$. ✻ ④

In a sample space with equally likely outcomes, it is easy to calculate the probability of any event by using the following formula.

> **CALCULATING PROBABILITY WHEN OUTCOMES ARE EQUALLY LIKELY** If *E* is an event in a sample space *S* with all *equally likely outcomes,* then the probability of *E* is given by the formula:
>
> $$P(E) = \frac{n(E)}{n(S)}. \ *$$

---

*Recall that $n(E)$ is the cardinal number of set *E* (see Section 2.1).

Math in Your Life*

Why Does It Always Happen to You?

When you wait at a toll booth, why does it seem that the line of cars next to you moves faster than your line? If you look into a sock drawer, do you notice how many unmatched socks there are? Why does the buttered side of a slice of bread almost always land face down if you drop the bread while making a sandwich? Do such annoyances affect only you? Or is there a mathematical explanation?

First let's consider the socks. Suppose you have 10 pairs of socks in a drawer and lose 1 sock, destroying a pair. Of the 19 remaining socks, there is only 1 unpaired sock. Therefore, if you lose a second sock, the probability of losing a paired sock is $\frac{18}{19}$. Now you have 2 unpaired socks and 16 paired socks. The probability that the third sock you lose will be part of a pair is still overwhelming. Continuing this line of thought, you see that it will be quite a while before probability theory predicts that you can expect to lose an unpaired sock.

The problem with the buttered bread is simple to explain. In fact you might conduct an experiment to simulate this situation with an object such as a computer mouse pad. If you slide the object off the edge of a table, as it begins to fall it rotates halfway around so that the top side is facing down. However, there is usually not enough time for the object to rotate back to the upward position before it hits the floor. You could conduct this experiment 100 times and determine the empirical probability that an object you slide off the table will land face down. So again, it's not bad luck—it's probability.

The slow-moving line at the toll booth is the easiest to explain. If we assume that delays in any line occur randomly, then one of the lines—yours, the one to the left, or the one to the right—will move fastest. Therefore, the probability that the fastest line will be yours is only $\frac{1}{3}$.

EXAMPLE 6 *Computing Probability of Events*

a) What is the probability in a family with three children that two of the children are girls?

b) What is the probability that a total of four shows when we roll two fair dice?

[†]c) If we draw a 5-card hand from a standard 52-card deck, what is the probability that all 5 cards are hearts?

[†]d) Harold, Kumar, Neil, and Vanessa are friends who belong to their college's 10-person international relations club. Two people from the club will be selected randomly to attend a conference at the United Nations building. What is the probability that two of these four friends will be selected?

SOLUTION: In each situation, we assume that the outcomes are equally likely.

a) We saw in Example 1 that there are eight outcomes in this sample space. We denote the event that two of the children are girls by the set $G = \{bgg, gbg, ggb\}$. Thus,

$$P(G) = \frac{n(G)}{n(S)} = \frac{3}{8}.$$

b) The sample space for rolling two dice has 36 ordered pairs of numbers. We will represent the event "rolling a four" by F. Then $F = \{(1, 3), (2, 2), (3, 1)\}$. Thus,

$$P(F) = \frac{n(F)}{n(S)} = \frac{3}{36} = \frac{1}{12}.$$

c) From Example 5, we know that there are $C(52, 5)$ ways to select a 5-card hand from a 52-card deck. If we want to draw only hearts, then we are selecting 5 hearts from the

---

*This Math in Your Life is based on Robert Matthews, "Murphy's Law or Coincidence." *Reader's Digest*, March 1998, pp. 25–30.
[†]Questions c) and d) require counting formulas from Chapter 13.

13 available, which can be done in $C(13, 5)$ ways. Thus, the probability of selecting all five cards to be hearts is

$$\frac{C(13, 5)}{C(52, 5)} = \frac{1{,}287}{2{,}598{,}960} \approx 0.000495.$$

d) The sample space, S, consists of all the ways we can select two people from the 10 members in the club. As you know from Chapter 13, we can choose 2 people from 10 in $C(10, 2) = \dfrac{10!}{8! \cdot 2!} = \dfrac{10 \cdot 9}{2} = 45$ ways. The event, call it E, consists of the ways we can choose two of the four friends. This can be done in $C(4, 2) = 6$ ways. Because all elements in S (choices of two people) are equally likely, the probability of E is

$$P(E) = \frac{n(E)}{n(S)} = \frac{C(4, 2)}{C(10, 2)} = \frac{6}{45} = \frac{2}{15}.$$

Now try Exercises 15 to 20. ※ **5**

 Some Good Advice

If the outcomes in a sample space are not equally likely, then you cannot use the formula $P(E) = \dfrac{n(E)}{n(S)}$. In that case, to find $P(E)$, you must add the probabilities of all the individual outcomes in E.

Suppose that we have a sample space with equally likely outcomes. An event, E, can contain none, some, or all of the outcomes in the sample space S, so we can say

$$0 \leq n(E) \leq n(S).$$

Dividing this inequality by the positive quantity $n(S)$, we get the inequality

$$\frac{0}{n(S)} \leq \frac{n(E)}{n(S)} \leq \frac{n(S)}{n(S)},$$

which simplifies to $0 \leq \dfrac{n(E)}{n(S)} \leq 1$. This gives us the first probability property listed below. The other properties are easy to see.

> **BASIC PROPERTIES OF PROBABILITY** Assume that S is a sample space for some experiment and E is an event in S.
>
> 1. $0 \leq P(E) \leq 1$ 2. $P(\varnothing) = 0$ 3. $P(S) = 1$

Probability and Genetics

In the nineteenth century, the Austrian monk Gregor Mendel noticed while cross-breeding plants that often a characteristic of the plants would disappear in the first-generation offspring but reappear in the second generation. He theorized that the first-generation plants contained a hidden factor (which we now call a *gene*) that was somehow transmitted to the second generation to enable the characteristic to reappear.

To check his theory, he selected a characteristic such as seed color—some peas had yellow seeds and some had green. Then when he was sure that he had bred plants that would produce only yellow seeds or green seeds, he was ready to begin his experiment. Mendel believed that one of the colors was *dominant* and the other was *recessive*. Which turned out to be the case, because when yellow-seeded plants were crossed with green-seeded plants, the offspring had yellow seeds. When Mendel crossed these offspring for a second generation, he found that 6,022 plants had yellow seeds and 2,001 had green seeds,

---

Sidebar (left column)

Quiz Yourself **5**

a) If we roll two fair dice, what is the probability of rolling a total of eight?

b) If we select 2 cards randomly from a standard 52-card deck, what is the probability that both are face cards?

 **KEY POINT**

Probability theory helps explain genetic theory.

which is almost exactly a ratio of 3 to 1. Because Mendel was skilled in mathematics as well as biology, he gave the following explanation for what he had observed.

We will represent the gene that produces the yellow seed by *Y* and the gene that produces the green seed by *g*. The uppercase *Y* indicates that yellow is dominant and the lowercase *g* indicates that green is recessive.*

Figure 14.3 shows the possible genetic makeup of the offspring from crossing a plant with pure yellow seeds and a plant with pure green seeds. Every one of these offspring has a *Yg* pair of genes. Because "yellow seed" is dominant over "green seed," every plant in the first generation will have yellow seeds.

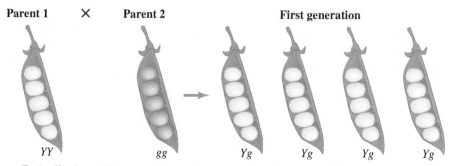

Each offspring will have one *Y* gene from parent 1 and one *g* gene from parent 2, and each will have yellow seeds.

FIGURE 14.3 The possible first-generation offspring we obtain by crossing pure yellow and pure green parents.

Figure 14.4 shows the possible genetic outcomes that can occur if we cross two first-generation pea plants. We summarize Figure 14.4 in Table 14.4, which is called a **Punnett square**.

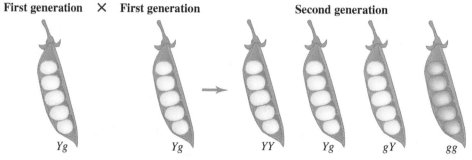

Each offspring will have either a *Y* gene or a *g* gene from each parent. Only the seeds of the offspring with the *gg* pair of genes will be green.

FIGURE 14.4 The possible second-generation offspring we obtain by crossing the first-generation offspring of pure yellow and pure green parents.

		First-Generation Plant	
		Y	**g**
First-Generation	**Y**	YY	Yg
Plant	**g**	gY	gg

TABLE 14.3 The genetic possibilities of crossing two plants that each have one yellow-seed and one green-seed gene.

As you can see in Table 14.3, there are four things that can happen when we cross two first-generation plants. We can get a *YY*, *Yg*, *gY*, or *gg* type of plant. Of these four possibilities, only the *gg* will result in green seeds, which explains why Mendel saw the recessive characteristic return in roughly one fourth of the second-generation plants.

---

*Biology books customarily use slightly different notation to indicate genes. For example, to indicate that yellow is dominant over green, you may see the notation *Yy*. The capital *Y* represents the yellow dominant gene and the lowercase *y* indicates the recessive green gene.

EXAMPLE 7   *Using Probability to Explain Genetic Diseases*

Sickle-cell anemia is a serious inherited disease that is about 30 times more likely to occur in African American babies than in non–African American babies. A person with two sickle-cell genes will have the disease, but a person with only one sickle-cell gene will be a carrier of the disease.

If two parents who are carriers of sickle-cell anemia have a child, what is the probability of each of the following:

a) The child has sickle-cell anemia?

b) The child is a carrier?

c) The child is disease free?

SOLUTION: Table 14.4 shows the genetic possibilities when two people who are carriers of sickle-cell anemia have a child. We will denote the sickle-cell gene by *s* and the normal gene by *n*. We use lowercase letters to indicate that neither *s* nor *n* is dominant.

		Second Parent	
		s	*n*
First Parent	*s*	*ss* has disease	*sn* carrier
	n	*ns* carrier	*nn* normal

TABLE 14.4 The genetic possibilities for children of two parents with sickle-cell trait.

From Table 14.4, we see that there are four equally likely outcomes for the child.

● The child receives two sickle-cell genes and therefore has the disease.

● The child receives a sickle-cell gene from the first parent and a normal gene from the second parent and therefore is a carrier.

● The child receives a normal gene from the first parent and a sickle-cell gene from the second parent and therefore is a carrier.

● The child receives two normal genes and therefore is disease-free.

From this analysis, it is clear that

a) $P(\text{the child has sickle-cell anemia}) = \frac{1}{4}$.

b) $P(\text{the child is a carrier}) = \frac{1}{2}$.

c) $P(\text{the child is normal}) = \frac{1}{4}$.

Now try Exercises 33 to 40. ✳

KEY POINT

In computing odds remember "against" versus "for."

Odds

We often use the word *odds* to express the notion of probability. When we do this, we usually state the odds *against* something happening. For example, before the 2008 Kentucky Derby, Las Vegas oddsmakers had set the odds against Big Brown, the eventual winner of the derby, to be 4 to 1.

When you calculate odds against an event, it is helpful to think of what is against the event as compared with what is in favor of the event. For example, if you roll two dice and want to find the odds against rolling a seven, you think that there are 30 pairs that will give you a nonseven and six that will give you a seven. Therefore, the odds against rolling a total of seven are 30 to 6. We write this as 30:6. Just like reducing a fraction, we can write these odds as 5:1. Sometimes you might see odds written as a fraction, such as 30/6, but, for the most part, we will avoid using this notation.

> **DEFINITION** If the outcomes of a sample space are equally likely, then the **odds against an event** *E* are simply the number of outcomes that are against *E* compared with the number of outcomes in favor of *E* occurring. We would write these odds as $n(E'):n(E)$, where *E'* is the complement of event *E*.*

---

*We discussed the complement of a set in Section 2.3.

Early Probability Theory

We can trace probability theory back to prehistoric times. Archaeologists have found numerous small bones, called *astrogali*, that are believed to have been used in playing various games of chance. Similar bones were later ground into the shape of cubes and decorated in various ways. They eventually evolved into modern dice. Games of chance were played for thousands of years, but it was not until the sixteenth century that a serious attempt was made to study them using mathematics.

Among the first to study the mathematics of games of chance was the Italian Girolamo Cardano. In addition to his interest in probability, Cardano was an astrologer. This caused him frequent misfortune. In one instance, Cardano cast the horoscope of Jesus and for this blasphemy he was sent to prison. Shortly thereafter, he predicted the exact date of his own death and, when the day arrived, Cardano made his prediction come true by taking his own life.

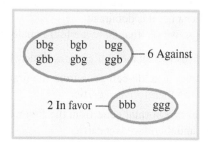

Recall that in Example 1, you saw there were eight ways for boys and girls to be born in order in a family. To find the odds against all children being of the same gender, you think of the six outcomes that are against this happening versus the two outcomes that are in favor, as in the accompanying diagram.

Therefore, the odds against all three children being of the same gender are 6:2, which we can reduce and rewrite as 3:1. We could also say that the *odds in favor* of all children being of the same gender are 1:3. It is important to understand that the odds in favor of an event are not the same as the probability of an event. In the example we are discussing, the probability of all children being the same gender is $\frac{2}{8} = \frac{1}{4}$.

 PROBLEM SOLVING

The Analogies Principle

Making an analogy with a real-life situation helps you to remember the meaning of mathematical terminology. For example, when General Custer fought Chief Sitting Bull at the battle of Little Big Horn, Custer had about 650 soldiers and Sitting Bull had 2,500 braves. If we think of how many were for Custer and how many were against him, we might say that the odds against Custer winning were 2,500 to 650. Similarly, the odds against Sitting Bull winning were 650 to 2,500.

EXAMPLE 8 *Calculating Odds on a Roulette Wheel*

A common type of roulette wheel has 38 equal-size compartments. Thirty-six of the compartments are numbered 1 to 36 with half of them colored red and the other half black. The remaining 2 compartments are green and numbered 0 and 00. A small ball is placed on the spinning wheel and when the wheel stops, the ball rests in one of the compartments. What are the odds against the ball landing on red?

SOLUTION: This is an experiment with 38 equally likely outcomes. Because 18 of these are in favor of the event "the ball lands on red" and 20 are against the event, the odds against red are 20 to 18. We can write this as 20:18, which we may reduce to 10:9. ✳

Although we have defined odds in terms of counting, we also can think of odds in terms of probability. Notice in the next definition we are comparing "probability against" with "probability for."

> **PROBABILITY FORMULA FOR COMPUTING ODDS** If E' is the complement of the event E, then the odds against E are
>
> $$\frac{P(E')}{P(E)}.$$

You may have been surprised that we have not used the "$a:b$" notation in this definition of odds. However, we have a good reason for doing this. If the probability of an event E is 0.30, then it is awkward to say that the odds against E are 0.70 to 0.30. It is better to say

$$\text{odds against } E = \frac{\text{probability of } E'}{\text{probability of } E} = \frac{0.70}{0.30} = \frac{70}{30}.$$

We could then say that the odds against E are 70 to 30, or 7 to 3. We will use this approach in Example 9.

EXAMPLE 9   *Using the Probability Formula for Computing the Odds in a Football Game*

Suppose that the probability of Green Bay winning the Super Bowl is 0.35. What are the odds against Green Bay winning the Super Bowl?

SOLUTION: Recall from Section 1.1 on problem solving that a diagram often helps us remember what to do. Call the event "Green Bay wins the Super Bowl" G. We illustrate this in Figure 14.5.

Thus, the odds against Green Bay winning the Super Bowl are

$$\frac{P(G')}{P(G)} = \frac{0.65}{0.35} = \frac{0.65 \times 100}{0.35 \times 100} = \frac{65}{35} = \frac{13}{7}.$$

In this case, we would say the odds against Green Bay winning the Super Bowl are 13 to 7.

Now try Exercises 21 to 24. ❋

Now that we have introduced some of the basic terminology and properties of probability, in the next section we will learn rules for calculating probabilities.

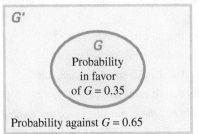

FIGURE 14.5 The odds against Green Bay winning are the probability of Green Bay losing versus the probability of Green Bay winning.

Exercises ⎨14.1⎬

Looking Back*

These exercises follow the general outline of the topics presented in this section and will give you a good overview of the material that you have just studied.

1. In Example 1(b), what method did we use to determine the sample space?

2. Although we usually describe events verbally, you should remember that an event is always what?

3. In Example 5(b), how did we find the number of objects in the sample space?

4. In Example 9, we knew that the probability of Green Bay winning the Super Bowl was 0.35. How did we find the odds against Green Bay winning?

5. In the Math in Your Life box, what was our explanation as to why the buttered side of a falling piece of bread lands face down? Why is it reasonable that your line at a toll booth would not be the fastest?

6. What was the point of our discussion about Custer and Sitting Bull?

Sharpening Your Skills

In Exercises 7–10, write each event as a set of outcomes. If the event is large, you may describe the event without writing it out.

7. When we roll two dice, the total showing is seven.

8. When we roll two dice, the total showing is five.

9. We flip three coins and obtain more (h)eads than (t)ails.

10. We select a red face card from a standard 52-card deck.

---

*Before doing these exercises, you may find it useful to review the note *How to Succeed at Mathematics* on page xix.

In Exercises 11–14, use the given spinner to write the event as a set of outcomes. Abbreviate "red" as "r," "blue" as "b," and "yellow" as "y."

11. Red appears exactly once when we spin the given spinner two times.

12. Yellow appears at least once when we spin the given spinner two times.

13. Blue appears exactly twice in three spins of the spinner.

14. Red does not appear in three spins of the spinner.

15. We are rolling two four-sided dice having the numbers 1, 2, 3, and 4 on their faces. Outcomes in the sample space are pairs such as (1, 3) and (4, 4).

   a. How many elements are in the sample space?

   b. Express the event "the total showing is even" as a set.

   c. What is the probability that the total showing is even?

   d. What is the probability that the total showing is greater than six?

16. You select three digital picture frames from a production line to determine if they are (d)efective or (n)ondefective. Outcomes in the sample space are represented by strings such as dnd and nnn.

   a. How many elements are in the sample space?

   b. Express the event "exactly one frame is defective" as a set.

   c. What is the probability that exactly one frame is defective?

   d. What is the probability that more frames are defective than nondefective?

17. Singers (C)arrie, (M)ariah, (K)eith, and (J)ustin are to perform in a talent contest and the order of their appearance will be chosen randomly. Outcomes in the sample space are represented by strings of letters such as CKMJ and JKCM.

   a. How many elements are in the sample space?

   b. Express the event "the women (C and M) do not perform consecutively" as a set.

   c. What is the probability that the women do not perform consecutively?

   d. What is the probability that Carrie will perform last?

18. We are flipping four coins. Outcomes in the sample space are represented by strings of Hs and Ts such as TTHT and HHTT.

   a. How many elements are in this sample space?

   b. Express the event "there are more heads than tails" as a set.

   c. What is the probability that there are more heads than tails?

   d. What is the probability that there are an equal number of heads and tails?

19. An experimenter testing for extrasensory perception has five cards with pictures of a (s)tar, a (c)ircle, (w)iggly lines, a (d)ollar sign, and a (h)eart. She selects two cards without replacement. Outcomes in the sample space are represented by pairs such as (s, d) and (h, c).

   a. How many elements are in this sample space?

   b. Express the event "a star appears on one of the cards" as a set.

   c. What is the probability that a star appears on one of the cards?

   d. What is the probability that a heart does not appear?

20. You have bought stock in Apple and Dell and each stock can either (i)ncrease in value, (d)ecrease in value, or (s)tay the same. Outcomes in the sample space are represented by pairs such as (i, d) and (d, d).

   a. How many elements are in this sample space?

   b. Express the event "Apple increases" as a set.

   c. What is the probability that Apple increases?

   d. What is the probability that Dell does not stay the same?

In Exercises 21–24, a) Find the probability of the given event. b) Find the odds against the given event.

21. A total of nine shows when we roll two fair dice.

22. A total of three shows when we roll two fair dice.

23. We draw a heart when we select 1 card randomly from a standard 52-card deck.

24. We draw a face card when we select 1 card randomly from a standard 52-card deck.

In Exercises 25–28, assume that we are drawing a 5-card hand from a standard 52-card deck.

25. What is the probability that all cards are diamonds?

26. What is the probability that all cards are face cards?

27. What is the probability that all cards are of the same suit?

28. What is the probability that all cards are red?

The residents of a small town and the surrounding area are divided over the proposed construction of a sprint car racetrack in the town. Use the following table to answer Exercises 29 and 30.

	Support Racetrack	Oppose Racetrack
Live in Town	1,512	2,268
Live in Surrounding Area	3,528	1,764

29. If a newspaper reporter randomly selects a person to interview from these people,

   a. what is the probability that the person supports the racetrack?

   b. what are the odds in favor of the person supporting the racetrack?

30. If a newspaper reporter randomly selects a person from town to interview,

   a. what is the probability that the person supports the racetrack?

   b. what are the odds in favor of the person supporting the racetrack?

Applying What You've Learned

31. In a given year, 2,048,861 males and 1,951,379 females were born in the United States. If a child is selected randomly from this group, what is the probability that it is a female?

32. Recently, the FBI reported that there were 7,160 hate crimes in the United States. Of these, 3,919 were based on race, 1,227 on religion, 1,017 on sexual orientation, 944 on ethnicity, and 53 on disability. (Assume that no crime was reported in two

categories.) If you selected one of these crimes randomly, what is the probability that it would not be based on race?

33. The following table lists some of the empirical results that Mendel obtained in his experiments in cross-breeding pea plants.

Characteristics That Were Crossbred	First-Generation Plants	Second-Generation Plants
Tall vs. short	All tall	787 tall 277 short
Smooth seeds vs. wrinkled seeds	All smooth seeds	5,474 smooth 1,850 wrinkled

Assume that we are cross-breeding genetically pure tall plants with genetically pure short plants. Use this information to assign the probability that a second-generation plant will be short. How consistent is this with the theoretical results that Mendel derived?

34. Assume that we are cross-breeding genetically pure smooth-seed plants with genetically pure wrinkled-seed plants. Use the information provided in Exercise 33 to assign the probability that a second-generation plant will have smooth seeds. How consistent is this with the theoretical results that Mendel derived?

In Exercises 35 and 36, construct a Punnett square as we did in Table 14.4 to show the probabilities for the offspring.

35. One parent who has sickle-cell anemia and one parent who is a carrier have a child. Find the probability that the child is a carrier of sickle-cell anemia.

36. One parent who has sickle-cell anemia and one parent who is a carrier have a child. Find the probability that the child has sickle-cell anemia.

In cross-breeding snapdragons, Mendel found that flower color does not dominate, as happens with peas. For example, a snapdragon with one red and one white gene will have pink flowers. In Exercises 37 and 38, analyze the cross-breeding experiment as we did in the discussion prior to Example 7.

37. a. Construct a Punnett square showing the results of crossing a purebred white snapdragon with a purebred red one.

   b. What is the probability of getting red flowers in the first-generation plants? What is the probability of getting white? Of getting pink?

38. a. If we cross two pink snapdragons, draw a Punnett square that shows the results of crossing two of these first-generation plants.

   b. What is the probability of getting red flowers in the second-generation plants? What about white? Pink?

39. Cystic fibrosis is a serious inherited lung disorder that often causes death in victims during early childhood. Because the gene for this disease is recessive, two apparently healthy adults, called *carriers*, can have a child with the disease. We will denote the normal gene by N and the cystic fibrosis gene by c to indicate its recessive nature.

   a. Construct a Punnett square as we did in Example 7 to describe the genetic possibilities for a child whose two parents are carriers of cystic fibrosis.

   b. What is the probability that this child will have the disease?

40. From the Punnett square in Exercise 39, what is the probability that a child of two carriers will

   a. be normal?

   b. be a carrier?

41. Assume that the following table summarizes a survey involving the relationship between living arrangements and grade point average for a group of students.

	On Campus	At Home	Apartment	Totals
Below 2.5	98	40	44	182
2.5 to 3.5	64	25	20	109
Over 3.5	17	4	8	29
Totals	179	69	72	320

If we select a student randomly from this group, what is the probability that the student has a grade point average of at least 2.5?

42. Using the data in Exercise 41, if a student is selected randomly, what is the probability that the student lives off campus?

Use this replica of the Monopoly game board to answer Exercises 43–46.

43. Assume that your game piece is on the Electric Company. If you land on either St. James Place, Tennessee Avenue, or New York Avenue, you will go bankrupt. What is the probability that you avoid these properties?

44. Assume that your game piece is on Pacific Avenue. If you land on either Park Place or Boardwalk, you will go bankrupt. What is the probability that you avoid these properties?

45. Your game piece is on Virginia Avenue. What is the probability that you will land on a railroad on your next move?

46. Your game piece is on Pennsylvania Avenue. What is the probability that you will have to pay a tax on your next move?

In Exercises 47–50 assume that we are randomly picking a person described in Table 14.2 from Example 4.

47. If we pick a divorced person, what is the probability that the person is a woman?

48. If we pick a woman, what is the probability that the person is married but not separated?

49. If we pick a never-married person, what is the probability that the person is a man?

50. If we pick a man, what is the probability that the person is a widower?

In horse racing, a trifecta is a race in which you must pick the first-, second-, and third-place winners in their proper order to win a payoff.

51. If eight horses are racing and you randomly select three as your bet in the trifecta, what is the probability that you will win? (Assume that all horses have the same chance to win.)

52. If 10 horses are racing and you randomly select 3 as your bet in the trifecta, what is the probability that you will win? (Assume that all horses have the same chance to win.)

53. If the odds against event E are 5 to 2, what is the probability of E?

54. If $P(E) = 0.45$, then what are the odds against E?

55. If the odds against the U.S. women's soccer team winning the World Cup are 7 to 5, what is the probability that they will win the World Cup?

56. If the odds against the U.S. men's volleyball team defeating China in the Summer 2008 Olympic Games is 9 to 3, what is the probability that the United States will defeat China?

57. Suppose the probability that the Yankees will win the World Series is 0.30.

  a. What are the odds in favor of the Yankees winning the World Series?

  b. What are the odds against the Yankees winning the World Series?

58. Suppose the probability that Rags to Riches will win the Triple Crown in horse racing is 0.15.

  a. What are the odds in favor of Rags to Riches winning the Triple Crown?

  b. What are the odds against Rags to Riches winning the Triple Crown?

59. In the New York Lotto, the player must correctly pick six numbers from the numbers 1 to 59. What are the odds against winning this lottery?

60. Go to the National Safety Council's Web site at www.nsc.org to find the odds against you being killed by lightning in your lifetime. How many more times likely is it that you will be killed by lightning than win the New York Lotto?

Communicating Mathematics

61. Suppose that we want to assign the probability of E empirically. Complete the following equation: $P(E) =$

62. What condition must we have in order to use the formula $P(E) = \dfrac{n(E)}{n(S)}$?

63. In the pea plant example, we found that all the first-generation plants had yellow seeds. Why was this the case?

64. If the odds against an event are a to b, what are the odds in favor of the event?

65. Explain the difference between an outcome and an event.

66. When rolling two dice, describe in words an event that is the empty set.

67. When rolling two dice, describe in words an event that is the whole sample space.

68. Can an event have just one single outcome in it? Give an example.

69. Explain the difference between the probability of an event and the odds *in favor* of the event.

70. You know that the probability of an event can never be greater than 1. Can the odds in favor of an event ever exceed 1? Explain.

Using Technology to Investigate Mathematics

71. See your instructor for a tutorial on using graphing calculators to demonstrate some of the ideas we have discussed in this section. Report on your findings.*

72. Search the Internet to find applets that illustrate some of the ideas we have discussed in this section. Report on your findings.

For Extra Credit

In Exercises 73 and 74, assume that to log in to a computer network you must enter a password. Assume that a hacker who is trying to break into the system randomly types one password every 10 seconds. If the hacker does not enter a valid password within 3 minutes, the system will not allow any further attempts to log in. What is the probability that the hacker will be successful in discovering a valid password for each type of password?

73. The password consists of two letters followed by three digits. Case does not matter for the letters. Thus, Ca154 and CA154 would be considered the same password.

74. The password consists of any sequence of two letters and three digits. Case does not matter for the letters. Thus, B12q5 and b12Q5 would be considered the same password.

75. Find some examples of advertising claims in the media. In what way are these claims probabilities?

76. a. Flip a coin 100 times. How do your empirical results compare with the theoretical probabilities for obtaining heads and tails?

b. Roll a pair of dice 100 times. How do your empirical results compare with the theoretical probabilities for rolling a total of two, three, four, and so on?

c. Toss an irregular object such as a thumbtack 1,000 times. After doing this, what probability would you assign to the thumbtack landing point up? What about point down? Does it matter what kind of thumbtack you use? Explain.

77. Investigate other genetic diseases, such as Tay-Sachs or Huntington's disease. Explain how the mathematics of the genetics of these diseases is similar or dissimilar to the examples we studied in this section.

78. Experiment with an object such as a mouse pad. Slide it off a table 100 times and record how often it lands face down. If the object slips off the table, what is the probability that the object will land face down?

79. Simulate the lost socks example discussed in the Math in Your Life box by doing the following. Take 20 three-by-five cards. Label two of them "pair one," two of them "pair two," two of them "pair three," and so on. Put the 20 cards into a box and draw cards randomly, without replacement, until you have drawn two cards that have the same label. Do this 30 times. On average, how many cards do you draw before you have drawn two cards with the same label?

14.2 Complements and Unions of Events

Objectives

1. Understand the relationship between the probability of an event and the probability of its complement.
2. Calculate the probability of the union of two events.
3. Use complement and union formulas to compute the probability of an event.

Suppose that you are attending a luncheon on your campus to develop a campaign to fight world hunger. Someone at your table might ask, "This room is pretty crowded. I wonder how many are here?" You look around and see that there are eight tables that seat 10 people each and notice that there are only six empty seats. So, without actually counting, you can quickly say that there are 74 people attending.

Similarly, you can often solve complex probability problems by applying a few simple, intuitive formulas. We will use some results from set theory in Chapter 2 to develop rules for computing the probability of the complement and the union of events.

KEY POINT

We can compute the probability of an event by finding the probability of its complement.

Complements of Events

You can frequently solve a mathematics problem by rephrasing it as an equivalent question that is easier to answer. For example, suppose that you want to calculate the probability of event E,* but find that E is too complicated to understand easily. If you remember that the total probability available in a sample space is 1, then it may be simpler to find the probability of E's complement and subtract that number from 1.

---

*Throughout the rest of this chapter, unless we state otherwise, E, F, and so on will represent events in the sample space S.

> **COMPUTING THE PROBABILITY OF THE COMPLEMENT OF AN EVENT** If E is an event, then $P(E') = 1 - P(E)$.

Of course we can state this result differently as $P(E) = 1 - P(E')$ or $P(E) + P(E') = 1$. We illustrate this formula in Figure 14.6.

Sample space ($\boldsymbol{S}$)

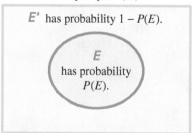

FIGURE 14.6 $P(E) + P(E') = 1$.

PROBLEM SOLVING

The Analogies Principle

The Analogies Principle in Section 1.1 says that you can learn a new area of mathematics more easily if you connect it with an area that you already know. By drawing Venn diagrams, you can visualize many of the rules of probability theory that will help you remember them and use them properly.

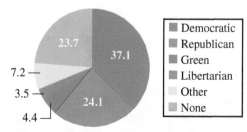

Percent of voters according to party affiliation

EXAMPLE 1 *Using the Complement Formula to Study Voter Affiliation*

The accompanying graph shows how a group of first-time voters are classified according to their party affiliation. If we randomly select a person from this group, what is the probability that the person has a party affiliation?

SOLUTION: Let A be the event that the person we select has some party affiliation. Rather than compute the probability of this event, it is simpler to calculate the probability of A' which is the event that the person we select has no party affiliation. We illustrate this situation in Figure 14.7.

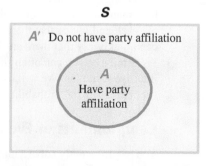

FIGURE 14.7 Calculate $P(A)$ by first finding $P(A')$.

Quiz Yourself

If a pair of dice are rolled, what is the probability of rolling a total that is less than 11? (Use the complement rule.)

Because 23.7% have no party affiliation, the probability of selecting such a person is 0.237. Thus, $P(A) = 1 - P(A') = 1 - 0.237 = 0.763$.

Now try Exercises 5 to 12. ✺ **6**

HIGHLIGHT ✳ ✳ ✳

Between the Numbers—What Are Your Chances?

Once, while we were studying the probability of lotteries and casino games, one of my students, upon realizing his slim chances of winning a lottery, blurted out, "I'm never going to gamble again!"

If you did Exercises 59 and 60 from Section 14.1, you saw that the odds against your winning the New York

Lotto are 45,057,474 to 1, which is much greater than being killed by lightning. To put in perspective what a long shot it is to win a big lottery, consider the odds on your dying from various events provided by the National Safety Council.

Event (Dying From . . .)	Odds Against This Event	Number of Times More Likely Than Winning The New York Lotto
Lightning	79,113 to 1	569
Drowning	9,641 to 1	4,674
Assault by Firearms	308 to 1	146,290
Motor Vehicle Accident	87 to 1	517,902

 **KEY POINT**

We often describe the union of events using the word *or.*

Unions of Events

We often combine objects in a mathematical system to obtain other objects in the system. For example, in number systems, we add and subtract pairs of numbers to get other numbers. In probability, we join events using the set operations union and intersection, which we discussed in Section 2.3. We will investigate the union of events in this section and the intersection of events in Section 14.3. We often describe the union of events using the word *or.*

Figure 14.8 shows the union of events E and F. In computing $P(E \cup F)$, it is a *common mistake* to simply add $P(E)$ and $P(F)$. Because some outcomes may be in both E and F, you will count their probabilities twice. To compute $P(E \cup F)$ properly, you must subtract $P(E \cap F)$.

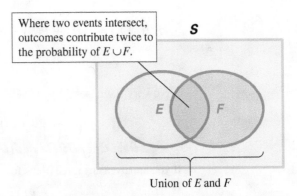

Where two events intersect, outcomes contribute twice to the probability of $E \cup F$.

Union of E and F

FIGURE 14.8 The union of two events.

> **RULE FOR COMPUTING THE PROBABILITY OF A UNION OF TWO EVENTS** If E and F are events, then
>
> $$P(E \cup F) = P(E) + P(F) - P(E \cap F). *$$
>
> If E and F have no outcomes in common, they are called *mutually exclusive events*. In this case, because $E \cap F = \varnothing$, the preceding formula simplifies to
>
> $$P(E \cup F) = P(E) + P(F).$$

---

*The counting version of this rule can be found in Section 2.3.

EXAMPLE 2   *Finding the Probability of the Union of Two Events*

If we select a single card from a standard 52-card deck, what is the probability that we draw either a heart or a face card?

SOLUTION: Let H be the event "draw a heart" and F be the event "draw a face card." We are looking for $P(H \cup F)$. There are thirteen hearts, twelve face cards, and three cards that are both hearts and face cards. Figure 14.9 helps us remember the formula to use.

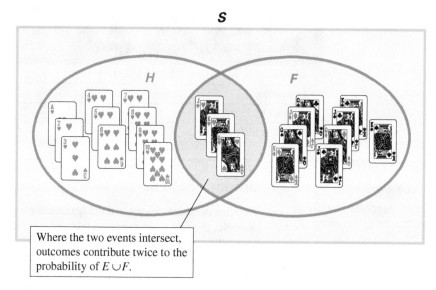

S

Where the two events intersect, outcomes contribute twice to the probability of $E \cup F$.

FIGURE 14.9 The union of the events "draw a heart" and "draw a face card."

Therefore,

$$P(H \cup F) = P(H) + P(F) - P(H \cap F) = \frac{13}{52} + \frac{12}{52} - \frac{3}{52} = \frac{22}{52} = \frac{11}{26}$$

probability of a heart ⌐   ⌐ probability of a face card

└ probability of a heart that is a face card

Now try Exercises 13 to 16. ✳

 Some Good Advice

If you are given any three of the four quantities in the formula

$$P(E \cup F) = P(E) + P(F) - P(E \cap F),$$

you can use algebra to solve for the other. See Example 3.

EXAMPLE 3   *Using Algebra to Find a Missing Probability*

A magazine conducted a survey of readers age 18 to 25 regarding their health concerns. The editors will use this information to choose topics relevant to their readers. The survey found that 35% of the readers were concerned with improving their cardiovascular fitness and 55% wanted to lose weight. Also, the survey found that 70% are concerned with either improving their cardiovascular fitness or losing weight. If the editors randomly select one of those surveyed to profile in a feature article, what is the probability that the person is concerned with both improving cardiovascular fitness *and* losing weight?

SOLUTION: If we let C be the event "the person wants to improve cardiovascular fitness" and W be the event "the person wishes to lose weight," then the word "and" tells us that we need to find $P(C \cap W)$.

We are given that 35% want to improve cardiovascular fitness, so $P(C) = 0.35$. Similarly, $P(W) = 0.55$. The event "a person wants to improve cardiovascular fitness or lose weight," is the event $C \cup W$, and we are told that $P(C \cup W) = 0.70$. Figure 14.10 will now help you to see what to do.

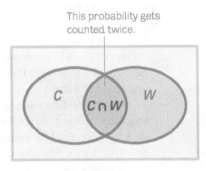

FIGURE 14.10 The union of events C and W.

From this diagram* you can see that

$$P(C \cup W) = P(C) + P(W) - P(C \cap W).$$

$$0.70 \qquad 0.35 \quad 0.55 \qquad \text{unknown}$$

This gives us the equation

$$0.70 = 0.35 + 0.55 - P(C \cap W).$$

Rewriting this equation as

$$P(C \cap W) = 0.35 + 0.55 - 0.70,$$

we find that $P(C \cap W) = 0.20$.

This means that there is a 20% chance that the person chosen will be interested in both improving cardiovascular fitness and losing weight.

Now try Exercises 17 to 20. ✳

Suppose that A and B are events such that $P(A) = 0.35$, $P(A \cap B) = 0.15$, and $P(A \cup B) = 0.65$. Find $P(B)$.

KEY POINT

We may use several formulas to calculate an event's probability.

Combining Complement and Union Formulas

In Example 4, we use both the complement formula and the union formula to compute an event's probability.

EXAMPLE 4 *Finding the Probability of the Complement of the Union of Two Events*

A survey of consumers comparing the amount of time they spend shopping on the Internet per month with their annual income produced the results in Table 14.5.[†]

Assume that these results are representative of all consumers. If we select a consumer randomly, what is the probability that the consumer neither shops on the Internet 10 or more hours per month nor has an annual income above $60,000?

---

*We will not always draw diagrams to illustrate the rule for calculating the probability of the union of two events; however, we do encourage you to do so to aid you in your computations.
[†]We will assume that all times are rounded to the nearest hour.

$n(T \cap A)$

Annual Income	10 + Hours (*T*)	3–9 Hours	0–2 Hours	Totals	
Above $60,000 (*A*)	192	176	128	496	— *n(A)*
$40,000–$60,000	160	208	144	512	
Below $40,000	128	192	272	592	
Totals	480	576	544	1,600	— *n(S)*

$n(T)$

TABLE 14.5 Survey results on Internet shopping.

SOLUTION: Although we could use the probability techniques that we introduced in Section 14.1 to answer this question, we will use instead the formulas for the complement and union of events.

We will let *T* be the event "the consumer selected spends 10 or more hours per month shopping on the Internet." Event *T* corresponds to the first column in Table 14.5. Also, let *A* be the event "the consumer selected has an annual income above $60,000," which is described by the first row in Table 14.5.

In Figure 14.11, you can see that the event "the consumer selected neither shops on the Internet 10 or more hours per month nor has an annual income above $60,000" is the region outside of $T \cup A$, which is the complement of $T \cup A$.

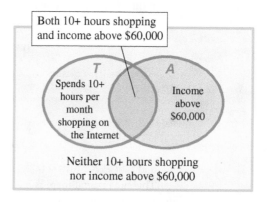

FIGURE 14.11 The event "neither *T* nor *A*" corresponds to the complement of $T \cup A$.

From Table 14.5, you see that the number of outcomes in *T* is

$$n(T) = 192 + 160 + 128 = 480.$$

The total number of outcomes in the sample space, *S*, is the total number of people surveyed, which is 1,600. Therefore,

$$P(T) = \frac{n(T)}{n(S)} = \frac{480}{1,600} = 0.30.$$

Similarly,

$$P(A) = \frac{n(A)}{n(S)} = \frac{496}{1,600} = 0.31.$$

Also, if you look at the intersection of the column labeled *T* and the row labeled *A*, you see that the number of people surveyed who shop on the Internet more than 10 hours per month and also earn above $60,000 is 192. Therefore,

$$P(T \cap A) = \frac{n(T \cap A)}{n(S)} = \frac{192}{1,600} = 0.12.$$

HISTORICAL HIGHLIGHT 🌸 🌸 🌸

Modern Probability Theory

Modern probability theory began in the seventeenth century when Blaise Pascal and his friend Pierre de Fermat began to study the mathematical principles of gambling. They were answering several questions posed to Pascal by Antoine Gombauld, the Chevalier de Mere:

"How many times should a single die be thrown before we could reasonably expect two sixes?"

"How should prize money in a contest be fairly divided in the case that the contest, for some reason, cannot be completed?"

In 1812, Pierre-Simon de Laplace presented classical probability theory in his work *Theorie Analytique des Probabilities*. Laplace boldly affirmed that all knowledge could be obtained by using the principles he set forth.

Physicists now use probability theory to study radiation and atomic physics, and biologists apply it to genetics and mathematical learning theory. Probability also is a theoretical basis for statistics, which is used in scientific, industrial, and social research.

We can now calculate the probability of the complement of $T \cup A$ as follows:

$$P((T \cup A)') = 1 - P(T \cup A) = 1 - [P(T) + P(A) - P(T \cap A)]$$
$$= 1 - [0.30 + 0.31 - 0.12] = 1 - 0.49 = 0.51.$$

This means that if we select a consumer randomly, there is a 51% chance that the consumer neither spends 10 or more hours per month shopping on the Internet nor has a yearly income above $60,000.

Now try Exercises 21, 22, and 25 to 28. 🌸

Exercises 14.2

Looking Back*

These exercises follow the general outline of the topics presented in this section and will give you a good overview of the material that you have just studied.

1. In Example 1, why did we compute the probability of A' rather than compute $P(A)$ directly?

2. Why did we subtract $\frac{3}{52}$ in calculating $P(H \cup F)$ in Example 2?

3. What was the point of the Between the Numbers Highlight?

4. How did Pascal and Fermat get interested in probability theory?

Sharpening Your Skills

In Exercises 5–12, use the complement formula to find the probability of each event.

5. If the probability that your DVD player breaks down before the extended warranty expires is 0.015, what is the probability that the player will not break down before the warranty expires?

6. If the probability that a vaccine you took will protect you from getting the flu is 0.965, what is the probability that you will get the flu?

7. If there is a 1 in 1,000 chance that you will pick the numbers correctly in tonight's lottery, what is the probability that you will not pick the numbers correctly?

8. If there is a 1 in 4 chance that it will rain for your Fourth of July barbecue, what is the probability that it won't rain?

9. If two dice are rolled, find the probability that neither die shows a five on it.

10. If two dice are rolled, find the probability that the total showing is less than 10.

11. If five coins are flipped, what is the probability of obtaining at least one head?

12. If five coins are flipped, what is the probability of obtaining at least one head and at least one tail?

13. If a single card is drawn from a standard 52-card deck, what is the probability that it is either a five or a red card?

14. If a single card is drawn from a standard 52-card deck, what is the probability that it is either a face card or a red card?

15. If a pair of dice is rolled, what is the probability that the total showing is either odd or greater than eight?

16. If a pair of dice is rolled, what is the probability that the total showing is either even or less than seven?

*Before doing these exercises, you may find it useful to review the note *How to Succeed at Mathematics* on page xix.

In Exercises 17–20, assume that A and B are events.

17. If $P(A \cup B) = 0.85$, $P(B) = 0.40$, and $P(A) = 0.55$, find $P(A \cap B)$.

18. If $P(A \cup B) = 0.75$, $P(B) = 0.45$, and $P(A) = 0.60$, find $P(A \cap B)$.

19. If $P(A \cup B) = 0.70$, $P(A) = 0.40$, and $P(A \cap B) = 0.25$, find $P(B)$.

20. If $P(A \cup B) = 0.60$, $P(B) = 0.45$, and $P(A \cap B) = 0.20$, find $P(A)$.

21. If we draw a card from a standard 52-card deck, what is the probability that the card is neither a heart nor a face card? (*Hint:* Draw a picture of this situation before trying to calculate the probability.)

22. If we draw a card from a standard 52-card deck, what is the probability that the card is neither red nor a queen? (*Hint:* Draw a picture of this situation before trying to calculate the probability.)

Applying What You've Learned

Use the following table from the U.S. Bureau of Labor Statistics, which shows the age distribution of those who earned less than the minimum wage in 2004, to answer Exercises 23 and 24.

Age	Working Below Minimum Wage (thousands)
16–19	329
20–24	420
25–34	320
35–44	175
45–54	125
55–64	61
65 and older	53

23. If we select a worker randomly from those surveyed, what is the probability that the person is younger than 55?

24. If we select a worker randomly from those surveyed, what is the probability that the person is older than 19?

Use the following table, that we presented in Example 4, relating the amount of time consumers spend shopping on the Internet per month with their annual income, to answer Exercises 25–28.

Annual Income	10+ Hours	3–9 Hours	0–2 Hours	Totals
Above $60,000	192	176	128	496
$40,000–$60,000	160	208	144	512
Below $40,000	128	192	272	592
Totals	480	576	544	1,600

25. What is the probability that a consumer we select randomly either spends 0–2 hours per month shopping on the Internet or has an annual income below $40,000?

26. What is the probability that a consumer we select randomly either spends 10 or more hours per month shopping on the Internet or has an annual income between $40,000 and $60,000?

27. What is the probability that a consumer we select randomly neither spends more than 2 hours per month shopping on the Internet nor has an annual income of $60,000 or less?

28. What is the probability that a consumer we select randomly neither spends more than 2 hours per month shopping on the Internet nor has an annual income below $40,000?

Probability of earning commissions. *Joanna earns both a salary and a monthly commission as a sales representative for an electronics store. The following table lists her estimates of the probabilities of earning various commissions next month. Use this table to calculate the probabilities in Exercises 29–32.*

Commission	Probability That This Will Happen
Less than $1,000	0.08
$1,000 to $1,249	0.11
$1,250 to $1,499	0.23
$1,500 to $1,749	0.30
$1,750 to $1,999	0.12
$2,000 to $2,249	0.05
$2,250 to $2,499	0.08
$2,500 or more	0.03

29. The probability that she will earn at least $1,000 in commissions

30. The probability that she will earn at least $1,500 in commissions

31. The probability that she will earn no more than $1,999 in commissions

32. The probability that she will earn less than $2,250 in commissions

A college administration has conducted a study of 200 randomly selected students to determine the relationship between satisfaction with academic advisement and academic success. They obtained the

following information: Of the 70 students on academic probation, 32 are not satisfied with advisement; however, only 20 of the students not on academic probation are dissatisfied with advisement. Use these data to answer Exercises 33–36. In each exercise, assume that we select a student at random.

33. What is the probability that the student is not on academic probation?

34. What is the probability that the student is satisfied with advisement?

35. What is the probability that the student is on academic probation and is satisfied with advisement?

36. What is the probability that the student is not on academic probation and is satisfied with advisement?

Communicating Mathematics

37. Why does $P(E) + P(E') = 1$?

38. What word in Example 4 suggested that we compute the probability of the *complement* of the union of T and A?

In Exercises 39–42, determine whether each statement is true or false for events A and B. Explain your answer.

39. $P(A) = P(A \cup B) - P(B)$

40. $P(A \cup B) - P(B) = P(A \cap B)$

41. $P(A) + P(B) - P(A \cup B) = P(A \cap B)$

42. $P(A \cup B) - P(B) = P(A)$

43. Many texts that discuss probability state that if events E and F are disjoint, then $P(E \cup F) = P(E) + P(F)$. Explain why it is really not necessary to state this formula.

44. If $P(E \cup F) = P(E) + P(F)$, what can you conclude about $P(E \cap F)$?

For Extra Credit

45. If events A, B, and C are as pictured in this Venn diagram, write a formula for $P(A \cup B \cup C)$. Explain your answer.

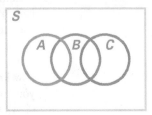

46. If events A, B, and C are as pictured in this Venn diagram, write a formula for $P(A \cup B \cup C)$. Explain your answer.

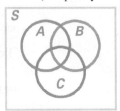

Use the given spinner to answer Exercises 47 to 50. Each green sector occupies 10% of the circle, each blue sector occupies 12%, each red sector occupies 9%, and the yellow sector occupies 4%. Assume that the spinner is spun once. What is the probability that

47. The spinner does not stop on yellow?

48. The spinner stops on an odd number or a green?

49. The spinner stops on neither an odd number nor a blue?

50. The spinner stops on neither green nor an even number?

Conditional Probability and Intersections of Events

14.3

Objectives

1. Understand how to compute conditional probability.
2. Calculate the probability of the intersection of two events.
3. Use probability trees to compute conditional probabilities.
4. Understand the difference between dependent and independent events.

You know how to compute the probability of complements and unions of events. We will now show you how to find the probability of intersections of events, but first you need to understand how the occurrence of one event can affect the probability of another event.

✎ KEY POINT

Conditional probability takes into account that one event occurring may change the probability of a second event.

Conditional Probability

Suppose that you and your friend Marcus cannot agree as to which video to rent and you decide to settle the matter by rolling a pair of dice. You will each pick a number and then roll the dice. The person whose total showing on the dice comes up first gets to pick the video. With your knowledge of probability, you know that the number you should pick is 7 because it has the highest probability of appearing, namely $\frac{1}{6}$.

To illustrate the idea of conditional probability, let's now change this situation slightly. Assume that your friend Janelle will roll the dice before you and Marcus pick your numbers. You are not allowed to see the dice, but Janelle will tell you something about the dice and then you will choose your number before looking at the dice.

Suppose that Janelle tells you that the total showing is an even number. Would you still choose a 7? Of course not, because once you know the *condition* that the total is even, you now know that the probability of having a 7 is 0. A good way to think of this is that once you know that the total is even, you must exclude all pairs from the sample space such as (1, 4), (5, 6), and (4, 3) that give odd totals.

In a similar way, suppose that you draw a card from a standard 52-card deck, put that card in your pocket, and then draw a second card. What is the probability that the second card is a king? How you answer this question depends on knowing what card is in your pocket. If the card in your pocket is a king, then there are three kings remaining in the 51 cards that are left, so the probability is $\frac{3}{51}$. If the card in your pocket is not a king, then the probability of the second card being a king is $\frac{4}{51}$. Why? This discussion leads us to the formal definition of conditional probability.

DEFINITION When we compute the probability of event *F* assuming that the event *E* has already occurred, we call this the **conditional probability** of *F*, given *E*. We denote this probability as $P(F \mid E)$. We read $P(F \mid E)$ as "the probability of *F* given that *E* has occurred," or in a quicker way, "the probability of *F* given *E*."

Do not let this new notation intimidate you. The notation $P(F \mid E)$ simply means that you are going to compute a probability knowing that something else has already happened. For example, in our earlier discussion of Janelle, we said, "The probability of having a total of 7 knowing that the total is even is 0." We will restate this several times, each time increasing our use of symbols. So, we could say instead,

$$P(\text{having a total of 7 given that the total is even}) = 0;$$

or,

$$P(\text{having a total of 7} \mid \text{the total is even}) = 0.$$

If we now represent the event "total is 7" by *F* and "total is even" by *E*, then we could write our original statement as

Total is even.

$$P(F \mid E) = 0.$$

Total is 7.

Similarly, let's return to the example of drawing two cards, and let *A* represent the event that we draw a king on our first card and put it in our pocket and, let *B* represent the event that we draw a king on our second card. Then we could write, "The probability that we draw a second king given that the first card was a king is $\frac{3}{51}$," as

First card was a king.

$$P(B \mid A) = \frac{3}{51}.$$

Second card is a king.

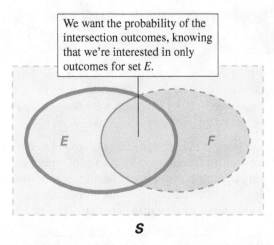

We want the probability of the intersection outcomes, knowing that we're interested in only outcomes for set *E*.

S

FIGURE 14.12 To compute the probability of *F* given *E*, we compare the outcomes in *E* ∩ *F* with the outcomes in *E*.

The Venn diagram in Figure 14.12 will help you remember how to compute conditional probability.

We drew *E* with a heavy line in Figure 14.12 to emphasize that when we assume that *E* has occurred, we can then think of the outcomes outside of *E* as being discarded from the discussion. In computing conditional probability, you will find it useful to consider the sample space to be *E* and the event as being *E* ∩ *F*, rather than *F*. We will first state a special rule for computing conditional probability when the outcomes are equally likely (all have the same probability of occurring). We will state the more general conditional probability rule later.

SPECIAL RULE FOR COMPUTING $P(F|E)$ BY COUNTING   If *E* and *F* are events in a sample space with equally likely outcomes, then $P(F|E) = \dfrac{n(E \cap F)}{n(E)}$.

EXAMPLE 1   *Computing Conditional Probability by Counting*

Assume that we roll two dice and the total showing is greater than nine. What is the probability that the total is odd?

SOLUTION: This sample space has 36 equally likely outcomes. We will let *G* be the event "we roll a total greater than nine" and let *O* be the event "the total is odd." Therefore,

$$G = \{(4, 6), (5, 5), (5, 6), (6, 4), (6, 5), (6, 6)\}.$$

The set *O* consists of all pairs that give an odd total. Figure 14.13 shows you how to use the special rule for computing conditional probability to find $P(O|G)$.

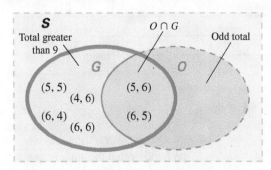

FIGURE 14.13 To compute $P(O|G)$, we compare the number of outcomes in *O* ∩ *G* with the number of outcomes in *G*.

Therefore,

$$P(O|G) = \frac{n(O \cap G)}{n(G)} = \frac{2}{6} = \frac{1}{3}.$$

Notice how the probability of rolling an odd total has changed from $\dfrac{1}{2}$ to $\dfrac{1}{3}$ when we know that the total showing is greater than nine.

Now try Exercises 5 to 22. ✳

PROBLEM SOLVING

The Order Principle

As we have emphasized often, the order in which we do things is important in mathematics. In Example 1, $P(O \mid G)$ does not mean the same thing as $P(G \mid O)$. To understand the difference, state what $P(G \mid O)$ represents and then compute $P(G \mid O)$.

It is important to remember that the special rule for computing conditional probability only works when the outcomes in the sample space are *equally likely*. Sometimes you may be solving a problem where that is not the case; or, you may have a situation where it is not possible to count the outcomes. In such cases, we need a rule for computing $P(F \mid E)$ that is based on probability rather than counting.

> **GENERAL RULE FOR COMPUTING** $P(F|E)$ If E and F are events in a sample space, then $P(F \mid E) = \dfrac{P(E \cap F)}{P(E)}$.

We still can use Figure 14.12 to remember this rule; however, now instead of comparing the number of outcomes in $E \cap F$ with the number of outcomes in E, we compare the probability of $E \cap F$ with the probability of E.

EXAMPLE 2   *Using the General Rule for Computing Conditional Probability*

The state bureau of labor statistics conducted a survey of college graduates comparing starting salaries to majors. The survey results are listed in Table 14.6.

Major	$30,000 and Below	$30,001 to $35,000	$35,001 to $40,000	$40,001 to $45,000	Above $45,000	Totals (%)
Liberal arts	6*	10	9	1	1	27
Science	2	4	10	2	2	20
Social sciences	3	6	7	1	1	18
Health fields	1	1	8	3	1	14
Technology	0	2	7	8	4	21
Totals (%)	12	23	41	15	9	100

*These numbers are percentages.

TABLE 14.6 Survey comparing starting salaries to major in college.

If we select a graduate who was offered between $40,001 and $45,000, what is the probability that the student has a degree in the health fields?

SOLUTION: Each entry in Table 14.6 is the probability of an event. For example, the 8% that we highlighted is the probability of selecting a graduate in technology who earns between $40,001 and $45,000, inclusive. The 14% that we highlighted tells us the probability of selecting a graduate who majored in the health fields.

Let R be the event "the graduate received a starting salary between $40,001 and $45,000" and H be the event "the student has a degree in the health fields." *It is important in doing this problem that you identify clearly what you are given and what you must find.* We are given R and must find the probability of H, so we want to find $P(H \mid R)$, not $P(R \mid H)$.

Because we want the probability of H given R, we can, in effect, ignore all the outcomes that do not correspond to a starting salary of $40,001 to $45,000. We darken the columns we want to ignore in Table 14.7.

Major	$30,000 or Below	$30,001 to $35,000	$35,001 to $40,000	$40,001 to $45,000	Above $45,000	Totals (%)
Liberal arts	6	10	9	1	1	27
Science	2	4	10	2	2	20
Social sciences	3	6	7	1	1	18
Health fields	1	1	8	3	1	14
Technology	0	2	7	8	4	21
Totals (%)	12	23	41	15	9	100

TABLE 14.7 The columns we want to ignore are darkened.

In order to use the general rule for computing conditional probability, we first need to know $P(R)$ and $P(H \cap R)$, as you can see from Figure 14.14.

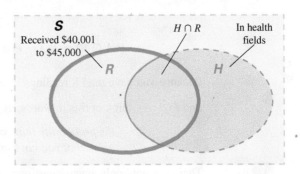

FIGURE 14.14 To compute $P(H \mid R)$, we compare $P(H \cap R)$ with $P(R)$.

Therefore,

$$P(H \mid R) = \frac{P(H \cap R)}{P(R)} = \frac{0.03}{0.15} = 0.20.$$

If a graduate receives an offer between $40,001 and $45,000, then the probability that the person is in the health fields is 0.20, or 20%.

Now try Exercises 49 to 52. ✳ **8**

The Intersection of Events

We can now find a formula to compute the probability of the intersection of two events. The general rule for computing conditional probability states that

$$P(F \mid E) = \frac{P(E \cap F)}{P(E)}.$$

If we multiply both sides of this equation by the expression $P(E)$, we get

$$P(E) \cdot P(F \mid E) = P(E) \cdot \frac{P(E \cap F)}{P(E)}.$$

Canceling $P(E)$ from the numerator and denominator of the right side of this equation gives us the rule for computing the probability of the intersection of events E and F.

> **RULE FOR COMPUTING THE PROBABILITY OF THE INTERSECTION OF EVENTS** If E and F are two events, then
>
> $$P(E \cap F) = P(E) \cdot P(F \mid E).$$

Quiz Yourself **8**

Assume that we select a graduate who received more than $45,000 as a starting salary. Use Table 14.7 to find the probability that the graduate has a degree in technology.

KEY POINT

We use conditional probability to find the probability of the intersection of two events.

This rule says that to find the probability of $P(E \cap F)$, you first find the probability of E and then multiply it by the probability of F, *assuming that E has occurred.*

EXAMPLE 3   *Estimating Your Grade in a Class*

Assume that for your literature final your professor has written questions on 10 assigned readings on cards and you are to randomly select two cards and write an essay on them. If you have read 8 of the 10 readings, what is your probability of getting two questions that you can answer? (We will assume that if you've done a reading, then you can answer the question about that reading; otherwise, you can't answer the question.)

SOLUTION: We can think of this event as the intersection of two events A and B where

     A is "you can answer the first question;"

     B is "you can answer the second question."

By the rule we just stated, you need to calculate

probability you can answer the first question

probability you can answer the second question, given that you answered the first question

$$P(A \cap B) = P(A) \cdot P(B \mid A).$$

Because you have read 8 readings from 10 that were assigned, we see that $P(A) = \dfrac{8}{10}$. To find $P(B \mid A)$, think of this in words, as we want to find

> *the probability that you can answer the second question,*
> *given that you have answered the first question.*

There are now only seven questions that you can answer on the remaining nine cards so $P(B \mid A) = \dfrac{7}{9}$. Thus the probability that you get two questions on readings that you have done is

$$P(A \cap B) = P(A) \cdot P(B \mid A) = \frac{8}{10} \cdot \frac{7}{9} = \frac{56}{90} \approx 0.62.$$

Now try Exercises 27 to 40. ✳

Quiz Yourself ❾

Suppose that we draw 2 cards without replacement from a standard 52-card deck. What is the probability that both cards are face cards?

◉ *Some Good Advice*

A common mistake that you can make when computing conditional probability is to use the formula $P(A \cap B) = P(A) \cdot P(B)$. That is, you may forget to take into account that event A has occurred. Notice that if we had used this incorrect formula in Example 3, the probability that you can answer the second question would have been $\dfrac{8}{10}$, not $\dfrac{7}{9}$. In effect, we would have computed the second probability as though the first question had been returned to the cards.

✎ **KEY POINT**

Trees help you visualize probability computations.

Probability Trees

Recall that the Three-Way Principle in Section 1.1 tells you that drawing a diagram is a good problem-solving technique. You will find that it is often very helpful to draw a probability tree to help you understand a conditional probability problem.

> **USING TREES TO CALCULATE PROBABILITIES**   We can represent an experiment that happens in stages with a tree whose branches represent the outcomes of the experiment. We calculate the probability of an outcome by multiplying the probabilities found along the branch representing that outcome. We will call these trees **probability trees**.

In order to show you how to use trees to visualize conditional probabilities, we will look at the situation in Example 3 again.

EXAMPLE 4   *Using a Tree to Compute Probabilities*

Recall that you are taking an exam and will pick two questions. Eight of the 10 questions are on readings that you have done and 2 are on readings you have not done. What is the probability that you will get questions on two readings that you have not done? (We will assume that if you've done a reading, then you can answer the question about that reading; otherwise, you can't answer the question.)

SOLUTION: A will represent the event, "you can answer a question," and N^* will represent the event "you can't answer a question." The tree in Figure 14.15(a) shows that when you draw your first card you either can answer the question or not. Because 8 of the 10 cards have questions you can answer, $P(A) = \dfrac{8}{10}$, and because there are two questions you can't answer, $P(N) = \dfrac{2}{10}$.

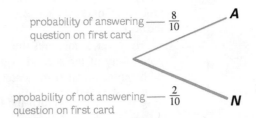

FIGURE 14.15 (a) Tree showing the probabilities on the first draw.

We have indicated the two possibilities for the first draw, namely, A or N. Notice how we place the probabilities for A and N on the branches of the tree. In Figure 14.15(b), we add more branches to show the possibilities for drawing the second card.

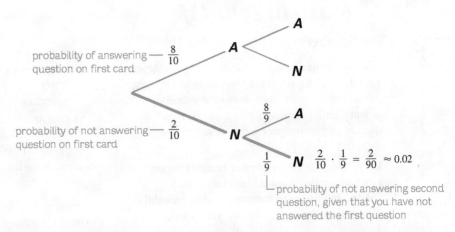

FIGURE 14.15 (b) Tree showing the probabilities when drawing two cards.

From Figure 14.15(b), you can see that the probability of not answering the first question is $P(N) = \dfrac{2}{10}$. If you did not answer the first question, then there is only one of the remaining nine cards with a question you can't answer. So the probability of not answering

---

*Recognize that the event N is just another name for A', the complement of A.

Quiz Yourself ❿

In Example 4, what is the probability that you can answer the first question, but not the second?

the second question is $\frac{1}{9}$. Thus, the probability that you can't answer the first question and also can't answer the second question is

$$P(N) \cdot P(N \mid N) = \frac{2}{10} \cdot \frac{1}{9} = \frac{2}{90} \approx 0.02.$$

probability of not — answering first question

— probability of not answering second question, given that you did not answer first question

 ❿

The probability tree in Figure 14.15(b), describes four (non-equally-likely) outcomes: (A, A), (A, N), (N, A), (N, N). We can find the probability of each of these outcomes by multiplying the probabilities along the branch that corresponds to that outcome. In Example 3, we found the probability of (A, A) without drawing a tree. In Example 4, we found the probability of (N, N), by multiplying the probabilities along the bottom branch of the tree.

KEY POINT

Independent events have no effect on each other's probabilities.

Dependent and Independent Events

As we have seen, knowing that a first event has occurred may affect the way we calculate the probability of a second event. Such was the case in Example 3 when we computed the probability of drawing a second card, given that a first card was drawn and not returned to the deck.

However, sometimes the occurrence of a first event has no effect whatsoever on the probability of the second event. This would be the case if you were drawing 2 cards with replacement from a standard 52-card deck. The probability of drawing a first king is $\frac{4}{52}$. If you return the king to the deck and draw again, the probability of the second king is also $\frac{4}{52}$. Therefore, drawing the first king would not affect the probability of drawing a second king. So you see that sometimes two events influence each other and other times they do not.

Math in Your Life

The Numbers Don't Lie—Or Do They?

- In an article in *Chance* magazine, Mary C. Meyer, a statistics professor at the University of Georgia, claims that a recent study shows the probability of your death in a automobile accident is slightly greater if your car has an airbag than if it doesn't.

- *The Ottowa Citizen* reports that Dennis Lindley, a professor of statistics at University College, London, has derived a formula based on probability that tells you the optimal age for you to settle down. His formula is $X + \frac{Y - X}{2.718}$, where X is the age at which you start looking for a spouse and Y is the age at which you expect to stop looking. According to Lindley's formula, if you start searching at age 16 and expect to stop looking at age 60, then

the best age for you to choose a mate is at age

$$16 + \frac{60 - 16}{2.718} \approx 32 \text{ years.}$$

- A third article from the Woods Hole Oceanographic Institute in Massachusetts states that commercial fishing is one of the least safe occupations. If you are a commercial fisherman, you are 16 times more likely to die on the job than a firefighter or a police officer.

Truly probability is all around us. Do you agree with the previous statements? Or do they go against your "common sense?" Do you feel that something is missing? As we have been emphasizing throughout this text, always remember that when someone builds a model, they decide what goes into the model and what is left out. Maybe the numbers don't lie—or, . . . maybe . . . sometimes they do.

> **DEFINITIONS** Events E and F are **independent** events if
>
> $$P(F \mid E) = P(F).$$
>
> If $P(F \mid E) \neq P(F)$, then E and F are **dependent**.

This definition says that if E and F are independent, then knowing that E has occurred does not influence the way we compute the probability of F.

PROBLEM SOLVING
The Analogies Principle

Recall that the Analogies Principle in Section 1.1 tells you that mathematical terminology, symbolism, and its equations are often based on real-life ideas. Although at times it may seem difficult, if you work hard to make the connection between the intuitive ideas and the mathematical formalism, you will be rewarded by your increased understanding of mathematics. If you understand how the everyday usage of the terms *independent* and *dependent* corresponds to their mathematical definitions, it will help you remember their meaning.

EXAMPLE 5 *Determining Whether Events Are Independent or Dependent*

Assume we roll a red and a green die. Are the events F, "a five shows on the red die," and G, "the total showing on the dice is greater than 10," independent or dependent?

SOLUTION: To answer this question, we must determine whether $P(G \mid F)$ and $P(G)$ are the same or different. There are three outcomes—(5, 6), (6, 5), and (6, 6)—that give a total greater than 10, so $P(G) = \dfrac{3}{36} = \dfrac{1}{12}$.

Now,

$$F = \{(5, 1), (5, 2), (5, 3), (5, 4), (5, 5), (5, 6)\}$$

and

$$G \cap F = \{(5, 6)\},$$

so

$$P(G \mid F) = \frac{P(G \cap F)}{P(F)} = \frac{1/36}{6/36} = \frac{1}{6}.$$

Because $P(G \mid F) \neq P(G)$, the events are dependent.

Now try Exercises 45 to 48. ✳ **11**

Quiz Yourself **11**

The situation is the same as in Example 5. Are the events F, "a five shows on the red die," and O, "an odd total shows on the dice," dependent or independent?

EXAMPLE 6 *Selecting a Dormitory Room*

Brianna is taking part in a lottery for a room in one of the new dormitories at her college. She is guaranteed a space, but she will have to draw a card randomly to determine exactly which room she will have. Each card has the name of one dormitory, X, Y, or Z, and also has a two-person room number or an apartment number. Thirty percent of the available spaces are in X, 50% in Y, and 20% of the spaces are in Z.

Half of the available spaces in X are in rooms, 40% of Y's spaces are in rooms, and 30% of the spaces in Z are in rooms.

a) Draw a probability tree to describe this situation.

b) Given that Brianna selects a card for dormitory Y, what is the probability that she will be assigned to an apartment?

c) What is the probability that Brianna will be assigned an apartment in one of the three dormitories?

SOLUTION:

a) In drawing the tree, we will think of Brianna's assignment happening in two stages. First, she is assigned a dormitory, and then she is assigned either a room or an apartment. We show the tree in Figure 14.16, which begins with three branches corresponding to the dormitories X, Y, and Z. Each of these three branches has two further branches representing the assignment of either a room or an apartment.

We wrote various probabilities along the tree's branches in Figure 14.16. If you look carefully at the lower branch, you see that the 0.20 is the probability that Brianna will be assigned to dormitory Z; thus, $P(Z) = 0.20$. The 0.70 is a conditional probability. Assuming the condition that she is assigned to dormitory Z, then there is a 0.70 chance that she will be assigned to an apartment. Symbolically, this means that $P(Apartment \mid Z) = 0.70$.

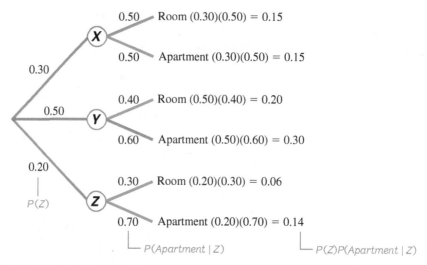

FIGURE 14.16 Probability tree for Brianna's room assignment.

The product $(0.20)(0.70) = 0.14$ is the probability that Brianna will be assigned to dormitory Z and also to an apartment.* We could have written this numeric equation more formally as

$$P(Z \cap Apartment) = P(Z) \cdot P(Apartment \mid Z),$$

which is the formula we gave you for computing the probability of the intersection of two events. In Quiz Yourself 12, we will ask you to interpret some more of these probabilities.

b) We can answer this question easily by looking at the branch that is highlighted in red in Figure 14.16. That branch shows that after Brianna has been assigned to dormitory Y, there is then a 0.60 chance that she will get an apartment. That is, $P(Apartment \mid Y) = 0.60$.

---

*It may seem that we have gotten away from thinking of events as subsets of the sample space, but we have not. The "Z" represents the set of cards that have dormitory Z written on them, and "*Apartment*" represents the set of all cards that have apartment written on them.

Quiz Yourself 12

a) Explain the meaning of the 0.30 on the top branch of the tree in Figure 14.16.

b) What is the probability that Brianna will be assigned a room, given that she is assigned to dormitory Y?

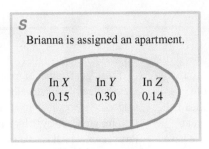

FIGURE 14.17 Probabilities that Brianna is assigned an apartment in dormitories X, Y, or Z.

c) Realize that if Brianna is assigned to an apartment, then she is in *exactly one* of dormitories X, Y, or Z. Figure 14.17 shows how to find the probability that she is assigned an apartment.

From Figure 14.17, we see that the event "Brianna is assigned an apartment" is the union of three mutually disjoint subevents with probabilities 0.15, 0.30, and 0.14. Therefore, the probability that Brianna is assigned an apartment is $0.15 + 0.30 + 0.14 = 0.59$.

Now try Exercises 57 to 60. 12

We will now return to the issue of drug testing that we mentioned in the chapter opener.

EXAMPLE 7 *Drug Testing**

Assume that you are working for a company that has a mandatory drug testing policy. It is estimated that 2% of the employees use a certain drug, and the company is giving a test that is 99% accurate in identifying users of this drug. What is the probability that if an employee is identified by this test as a drug user, the person is innocent?

SOLUTION: Let D be the event "the person is a drug user" and let T be the event "the person tests positive for the drug." We are asking, then, "if we are given that the person tests positive, what is the probability that the person does not use the drug?" Realize that the complement of D, namely D', is the event "the person does not use the drug." So, we are asking for the conditional probability

$$P(D' \mid T).$$

Person does not use drug ⌐　└─ given that person tests positive.

The probability tree in Figure 14.18 will give you some insight into this problem.

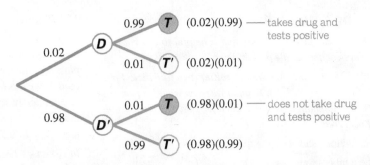

FIGURE 14.18 Tree showing probabilities for drug testing.

Recall that $P(D' \mid T) = \dfrac{P(D' \cap T)}{P(T)}$. Branches 1 and 3 in Figure 14.18 correspond to the drug test being positive. This means that $P(T) = (0.02)(0.99) + (0.98)(0.01)$. The event $D' \cap T$ corresponds to branch 3. Therefore, $P(D' \cap T) = (0.98)(0.01)$. From this, we see that the probability that an innocent person will test positive for the drug is

$$P(D' \mid T) = \frac{P(D' \cap T)}{P(T)} = \frac{(0.98)(0.01)}{(0.02)(0.99) + (0.98)(0.01)} = \frac{0.0098}{.0296} \approx 0.331.$$

In other words, if a person tests positive, there is a roughly $\dfrac{1}{3}$ chance that the person is innocent!

Now try Exercises 71 and 72. ✳

---

*This example is based on an article that can be found at www.intuitor.com/statistics/BadTestResults.html.

✾ ✾ ✾ HIGHLIGHT

Expert Systems

Whether playing chess, doing mathematics, making soup, or practicing law, what makes an expert different from the rest of us? Scientists studying this question have learned that organizing knowledge effectively makes a person an expert. Researchers in the area of artificial intelligence have developed complex computer programs called expert systems that rely heavily on conditional probability to draw conclusions from an organized body of information.

The "grandfather of expert systems" is an ingenious program called Mycin, developed at Stanford University, which diagnoses blood infections. Some other well-known expert systems are Hearsay, which understands spoken language; Prospector, which is able to predict the location of valuable mineral resources; and Internist, which can diagnose many internal diseases. With ongoing research in this area, expert systems continue to be a major application of probability theory.

Exercises 14.3

Looking Back*

These exercises follow the general outline of the topics presented in this section and will give you a good overview of the material that you have just studied.

1. In Example 1, what were we computing when we found $P(O|G)$?

2. We blanked out all columns in Table 14.7, except one. Why did we do this?

3. In Example 5, how did we determine that the events F and G were independent?

4. What is an expert system?

Sharpening Your Skills

In many of these exercises, you may find it helpful to draw a tree diagram before computing the probabilities.

In Exercises 5–8, assume that we are rolling two fair dice. First compute $P(F)$ *and then* $P(F|E)$. *Explain why you would expect the probability of* F *to change as it did when we added the condition that* E *had occurred.*

5. *E*—an odd total shows on the dice.
   F—the total is seven.

6. *E*—an even total shows on the dice.
   F—the total is four.

7. *E*—a three shows on at least one of the dice.
   F—the total is less than five.

8. *E*—a two shows on at least one of the dice.
   F—the total is greater than five.

In Exercises 9–12, we are drawing a single card from a standard 52-card deck. Find each probability.

9. *P*(heart | red)

10. *P*(king | face card)

11. *P*(seven | nonface card)

12. *P*(even-numbered card | nonface card)

You are to randomly pick one disk from a bag that contains the disks shown below. Find each of the following probabilities. For example, P(heart | yellow) *means you are to find the probability of a heart being on the disk, given that the disk is yellow.*

13. *P*(heart | yellow)

14. *P*(pink | smiley face)

15. *P*(yellow | heart)

16. *P*(heart | blue)

17. *P*(heart | pink)

18. *P*(smiley face | blue)

Playing a store's discount game. *To stimulate business, a department store has introduced a game called "Register Roulette." To play, a customer selects a first purchase and a second purchase to qualify for a discount. The customer then reaches into a container and randomly selects two game tokens. There are 50 green tokens that qualify a purchase for a 10% discount, 10 blue tokens that result in a 20% discount, and 2 red tokens that give a 50% discount.*

In Exercises 19–22, assume that you are randomly selecting two of these tokens, without replacement. Compute $P(F|E)$.

19. *E*—you select a red token first.
    F—the second token is green.

20. *E*—you select a red token first.
    F—the second token is red.

21. *E*—you select a nonred token first.
    F—the second token is red.

22. *E*—you select a nonred token first.
    F—the second token is nonred.

According to U.S. government statistics, mononucleosis (mono) is four times more common among college students than the rest of the population. Blood tests for the disease are not 100% accurate. Assume that

---

the following table of data was obtained regarding students who came to your school's health center complaining of tiredness, a sore throat, and slight fever. Use these data to answer Exercises 23–26.

	Has Mono	Doesn't Have Mono	Totals
Positive Blood Test	72	4	76
Negative Blood Test	8	56	64
Totals	80	60	140

If a student is selected from this group, what is the probability of each of the following?

23. The student has mono, given that the test is positive.

24. The student does not have mono, given that the test is positive.

25. The test is positive, given that the student has mono.

26. The test is negative, given that the student does not have mono.

Probability and drawing cards. *In Exercises 27–32, assume that we draw 2 cards from a standard 52-card deck. Find the desired probabilities.*

a) *First assume that the cards are drawn without replacement.*

b) *Next assume that the cards are drawn with replacement.*

27. The probability that we draw two jacks

28. The probability that we draw two hearts

29. The probability that we draw a face card followed by a non-face card

30. The probability that we draw a heart followed by a spade

31. The probability that we draw a jack and a king

32. The probability that we draw a heart and a spade

33. We are drawing 2 cards without replacement from a standard 52-card deck. Find the probability that we draw at least one face card. (*Hint:* Consider the complement.)

34. We are drawing 2 cards with replacement from a standard 52-card deck. Find the probability that we draw at least one heart. (*Hint:* Consider the complement.)

35. We draw 3 cards without replacement from a standard 52-card deck. Find the probability of drawing three face cards.

36. We draw 3 cards without replacement from a standard 52-card deck. Find the probability of drawing three spades.

37. We draw 3 cards without replacement from a standard 52-card deck. Find the probability of drawing exactly two hearts.

38. We draw 3 cards without replacement from a standard 52-card deck. Find the probability of drawing exactly two kings.

39. We roll a pair of dice three times. Find the probability that a total of five is rolled each time.

40. We roll a pair of dice three times. Find the probability that a total of five is rolled exactly twice.

Assume that the Political Action Club on your campus has gathered the following information about the 2008 Democratic presidential election. Use this table to answer Exercises 41–44.

	Democrat	Republican	Independent	Totals
Preferred Obama	15	68	15	98
Preferred McCain	105	12	25	142
Totals	120	80	40	240

If a student is selected from this group, what is the probability of each of the following?

41. The student is a Democrat, given that he preferred McCain.

42. The student is an Independent, given that he preferred McCain.

43. The student preferred McCain, given that the student is an Independent.

44. The student preferred Obama, given that the student is a Republican.

Probability and rolling dice. *In Exercises 45–48, we are rolling a pair of fair dice. For each pair of events, determine whether E and F are dependent.*

45. *E*—the total showing is greater than nine.

   F—the total showing is even.

46. *E*—at least one 2 shows on the dice.

   F—the total showing is less than six.

47. *E*—a three shows on the first die.

   F—the total showing is even.

48. *E*—the total showing is odd.

   F—the total showing is greater than four.

Applying What You've Learned

Probability and starting salaries. *The following table from Example 2 relates starting salaries of college graduates and their majors. In Exercises 49–52, find* P(F | E).

Major	$30,000 or Below	$30,001 to $35,000	$35,001 to $40,000	$40,001 to $45,000	Above $45,000	Totals (%)
Liberal arts	6*	10	9	1	1	27
Science	2	4	10	2	2	20
Social sciences	3	6	7	1	1	18
Health fields	1	1	8	3	1	14
Technology	0	2	7	8	4	21
Totals (%)	12	23	41	15	9	100

*These numbers are percentages.

49. *E*—a person majored in social science.

   F—a person received a starting salary between $30,001 and $35,000.

50. *E*—a person majored in science.

   F—a person received a starting salary between $35,001 and $40,000.

51. *E*—a person received a starting salary between $40,001 and $45,000.

   F—a person majored in technology.

52. *E*—a person received a starting salary between $30,001 and $35,000.

   F—a person majored in liberal arts.

Assume that a softball player has a .300 batting average—to keep this simple we'll assume that this means the player has 0.30 probability of getting a hit in each at bat. Use this information to answer Exercises 53–56. Assume that the player bats four times.

53. What is the probability that she gets a hit only in her first at bat?

54. What is the probability that she gets exactly one hit? (Realize that there are four ways to do this.)

55. What is the probability that she gets exactly two hits?

56. What is the probability that she gets at least one hit? (*Hint:* Think complement.)

Selecting a dormitory room. *Exercises 57–60 refer to the tree diagram that we drew in Figure 14.16 of Example 6.*

57. What is the meaning of the number 0.40 on the top middle branch of Figure 14.16?

58. What is *P*(*Room* ∩ *Y*)?

59. What is *P*(*Apartment* | *X*)?

60. If Brianna gets an apartment, what is the probability that she is in dorm *Z*?

Testing a cold medication. *Imagine that you are taking part in a study to test a new cold medicine. Although you don't know exactly what drug you are taking, the probability that it is drug A is 10%, that it is drug B is 20%, and that it is drug C, 70%. From past clinical trials, the probabilities that these drugs will improve your condition are: A (30%), B (60%), and C (70%).*

61. Draw a tree to illustrate this drug trial situation.

62. What is the probability that you will improve given that you are taking drug B?

63. What is the probability that you will improve?

64. If you improve, what is the probability that you are taking drug B?

65. **Probability and exam questions.** Assume that either Professor Ansah or Professor Brunich has constructed the comprehensive exam that you must pass for graduation. Because each professor has extremely different views, it would be useful for you to know who has written the exam questions so that you can slant your answers accordingly. Assume that there is a 60% chance that Ansah wrote the exam. Ansah asks a question about international relations 30% of the time and Brunich asks a similar question 75% of the time. If there is a question on the exam regarding international relations, what is the probability that Ansah wrote the exam?

66. **Probability and exam questions.** Assume now that a third professor, Professor Ubaru, writes the exam 20% of the time, Brunich 30% of the time, and Ansah the rest. Ubaru asks a question about international relations 40% of the time, Brunich 35% of the time, and Ansah 25% of the time. If there is an international relations question on the exam, what is the probability that Brunich did not write the exam?

Product reliability. *You want to purchase a DVD drive for your laptop computer. Assume that 65% of the drives are made outside the United States. Of the U.S.-made drives, 4% are defective; of the foreign-made drives, 6% are defective. Determine each probability rounded to three decimal places.*

67. The probability that the drive you purchase is U.S. made and is not defective

68. The probability that the drive you purchase is foreign made and is defective

69. If your drive is defective, the probability that it is foreign made

70. If your drive is defective, the probability that it is made in the United States

Drug testing. *In Exercises 71 and 72, do computations similar to those in Example 7 using this revised information. Assume that 4% of the employees use the drug and that the test correctly identifies a drug user 98% of the time. Also assume that the test identifies a nonuser as a drug user 3% of the time.*

71. If an employee tests positive, what is the probability that the person is innocent?

72. If an employee tests negative, what is the probability that the person is a user?

Communicating Mathematics

73. If you know the conditional probability formula $P(F\,|\,E) = \dfrac{P(E \cap F)}{P(E)}$, how do you find the probability formula for $P(E \cap F)$?

74. We say that events *E* and *F* are independent if $P(F\,|\,E) = P(F)$. Give an intuitive explanation of what this equation is saying.

75. In what ways are the special and general rules for computing conditional events similar? How are they different?

76. If *A* and *B* are events, can $P(B\,|\,A) = P(B)$? When?

77. Explain how the formal definition of dependent and independent events corresponds to your intuitive understanding of these words in English.

78. The formula $P(E \cap F) = P(E) \cdot P(F)$ is, in general, not true. When can we use this formula instead of the correct formula, $P(E \cap F) = P(E) \cdot P(F\,|\,E)$?

Using Technology to Investigate Mathematics

79. Search the Internet for "expert systems." Report on an interesting site that you find.

80. Search the Internet for "amazing applications of probability and statistics." Report on an interesting site that you find.

For Extra Credit

The birthday problem. *A surprising result that appears in many elementary discussions on probability is called the birthday problem. The question simply stated is this: "If we poll a certain number of people, what is the probability that at least two of those people were born on the same day of the year?" For example, it may be that in the survey two people were both born on March 29.*

To solve this problem, we will use the formula for computing the probability of a complement of an event. It is clear that

P(*duplication of some birthdays*) = 1 − P(*no duplications*)

To illustrate this, assume that we have three people. To have no duplications, the second person must have a birthday that is different

from that of the first person, and the third person must have a birthday that is different from the first two. The probability that the second birthday is different from the first is $\frac{364}{365}$. The probability that the third person has a birthday different from the first two is $\frac{363}{365}$.

Therefore, for three people,

P(*duplication of birthdays*) = 1 − P(*no duplication of birthdays*)

$$= 1 - \left(\frac{364}{365}\right)\left(\frac{363}{365}\right) = 0.0082.$$

In Exercises 81–84, we will look at several other cases.

81. Assume that we have 10 people. Find the probability that at least 2 of the 10 people were born on the same day of the year.

82. Repeat Exercise 81 for 20 people.

83. Find the smallest number of people such that the probability of two of them being born on the same day of the year is greater than 0.50.

84. Conduct an experiment by surveying groups of various sizes* to see how your surveys conform to the predicted probabilities. If five people are working in a group, each person can survey four groups of 20, 30, 40, and so on to generate a reasonable amount of data.

---

*Instead of surveying people, you can write the numbers 1 to 365 on pieces of paper or cardboard and draw these from a box *with replacement.* Be sure to shake the container well before each draw. In this way you can quickly simulate interviews of groups of 20, 30, or 40 people, with the purpose of determining how close your experimental results conform to the predicted probabilities.

Expected Value

Objectives

1. Understand the meaning of expected value.
2. Calculate the expected value of lotteries and games of chance.
3. Use expected value to solve applied problems.

Life and Health Insurers' Profits Skyrocket 213% . . .*

How do insurance companies make so much money? When you buy car insurance, you are playing a sort of mathematical game with the insurance company. You are betting that you are going to have an accident—the insurance company is betting that you won't. Similarly, with health insurance, you are betting that you will be sick—the insurance company is betting that you will stay well. With life insurance, you are betting that, . . . well, . . . you get the idea.

Expected Value

Casinos also amass their vast profits by relying on this same mathematical theory—called **expected value**, which we will introduce to you in this section. Expected value uses probability to compare alternatives to help us make decisions.

Because of an increase in theft on campus, your school now offers personal property insurance that covers items such as laptops, iPods, cell phones, and even books. Although

---

*According to a report by Weiss Ratings, Inc., a provider of independent ratings of financial institutions.

the premium seems a little high, the insurance will fully replace any lost or stolen items. Our first example will help you get an idea of how probability can help you understand situations such as this.

EXAMPLE 1   *Evaluating an Insurance Policy*

Suppose that you want to insure a laptop computer, an iPhone, a trail bike, and your textbooks. Table 14.8 lists the values of these items and the probabilities that these items will be stolen over the next year.

a) Predict what the insurance company can expect to pay in claims on your policy.

b) Is $100 a fair premium for this policy?

Item	Value	Probability of Being Stolen	Expected Payout by Insurance Company
Laptop	$2,000	0.02	0.02($2,000) = $40
iPhone	$400	0.03	0.03($400) = $12
Trail bike	$600	0.01	0.01($600) = $6
Textbooks	$800	0.04	0.04($800) = $32

TABLE 14.8 Value of personal items and the probability of their being stolen.

SOLUTION:

a) From Table 14.8 the company has a 2% chance of having to pay you $2,000, or, another way to look at this is the company expects to lose on average 0.02($2,000) = $40 by insuring your computer. Similarly, the expected loss on insuring your iPhone is 0.03($400) = $12. To estimate, on average, what it would cost the company to insure all four items, we compute the following sum:

probability of iPhone being stolen ── ┌cost of iPhone probability of books being stolen ── ┌cost of books

$$0.02(\$2,000) + 0.03(\$400) + 0.01(\$600) + 0.04(\$800) = \$90.$$

probability of computer being stolen ──┘ └cost of computer probability of bike being stolen ──┘ └cost of bike

The $90 represents, *on average*, what the company can expect to pay out on a policy such as yours.

b) The $90 in part a) is telling us that if the insurance company were to write one million policies like this, it would expect to pay 1,000,000 × ($90) = $90,000,000 in claims. If the company is to make a profit, it must charge more than $90 as a premium, so it seems like a $100 premium is reasonable. ✳ ⑬

The amount of $90 we found in Example 1 is called the *expected value* of the claims paid by the insurance company. We will now give the formal definition of this notion.

> **DEFINITION** Assume that an experiment has outcomes numbered 1 to *n* with probabilities $P_1, P_2, P_3, \ldots, P_n$. Assume that each outcome has a numerical value associated with it and these are labeled $V_1, V_2, V_3, \ldots, V_n$. The **expected value** of the experiment is
>
> $$(P_1 \cdot V_1) + (P_2 \cdot V_2) + (P_3 \cdot V_3) + \cdots + (P_n \cdot V_n).$$

In Example 1, the probabilities were $P_1 = 0.02$, $P_2 = 0.03$, $P_3 = 0.01$, and $P_4 = 0.04$. The values were $V_1 = 2,000$, $V_2 = 400$, $V_3 = 600$, and $V_4 = 800$.

Quiz Yourself ⑬

In Example 1, if you were to drop coverage on your iPhone and add coverage on your saxophone that cost $1,400, what would the insurance company now expect to pay out in claims if the probability of the saxophone being stolen is 4% and the probability of your books being stolen is reduced to 3%?

Some Good Advice

Pay careful attention to what notation tells you to do in performing a calculation. In calculating expected value, you are told to *first* multiply the probability of each outcome by its value and *then* add these products together.

Expected Value of Games of Chance

EXAMPLE 2 *Computing Expected Value When Flipping Coins*

What is the number of heads we can expect when we flip four fair coins?

SOLUTION: Recall that there are 16 ways to flip four coins. We will consider the outcomes for this experiment to be the different numbers of heads that could arise. Of course, these outcomes are not equally likely, as we indicate in Table 14.9. If you don't see this at first, you could draw a tree to show the 16 possible ways that four coins can be flipped. You would find that 1 of the 16 branches corresponds to no heads, 4 of the 16 branches would represent flipping exactly one head, and 6 of the 16 branches would represent flipping exactly two heads, and so on.

We calculate the expected number of heads by first multiplying each outcome by its probability and then adding these products, as follows:

$$\left(\frac{1}{16}\cdot 0\right) + \left(\frac{4}{16}\cdot 1\right) + \left(\frac{6}{16}\cdot 2\right) + \left(\frac{4}{16}\cdot 3\right) + \left(\frac{1}{16}\cdot 4\right) = \frac{32}{16} = 2$$

probability of 0 heads — probability of 1 head

Thus we can expect to flip two heads when we flip four coins, which corresponds to our intuition. ✹

Number of Heads	Probability
0	$\frac{1}{16}$
1	$\frac{4}{16}$
2	$\frac{6}{16}$
3	$\frac{4}{16}$
4	$\frac{1}{16}$

TABLE 14.9 Probabilities of obtaining a number of heads when flipping four coins.

We can use the notion of expected value to predict the likelihood of winning (or more likely losing) at games of chance such as blackjack, roulette, and even lotteries.

EXAMPLE 3 *The Expected Value of a Roulette Wheel*

Although there are many ways to bet on the 38 numbers of a roulette wheel,* one simple betting scheme is to place a bet, let's say $1, on a single number. In this case, the casino pays you $35 (you also keep your $1 bet) if your number comes up and otherwise you lose the $1. What is the expected value of this bet?

SOLUTION: We can think of this betting scheme as an experiment with two outcomes:

1. Your number comes up and the value to you is +$35.
2. Your number doesn't come up and the value to you is −$1.

Because there are 38 equally likely numbers that can occur, the probability of the first outcome is $\frac{1}{38}$ and the probability of the second is $\frac{37}{38}$. The expected value of this bet is therefore

$$\left(\frac{1}{38}\cdot 35\right) + \left(\frac{37}{38}\cdot(-1)\right) = \frac{35-37}{38} = \frac{-2}{38} = -\frac{1}{19} = -0.0526.$$

probability of winning — amount won
probability of losing — amount lost

*See Example 8 in Section 14.1 for a description of a roulette wheel.

This amount means that, on the average, the casino expects you to lose slightly more than 5 cents for every dollar you bet.

Now try Exercises 3 to 8. ✣

The roulette wheel in Example 3 is an example of an unfair game.

> **DEFINITIONS** If a game has an expected value of 0, then the game is called **fair**. A game in which the expected value is not 0 is called an **unfair game**.

Although it would seem that you would not want to play an unfair game, in order for a casino or a state lottery to make a profit, the game has to be favored against the player.

EXAMPLE 4   *Determining the Fair Price of a Lottery Ticket*

Assume that it costs $1 to play a state's daily number. The player chooses a three-digit number between 000 and 999, inclusive, and if the number is selected that day, then the player wins $500 (this means the player's profit is $500 − $1 = $499.)

a) What is the expected value of this game?

b) What should the price of a ticket be in order to make this game fair?

Outcome	Value	Probability
You win	$499	$\dfrac{1}{1,000}$
You lose	−$1	$\dfrac{999}{1,000}$

TABLE 14.10 Values and probabilities associated with playing the daily number.

SOLUTION:

a) There are 1,000 possible numbers that can be selected. One of these numbers is in your favor and the other 999 are against your winning. So, the probability of you winning is $\dfrac{1}{1,000}$ and the probability of you losing is $\dfrac{999}{1000}$. We summarize the values for this game with their associated probabilities in Table 14.10. The expected value of this game is therefore

$$\left(\frac{1}{1,000} \cdot 499 \right) + \left(\frac{999}{1,000} \cdot (-1) \right) = \frac{499 - 999}{1,000} = \frac{-500}{1,000} = -0.50.$$

This means that the player, on average, can expect to lose 50 cents per game. Notice that playing this lottery is 10 times as bad as playing a single number in roulette.

b) Let x be the price of a ticket for the lottery to be fair. Then if you win, your profit will be $500 − x$ and if you lose, your loss will be x. With this in mind, we will recalculate the expected value to get

$$\left(\frac{1}{1,000} \cdot (500 - x) \right) + \left(\frac{999}{1,000} \cdot (-x) \right) = \frac{(500 - x) - 999x}{1,000} = \frac{500 - 1,000x}{1,000}.$$

We want the game to be fair, so we will set this expected value equal to zero and solve for x, as follows:

$$\frac{500 - 1,000x}{1,000} = 0$$

$$\cancel{1,000} \cdot \frac{500 - 1,000x}{\cancel{1,000}} = 1,000 \cdot 0 = 0 \qquad \text{Multiply both sides of the equation by 1,000.}$$

$$500 - 1,000x = 0 \qquad \text{Cancel 1,000 and simplify.}$$

$$500 = 1,000x \qquad \text{Add 1,000x to both sides.}$$

$$\frac{500}{1,000} = \frac{\cancel{1,000}x}{\cancel{1,000}} = x \qquad \text{Divide both sides by 1,000.}$$

$$x = \frac{500}{1,000} = 0.50 \qquad \text{Simplify.}$$

HISTORICAL HIGHLIGHT ✣ ✣ ✣

The History of Lotteries

Lotteries have existed since ancient times. The Roman emperor Nero gave slaves or villas as door prizes to guests attending his banquets, and Augustus Caesar used public lotteries to raise funds to repair Rome.

The first public lottery paying money prizes began in Florence, Italy, in the early 1500s; when Italy became consolidated in 1870, this lottery evolved into the Italian National Lottery. In this lottery, five numbers are drawn from 1 to 90. A winner who guesses all five numbers is paid at a ratio of 1,000,000 to 1. The number of possible ways to choose these five numbers is $C(90, 5) = 43,949,268$. Thus, as with most lotteries, these odds make the lottery a very good bet for the state and a poor one for the ordinary citizen.

Lotteries also played an important role in the early history of the United States. In 1612, King James I used lotteries to finance the Virginia Company to send colonists to the New World. Benjamin Franklin obtained money to buy cannons to defend Philadelphia, and George Washington built roads through the Cumberland mountains by raising money through another lottery he conducted. In fact, in 1776, the Continental Congress used a lottery to raise $10 million to finance the American Revolution.

This means that 50 cents would be a fair price for a ticket to play this lottery. Of course, such a lottery would make no money for the state, which is why most states charge $1 to play the game.

Now try Exercises 9 to 12. ✳

Other Applications of Expected Value

Calculating expected value can help you decide what is the best strategy for answering questions on standardized tests such as the GMATs.

EXAMPLE 5 *Expected Value and Standardized Tests*

A student is taking a standardized test consisting of multiple-choice questions, each of which has five choices. The test taker earns 1 point for each correct answer; $\frac{1}{3}$ point is subtracted for each incorrect answer. Questions left blank neither receive nor lose points.

a) Find the expected value of randomly guessing an answer to a question. Interpret the meaning of this result for the student.

b) If you can eliminate one of the choices, is it wise to guess in this situation?

SOLUTION:

a) Because there are five choices, you have a probability of $\frac{1}{5}$ of guessing the correct result, and the value of this is +1 point. There is a $\frac{4}{5}$ probability of an incorrect guess, with an associated value of $-\frac{1}{3}$ point. The expected value is therefore

$$\left(\frac{1}{5} \cdot 1\right) + \left(\frac{4}{5} \cdot \left(-\frac{1}{3}\right)\right) = \frac{1}{5} + \frac{-4}{15} = \frac{3}{15} - \frac{4}{15} = -\frac{1}{15}.$$

Thus, you will be penalized for guessing and should not do so.

Quiz Yourself 🔟4

Calculate the expected value as in Example 5(b), but now assume that the student can eliminate two of the choices. Interpret this result.

b) If you eliminate one of the choices and choose randomly from the remaining four choices, the probability of being correct is $\frac{1}{4}$ with a value of $+1$ point; the probability of being incorrect is $\frac{3}{4}$ with a value of $-\frac{1}{3}$. The expected value is now

$$\left(\frac{1}{4} \cdot 1\right) + \left(\frac{3}{4} \cdot \left(-\frac{1}{3}\right)\right) = \frac{1}{4} + \frac{-1}{4} = 0.$$

You now neither benefit nor are penalized by guessing.
Now try Exercises 19 to 22. ✳ 🔟4

Businesses have to be careful when ordering inventory. If they order too much, they will be stuck with a surplus and might take a loss. On the other hand, if they do not order enough, then they will have to turn customers away, losing profits.

EXAMPLE 6   *Using Expected Value in Business*

Cher, the manager of the U2 Coffee Shoppe, is deciding on how many of Bono's Bagels to order for tomorrow. According to her records, for the past 10 days the demand has been as follows:

Demand for Bagels	40	30
Number of Days with These Sales	4	6

She buys bagels for $1.45 each and sells them for $1.85. Unsold bagels are discarded. Find her expected value for her profit or loss if she orders 40 bagels for tomorrow morning.

SOLUTION: We can describe the expected value in words as

P(demand is 40) $\times$ (the profit or loss if demand is 40)

$\qquad\qquad\qquad + P$(demand is 30) $\times$ (the profit or loss if demand is 30).

For 4 of the last 10 days the demand has been for 40 bagels, so P(demand is 40) $= \frac{4}{10} = 0.4$. Similarly, P(demand is 30) $= \frac{6}{10} = 0.6$.

   We will now consider her potential profit or loss. If the demand is for 40 bagels, she will sell all of the bagels and make $40(\$1.85 - \$1.45) = 40(\$0.40) = \$16.00$ profit. If the demand is for 30 bagels, she will make $30(\$0.40) = \$12.00$ profit on the sold bagels, but will lose $10(\$1.45) = \$14.50$ on the 10 unsold bagels. So, she will lose $2.50. The following table summarizes our discussion so far if she orders 40 bagels.

Demand	Probability	Profit or Loss
40	0.4	$16.00
30	0.6	−$2.50

Quiz Yourself 🔟5

Redo Example 6 assuming that Cher orders 30 bagels.

Thus, the expected value in profit or loss for ordering 40 bagels is

$$(0.40)(16) + (0.60)(-2.50) = +6.40 + (-1.50) = 4.90.$$

So she can expect a profit of $4.90 if she orders 40 bagels. ✳ 🔟5

Exercises 14.4

Looking Back*

These exercises follow the general outline of the topics presented in this section and will give you a good overview of the material that you have just studied.

1. How did we arrive at the term 0.02($2,000) in the equation that we wrote for the expected value in Example 1?

2. What did Examples 3 and 4 show us about the expected values of playing roulette versus playing the daily number?

Sharpening Your Skills

In Exercises 3 and 4, you are playing a game in which a single die is rolled. Calculate your expected value for each game. Is the game fair? (Assume that there is no cost to play the game.)

3. If an odd number comes up, you win the number of dollars showing on the die. If an even number comes up, you lose the number of dollars showing on the die.

4. You are playing a game in which a single die is rolled. If a four or five comes up, you win $2; otherwise, you lose $1.

In Exercises 5 and 6, you pay $1 to play a game in which a pair of fair dice are rolled. Calculate your expected value for the game. (Remember to subtract the cost of playing the game from your winnings.) Calculate the price of the game to make the game fair.

5. If a six, seven, or eight comes up, you win $5; if a two or 12 comes up, you win $3; otherwise, you lose the dollar you paid to play the game.

6. If a total lower than five comes up, you win $5; if a total greater than nine comes up, you win $2; otherwise, you lose the dollar you paid to play the game.

In Exercises 7 and 8, a card is drawn from a standard 52-card deck. Calculate your expected value for each game. You pay $5 to play the game, which must be subtracted from your winnings. Calculate the price of the game to make the game fair.

7. If a heart is drawn, you win $10; otherwise, you lose your $5.

8. If a face card is drawn, you win $20; otherwise, you lose your $5.

In Exercises 9–12, first calculate the expected value of the lottery. Determine whether the lottery is a fair game. If the game is not fair, determine a price for playing the game that would make it fair.

9. The Daily Number lottery costs $1 to play. You must pick three digits in order from 0 to 9 and duplicates are allowed. If you win, the prize is $600.

10. The Big Four lottery costs $1 to play. You must pick four digits in order from 0 to 9 and duplicates are allowed. If you win, the prize is $2,000.

11. Five hundred chances are sold at $5 apiece for a raffle. There is a grand prize of $500, two second prizes of $250, and five third prizes of $100.

12. One thousand chances are sold at $2 apiece for a raffle. There is a grand prize of $300, two second prizes of $100, and five third prizes of $25.

13. Grace Adler is planning to buy a franchise from Home Deco to sell decorations for the home. The table below shows average weekly profits, rounded to the nearest hundred, for a number of the current franchises. If she were to buy a franchise, what would her expected weekly profit be?

Average Weekly Profit	Number Who Earned This
$100	4
$200	8
$300	13
$400	21
$500	3
$600	1

14. For the past several years, the Metrodelphia Fire Department has been keeping track of the number of fire hydrants that have been opened illegally daily during heat waves. These data (rounded to the nearest ten) are given in the table below. Use this information to calculate how many hydrants the department should expect to be opened per day during the upcoming heat wave.

Hydrants Opened	Days
20	13
30	11
40	15
50	11
60	9
70	1

Applying What You've Learned

In Exercises 15–18, we describe several ways to bet on a roulette wheel. Calculate the expected value of each bet. We show a portion of a layout for betting on roulette in the diagram on page 702. When we say that a bet pays "k to 1," we mean that if a player wins, the player wins k dollars as well as keeping his or her bet. When the player loses, he or she loses $1. Recall that there are 38 numbers on a roulette wheel.

15. A player can "bet on a line" by placing a chip at location A in the figure. By placing the chip at A, the player is betting on 1, 2, 3, 0, and 00. This bet pays 6 to 1.

---

*Before doing these exercises, you may find it useful to review the note *How to Succeed at Mathematics* on page xix.

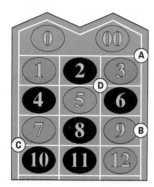

Figure for Exercises 15–18

16. A player can "bet on a square" by placing a chip at the intersection of two lines, as at location D. By placing a chip at D, the player is betting on 2, 3, 5, and 6. This bet pays 8 to 1.

17. A player can "bet on a street" by placing a chip on the table at location B. The player is now betting on 7, 8, and 9. This bet pays 8 to 1.

18. Another way to "bet on a line" is to place a chip at location C. By placing a chip at location C, the player is betting on 7, 8, 9, 10, 11, and 12. This bet pays 5 to 1.

In Exercises 19–22, a student is taking the GRE consisting of several multiple-choice questions. One point is awarded for each correct answer. Questions left blank neither receive nor lose points.

19. If there are four options for each question and the student is penalized $\frac{1}{4}$ point for each wrong answer, is it in the student's best interest to guess? Explain.

20. If there are three options for each question and the student is penalized $\frac{1}{3}$ point for each wrong answer, is it in the student's best interest to guess? Explain.

21. If there are five options for each question and the student is penalized $\frac{1}{2}$ point for each wrong answer, how many options must the student be able to rule out before the expected value of guessing is zero?

22. If there are four options for each question and the student is penalized $\frac{1}{2}$ point for each wrong answer, how many options must the student be able to rule out before the expected value of guessing is zero?

23. Assume that the probability of a 25-year-old male living to age 26, based on mortality tables, is 0.98. If a $1,000 one-year term life insurance policy on a 25-year-old male costs $27.50, what is its expected value?

24. Assume that the probability of a 22-year-old female living to age 23, based on mortality tables, is 0.995. If a $1,000 one-year term life insurance policy on a 22-year-old female costs $20.50, what is its expected value?

25. Your insurance company has a policy to insure personal property. Assume you have a laptop computer worth $2,200, and there is a 2% chance that the laptop will be lost or stolen during the next year. What would be a fair premium for the insurance? (We are assuming that the insurance company earns no profit.)

26. Assume that you have a used car worth $6,500 and you wish to insure it for full replacement value if it is stolen. If there is a 1% chance that the car will be stolen, what would be a fair premium for this insurance? (We are assuming that the insurance company earns no profit.)

27. A company estimates that it has a 60% chance of being successful in bidding on a $50,000 contract. If it costs $5,000 in consultant fees to prepare the bid, what is the expected gain or loss for the company if it decides to bid on this contract?

28. In Exercise 27, suppose that the company believes that it has a 40% chance to obtain a contract for $35,000. If it will cost $2,000 to prepare the bid, what is the expected gain or loss for the company if it decides to bid on this contract?

Communicating Mathematics

29. Explain in your own words the definition of expected value.

30. Explain in your own words how we determined the fair price of the game in Example 4. Why would the state not set this as the price to play the daily number?

Using Technology to Investigate Mathematics

31. Search the Internet for "the mathematics of lotteries." You might be surprised by the number of sites that you find selling software that can predict winning numbers. What is your reaction to these claims? Report on your findings.

32. Search the Internet for "expected value applets." Run some of these applets and report on your findings.

For Extra Credit

33. Nell's Bagels & Stuff, a local coffee shop, sells coffee, bagels, magazines, and newspapers. Nell has gathered information for the past 20 days regarding the demand for bagels. We list this information in the following table.

Demand for Bagels Sold	150	140	130	120
Number of Days with These Sales	3	6	5	6

Nell wants to use expected value to compute her best strategy for ordering bagels for the next week. She intends to order the same number each day and must  order in multiples of 10; therefore, she will order either 120, 130, 140, or 150 bagels. She buys the bagels for 65 cents each and sells them for 90 cents.

a. What is Nell's expected daily profit if she orders 130 bagels per day? (*Hint:* First compute the profit Nell will earn if she can sell 150, 140, 130, and 120 bagels.)

b. What is Nell's expected daily profit if she orders 140 bagels per day?

34. Mike sells the *Town Crier*, a local paper, at his newsstand. Over the past 2 weeks, he has sold the following number of copies.

Number of Copies Sold	90	85	80	75
Number of Days with These Sales	2	3	4	1

Each copy of the paper costs him 40 cents, and he sells it for 60 cents. Assume that these data will be consistent in the future.

a. What is Mike's expected daily profit if he orders 80 copies per day? (*Hint:* First compute the profit Mike will earn if he can sell 90, 85, 80, and 75 papers.)

b. What is Mike's expected daily profit if he orders 85 copies per day?

35. a. Calculate the expected total if you roll a pair of standard dice.

b. Unusual dice, called *Sicherman dice*, are numbered as follows.

Red: 1, 2, 2, 3, 3, 4   Green: 1, 3, 4, 5, 6, 8

Calculate the expected total if you roll a pair of these dice.

36. Suppose we have two pairs of dice (these are called *Efron's dice*) numbered as follows.

Pair One: Red: 2, 2, 2, 2, 6, 6   Green: 5, 5, 6, 6, 6, 6

Pair Two: Red: 1, 1, 1, 5, 5, 5   Green: 4, 4, 4, 4, 12, 12

If you were to play a game in which the highest total wins when you roll, what is the better pair to play with?

37. In playing a lottery, a person might buy several chances in order to improve the likelihood (probability) of winning. Discuss whether this is the case. Does buying several chances change your expected value of the game? Explain.

38. A lottery in which you must choose 6 numbers correctly from 40 possible numbers is called a $\frac{40}{6}$ lottery. In general, an $\frac{m}{n}$ lottery is one in which you must correctly choose n numbers from m possible numbers. Investigate what kind of lotteries there are in your state. What is the probability of winning such a lottery?

CHAPTER SUMMARY*

You will learn the items listed in this chapter summary more thoroughly if you keep in mind the following advice:

1. Focus on "remembering how to remember" the ideas. What pictures, word analogies, and examples help you remember these ideas?

2. Practice writing each item without looking at the book.

3. Make 3×5 flash cards to break your dependence on the text. Use these cards to give yourself practice tests.

SECTION	SUMMARY	EXAMPLE
SECTION 14.1	An observation of a **random phenomenon** is called an **experiment**. The different possible observations of the experiment are called **outcomes**. The set of all possible outcomes is called the **sample space** of the experiment. An **event** is a subset of the sample space. The **probability of an outcome** in a sample space is a number between 0 and 1, inclusive. The **probability of an event** is the sum of the probabilities of the outcomes in the event. We can assign the probability of an event **empirically** as	Definitions, p. 659 Example 1, p. 659 Example 2, p. 661
	$$P(E) = \frac{\text{the number of times } E \text{ occurs}}{\text{the number of times the experiment is performed}}.$$	
	This ratio is called the **relative frequency** of E. If E is an event in a sample space S with all equally likely outcomes, then	Examples 3 and 4, p. 662
	$$P(E) = \frac{n(E)}{n(S)}.$$	
	We can use **counting formulas** to compute probabilities. If E is an event in some sample space S, then	Example 5, p. 663 Example 6, p. 664
	1. $0 \le P(E) \le 1$　　2. $P(\varnothing) = 0$　　3. $P(S) = 1$.	Discussion, p. 665
	Probability can help explain **genetic theory**.	Discussion, p. 666 Example 7, p. 667
	If the outcomes in the sample space are equally likely, the **odds against** event E are the number of outcomes against E occurring compared to the number of outcomes in favor of E occurring. That is, $\dfrac{n(E')}{n(E)}$. An alternate formula for computing odds using probability is $\dfrac{P(E')}{P(E)}$.	Definition, p. 667 Examples 8 and 9, pp. 668, 669
SECTION 14.2	We can find the probability of event E by subtracting the probability of its **complement** from 1. That is, $P(E) = 1 - P(E')$.	Example 1, p. 674
	If E and F are events, we find the probability of their **union** as follows: $P(E \cup F) = P(E) + P(F) - P(E \cap F)$.	Examples 2 and 3, p. 676
	If E and F and disjoint, this formula simplifies to $P(E \cup F) = P(E) + P(F)$. We sometimes combine the complement and union formulas to solve a problem.	Example 4, p. 677
SECTION 14.3	If we compute the probability of an event F assuming that event E has already occurred, this is called the **conditional probability of F given E**. We denote this probability by $P(F \mid E)$. If E and F are events in a sample space with *equally likely outcomes*, then $P(F \mid E) = \dfrac{n(E \cap F)}{n(E)}$. In general, $P(F \mid E) = \dfrac{P(E \cap F)}{P(E)}$.	Definition, p. 682 Example 1, p. 683 Example 2, p. 684
	If E and F are events, then we calculate the probability of their **intersection** by using the following formula:	
	$$P(F \cap E) = P(E) \cdot P(F \mid E).$$	Example 3, p. 686

---

*Before studying this chapter's material, it would be useful to reread the note *How to Succeed at Mathematics* on page xix.

	We use **probability trees** to visualize probability problems.	Example 4, p. 687 Example 6, p. 689 Example 7, p. 691
	Events E and F are **independent** if $P(F \mid E) = P(F)$. Otherwise, they are **dependent**.	Definition, p. 689 Example 5, p. 689
SECTION 14.4	If an experiment has n outcomes with probabilities $P_1, P_2, P_3, \ldots, P_n$, and $V_1, V_2, V_3, \ldots, V_n$, are values associated with the outcomes, the **expected value** of the experiment is $(P_1 \cdot V_1) + (P_2 \cdot V_2) + (P_3 \cdot V_3) + \cdots + (P_n \cdot V_n)$. We use expected value to analyze games of chance.	Example 1, p. 696 Definition, p. 696 Examples 2 and 3, p. 697 Example 4, p. 698
	Expected value has many applications, such as evaluating test-taking strategies and business decision making.	Example 5, p. 699 Example 6, p. 700
SECTION 14.5	A **binomial trial** is an experiment that has two outcomes, labeled "success" and "failure." A binomial is a sequence of binomial trials that has the following properties:	Definitions, p. 703 Examples 1 and 2, p. 704
	1. The experiment is performed for a fixed number of trials. 2. Each trial has only two outcomes. 3. The probability of success is the same from trial to trial. 4. The trials are independent of each other.	
	In a binomial experiment with n trials, if the probability of success in each trial is p, the probability of exactly k successes is given by $C(n, k)(p)^k (1-p)^{(n-k)}$. We denote this probability by $B(n, k; p)$.	Discussion, p. 706
	Binomial probability can be used to solve wide-ranging applied problems.	Examples 3 and 4, p. 706 Example 5, p. 707

CHAPTER REVIEW EXERCISES

Section 14.1

1. Describe each event as a set of outcomes.

   a. When three coins are flipped, we obtain exactly two heads.

   b. When two dice are rolled, we obtain a total of eight.

2. If a single card is selected from a standard 52-card deck, what is the probability that a red face card is selected?

3. Explain the difference between empirical and theoretical probability. Give an example of each type of probability.

4. In cross-breeding pea plants, Mendel found that the characteristic "tall" dominated the characteristic "short." If we cross pure tall plants with pure short plants, what is the probability of tall plants in the second generation?

5. a. If the odds against the Dodgers winning the World Series are 17 to 2, what is the probability of them winning the Series?

   b. If the probability of rain tomorrow is 0.55, what are the odds against rain?

Section 14.2

6. a. State the formula for computing the probability of the complement of an event.

   b. Draw a diagram to explain this formula.

   c. In what sort of situations would you be likely to use this formula?

7. If a single card is drawn from a standard 52-card deck, what is the probability that we obtain either a face card or a red card? Draw a diagram to illustrate this situation.

8. On the given spinner, each green sector occupies 10% of the circle, each blue sector occupies 12%, each red sector occupies 9%, and the yellow sector occupies 4%. Assume that the spinner is spun once. What is the probability that

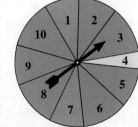

   a. The spinner does not stop on red?

   b. The spinner stops on an even number or blue?

Section 14.3

9. Explain in your own words what we mean by *conditional probability*.

10. If a pair of fair dice is rolled, what is the probability that we roll a total of five if we are given that the total is less than nine?

11. Assume that 2 cards are drawn without replacement from a standard 52-card deck.

   a. What is the probability that two hearts are drawn?

   b. What is the probability that a queen and then an ace is drawn?

12. A pair of fair dice are rolled. Are events E and F independent?

    E—an odd total is obtained.

    F—the total showing is less than six.

13. Assume that the incidence of the HIV virus in a particular population is 4% and that the test correctly identifies the virus 90% of the time. Assume that false positives occur 6% of the time. If a person tests positive for the virus, what is the probability that the person actually has the virus?

Section 14.4

14. Based on mortality tables, the probability of a 20-year-old male living to age 21 is 0.99. What is the expected value of a $1,000 one-year term life insurance on 20-year-old male from the insurance company's point of view? Assume that the yearly premium is $25.25.

15. A card is drawn from a standard 52-card deck. If a face card is drawn, you win $15; otherwise, you lose $4. Calculate the expected value for the game.

16. You are playing a game in which four fair coins are flipped. If all coins show the same (all heads or all tails), you win $5. Calculate the price to play the game that would make the game fair.

Section 14.5

17. Calculate $B\left(8, 3; \dfrac{1}{2}\right)$.

18. If you are guessing on a 10-question true–false quiz, what is the probability that you will get 8 correct?

CHAPTER TEST

1. Describe each event as a set of outcomes.

    a. When two dice are rolled, we obtain a total greater than nine.

    b. When four coins are flipped, we get more heads than tails.

2. If we select a single card from a standard 52-card deck, what is the probability that we select a black king?

3. a. If the odds against the Dolphins winning the Super Bowl are 28 to 3, what is the probability of them winning the Super Bowl?

    b. If the probability of rain tomorrow is 0.15, what are the odds against rain?

4. If we draw a single card from a standard 52-card deck, what is the probability that we obtain either a heart or a king?

5. What is the difference in the meaning between $P(B\,|\,A)$ and $P(A\,|\,B)$?

6. We are rolling a pair of fair dice. Are events E and F independent?

    E—both dice show the same number.

    F—the total is greater than eight.

7. It costs $1 to play a game in which two dice are rolled. If both dice show the same number, you win $5; otherwise, you lose. What is the expected value of this game?

8. Calculate $B\left(10, 2; \dfrac{1}{4}\right)$.

9. If you are guessing on a five-question multiple-choice quiz where each question has four possible answers, what is the probability that you will get three correct?

10. a. Complete the following equation $P(E) + \underline{\hspace{1cm}} = 1$.

    b. Draw a diagram to illustrate this formula.

11. In pea plants, purple flower color dominates white. With snapdragons, however, a pure red flowering plant crossed with pure white produces a pink flowering plant. If we begin by crossing pure red and white snapdragons, what is the probability of pink flowers in the second-generation plants?

12. Assume that 2% of the Brazilian population have dengue fever in 2008 and that a test correctly identifies the fever 95% of the time. Assume that a false positive occurs 5% of the time. If a person tests positive for the fever, what is the probability that the person actually has the fever?

13. It costs $2 to buy a raffle ticket. If there are 500 tickets sold, and there is one first prize of $250, three second prizes of $100, and five third prizes of $50, what is the expected value of this raffle?

14. If a pair of dice is rolled, what is the probability of rolling an even total given that the total is less than five?

15. Assume that 2 cards are drawn without replacement from a standard 52-card deck.

    a. What is the probability that two face cards are drawn?

    b. What is the probability that a king and an ace are drawn? (*Hint:* There are two cases.)

GROUP EXERCISES

1. **a.** Graphing calculators have random number generators built into them. For example, on the TI-83 and TI-84, if you press [MATH], then move the cursor to the right to [PRB], then press [ENTER] twice, you will get a number like .5489861799. If you generate a list of such numbers, you can use the digits in the list to simulate flipping a coin. For example, if you think of an odd digit as heads and an even digit as tails, then the number above corresponds to HTTHTTHHHH. Generate 1,000 digits to see how close your simulated coin flipping probability of a head corresponds to the theoretical probability of $\frac{1}{2}$.

    b. Make up a similar simulation for flipping two coins and compare some simulated probabilities with the theoretical ones. For example, if you generate 1,000 pairs of numbers, how close do you get to the theoretical probability of $\frac{1}{4}$ for getting two heads on two coins?

    c. Do similar simulations for rolling one die and rolling two dice.

2. Look up some real statistics regarding seat belt usage and traffic fatalities. Then compute the conditional probabilities P(driver is killed | driver was wearing a seat belt) versus P(driver is killed | driver was not wearing a seat belt).

Answers to Exercises

Chapter 9

Section 9.1

1. We represented 19% as 19 hundredths, or 0.19, then positioned the 32 in the two decimal places to the right of 0.19.

3. We found the selling price minus the dealer's cost and divided this difference by the dealer's cost.

5. 0.78　**7.** 0.08　**9.** 0.2735　**11.** 0.0035　**13.** 43%

15. 36.5%　**17.** 145%　**19.** 0.2%　**21.** 75%

23. 31.25%　**25.** 250%　**27.** 1.6%　**29.** 15%

31. 350　**33.** 19.6　**35.** 17.5%　**37.** 128　**39.** 9.4%

41. $397,000　**43.** 26.06%　**45.** 114.41%　**47.** 24.9%

49. 41.3%　**51.** 1,269　**53.** 7.3%　**55.** 27.6 million

57. a. 8%　**b.** She divided by 16,065 instead of 14,875.

59. $37,800　**61.** $680　**63.** 11.5%　**65.** $12,800

67. $35,771.50　**69.** $8,507.50　**75.** per hundred

77. We could have used the dealer's cost for the base, the markup as the amount, and then solved for percent.

79. $10,794.52

81. No. The price after the reduction will be less than the original price.

83. No. It is the same as an increase by 32%.

Section 9.2

1. We substituted values for A, r, and t in the equation $A = P(1 + rt)$, and then solved for P.

3. $\log(3^x) = x \log(3)$

5. $I = \$240$, $P = \$1,000$, $r = 8\%$, $t = 3$ years

7. $I = \$700$, $P = \$3,500$, $r = 5\%$, $t = 4$ years

9. $A = \$3,100$, $P = \$2,500$, $r = 8\%$, $t = 3$ years

11. $A = \$1,770$, $P = \$1,500$, $r = 6\%$, $t = 3$ years

13. $A = \$1,400$, $P = \$1,250$, $r = 6\%$, $t = 2$ years

15. 1.5%　**17.** 12/365%　**19.** $6,381.41

21. $4,686.64　**23.** $23,457.76　**25.** $4,885.48

27. 7.76%　**29.** 6.14%　**31.** 4.95% compounded quarterly

33. $12,278.88　**35.** 2.096　**37.** 14.207　**39.** 2.1544

41. 1.7783　**43.** 4.56%　**45.** 10.34

47. a. $4,896　**b.** $1,296　**49.** $66.67　**51.** 12.5%

53. 75%　**55.** $6.07　**57.** $4.29　**59.** $1,712.15

61. a. 4.74%　**b.** 4.67%　**63.** 10.07 years　**65.** $I = Prt$

67. A is the future amount, P is the principal, r is the yearly interest rate, m is the number of compounding periods per year, and n is the total number of compounding periods.

69. $m = 1$　**73.** 10.5170863%　**75.** 10.5170918%

Section 9.3

1. We added the loan amount and the interest, and then divided the sum by the number of payments.

3. It shows the balance for the loan for each day of September.

5. $46.50　**7.** $37.40　**9.** $243.20; $63.47

11. $3,019.68; $197.91　**13.** 288%　**15.** 384%

17. a. $313.50　**b.** down to $256.50　**c.** $3,982.46

19. a. $536.67　**b.** down to $429.34　**c.** $6,614.91

21. $4.38　**23.** $7.96　**25.** $9.67　**27.** $5.37

29. $4.95　**31.** $6.77　**33.** $5.03

35. add-on method, $87.50; credit card, $82.50　**37.** $61.44

39. We "add on" the interest for the loan before calculating the payments.

41. Charge a large purchase to your card early in the month and then pay off the debt before the end of the month so no interest is charged for that purchase.

Section 9.4

1. The expression $\frac{r}{m}$ is the monthly interest rate; n is the number of compounding periods; R is the monthly payment.

3. $\dfrac{x^8 - 1}{x - 1}$　**5.** $710.59　**7.** $21,669.48

9. $23,008.28　**11.** $85,785.11　**13.** $12,148.68

15. $7,463.67　**17.** $162.14　**19.** $193.75　**21.** 2.7268

23. 1.1073　**25.** 2.3219　**27.** 1.9527　**29.** 42.62

31. 30.91　**33.** 22.43　**35.** $2,435.99　**37.** $6,286.36

39. $121,417.91　**41.** $102.78　**43.** $98.31

45. a. $301,354.51; $226,015.88

　　b. $193,354.51; $145,015.88

　　c. $247,110.70 ; $199,913.02; tax-deferred earns $47,197.68 more

47. a. $146,709.85; $102,696.90

　　b. $50,709.85; $35,496.90

　　c. $102,696.90; $92,047.83; tax-deferred earns $10,649.07 more

49. a. $402,627.32; $301,970.49

　　b. $192,627.32; $144,470.49

　　c. $281,839.12; $258,629.34; tax-deferred earns $23,209.78 more

51. 61 months **53.** 47 months

55. The exponent property: $\log a^x = x \log a$

59. $141.33 **61.** $197,395.14

Section 9.5

1. The left side represents the amount owed on the loan after 48 months of compounding. The right side represents the amount that must be in the annuity to pay off the loan.

3. $126.82 **5.** $193.44 **7.** $306.64 **9.** $112.37

11.

Payment Number	Amount of Payment	Interest Payment	Applied to Principal	Balance
				$5,000.00
1	$126.82	$41.67	$85.15	$4,914.85
2	$126.82	$40.96	$85.86	$4,828.99
3	$126.82	$40.24	$86.58	$4,742.41

13.

Payment Number	Amount of Payment	Interest Payment	Applied to Principal	Balance
				$12,500.00
1	$306.64	$85.94	$220.70	$12,279.30
2	$306.64	$84.42	$222.22	$12,057.08
3	$306.64	$82.89	$223.75	$11,833.33

15. a.

Payment Number	Amount of Payment	Interest Payment	Applied to Principal	Balance
				$100,000.00
1	$665.31	$583.33	$81.98	$99,918.02
2	$665.31	$582.86	$82.45	$99,835.57
3	$665.31	$582.37	$82.94	$99,752.63

b.

Payment Number	Amount of Payment	Interest Payment	Applied to Principal	Balance
				$100,000.00
1	$765.31	$583.33	$181.98	$99,818.02
2	$765.31	$582.27	$183.04	$99,634.98
3	$765.31	$581.20	$184.11	$99,450.87

c. $1.76

17. a. $276.46 **b.** $1,770.08

19. a. $57.50 **b.** $12.50

21. a. $954.83 **b.** $2,057.23

23. a. $1,101.68 **b.** $2,128.43

25. The present value of the lottery winnings is $425,678.19; this is slightly better than the lump sum of $425,000.

27. $13,593.02

29. The present value of the retirement plan is $38,900.73; this is slightly worse than the lump sum of $40,000.

31. $5,416.17 **33.** $107,389.08 **35.** $4,159.37

37. a. $240.46 **b.** $88.08

39. a. $786.70 **b.** $8,955

41. a. $971.60 **b.** $118.08

43. We saw the left expression in calculating compound interest and the right expression in computing the future value of annuities.

Section 9.6

1. You had paid $300 on an outstanding balance of $1,000, so the interest rate was $\frac{300}{1,000} = 0.30$, or 30%.

3. 12% **5.** $15 **7.** $13 **9.** 13% **11.** 14%

13. 12.45% **15.** 13.67% **17.** 15% **19.** 11%

21. 15% **23.** 15% **25. b.** (b) is better.

27. b. (b) is better. **29.** over 16%

31. First calculate the finance charge per $100 on the loan. Next, use the line corresponding to the number of loan payments to locate the amount that is closest to the finance charge per $100. The percent shown at the top of that column is the approximate APR for the loan.

Chapter Review Exercises

1. 12.45% **3.** 68.75% **5.** $1,806 million

7. $1,770 **9.** $12,465.25 **11.** 131 months

13. $326.70; $45.75 **15.** $4.57 **17.** $50.85

19. 30 months **21.** $126.82

23. The present value is $490,907.37; the lump sum is the better option.

25. $912.04; $1,921.07 **27.** 15.2%

Chapter Test

1. 36.24% **3.** 43.75% **5.** $3,655 **7.** 11.77%

9. 15% **11.** 174 months **13.** $7,052.42

15. 4.55% **17.** $6.74 **19.** 2.19 **21.** $47.15

23. about 20 months

25. The annuity is the better choice because it has a present value of $811,089.58.

27. a. $347.34 **b.** $10,827.27

Chapter 10

Section 10.1

1. a. acute **b.** right **c.** obtuse **d.** straight

3. The length of arc AB is proportional to the measure of the central angle ACB.

5. 7 and 9 **7.** 7 and 3 **9.** 10 **11.** 9 and 10

13. true **15.** false **17.** true **19.** false **21.** false

23. e, d **25.** c, g **27.** 60°, 150°

29. No complementary angle; supplementary angle is 60°.

31. 38.8°, 128.8°

33. $m\angle a = 144°$, $m\angle b = 36°$, $m\angle c = 144°$

35. $m\angle a = 45°$, $m\angle b = 135°$, $m\angle c = 45°$

37. $m\angle a = 52°$, $m\angle b = 90°$, $m\angle c = 128°$

39. Arc AB has length 6 ft.   **41.** $m\angle ACB = 120°$

43. circumference = 1,200 mm   **45.** 6 ft   **47.** 144°

49. 60°   **51.** 18°   **53.** 12   **55.** 14.4°

57. The sum of supplementary angles is 180°; the sum of complementary angles is 90°.

59. "Alternate" means that they are on opposite sides of the transversal. "Exterior angles" means that they are outside the parallel lines.

61. yes, if the lines are perpendicular

63. No more than two could be obtuse. Because verticals are equal, if there were a third obtuse angle, then the fourth would also have to be obtuse, giving an angle sum of more than 360°.

65. yes, if the angles are both 45-degree angles

69.

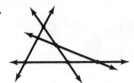

71. 180

Section 10.2

1. Alternate interior angles are equal; $m\angle 1 = m\angle 4$, $m\angle 3 = m\angle 5$.

3. It was the supplement of $\angle WVZ$, which had measure 108°.

5. false   **7.** true   **9.** false   **11.** polygon

13. not a polygon; not made of line segments

15. $m\angle A = 30°$, $m\angle B = 60°$, $m\angle C = 90°$

17. $m\angle A = 45°$, $m\angle B = 55°$, $m\angle C = 80°$

19. 4; 720°   **21.** 162°   **23.** 18   **25.** $\frac{5}{3}$ in.   **27.** 5 in

29. $m\angle E = 40°$, length of EH is 7

31. $m\angle I = 35°$, length of HI is 84

33. 450 ft   **35.** 75 ft   **37.** 192.5 feet

39. 54°   **41.** 20.88 feet

43. Isosceles triangles have two equal sides; equilateral triangles have all three sides equal.

45. No, a scalene triangle has no sides equal.

47. Both have four equal sides. A rhombus does not necessarily have right angles.

51. possible

53. Not possible; the angle sum would be greater than 180°.

57. The measure of the interior angles gets larger. For very large n, the interior angles have measures close to 180°.

59. $\frac{(n-2)90}{n}$ degrees

Section 10.3

1. In both cases, the area is the height times the base.

3. The area of the trapezoid is the sum of the areas of two triangles.

5. 160 ft   **7.** 140 in.^{2} **9.** 108 cm^2 **11.** 72 yd^2

13. 78.5 cm^2 **15.** 50.24 m^2 **17.** 72 yd^2 **19.** 6.88 m^2

21. 0.86 m^2 **23.** 24 in.^{2} **25.** 12 yd^2 **27.** 7 in.^{2}

29. 3.5 in.^{2} **31.** 42.15 cm^2 **33.** 59.81 m^2

35. 6.62 cm   **37.** 13 m   **39.** 6.93 yd   **41.** 69 m^2

43. area   **45.** perimeter   **47.** 127.28 ft   **49.** 2 m

51. 86.13 ft^2

53. The large pizza is the better buy; it costs 4.5 cents per square inch versus 5.3 cents per square inch for the medium.

55. 1,000.96 m^2 **57.** 186.38 m

59. a. 22.61 ft   **b.** 203.47 ft^2

61. rectangle, parallelogram, triangle, trapezoid

63. We had the length of the hypotenuse of $\triangle TMC$ and needed the length of another leg to find the height h.

67. 2,779.11 ft^2 **69.** false

71. The area of $WXYZ$ is one-half of the area of $ABCD$.

73. 50 ft by 50 ft   **75.** about 21,195 ft^2

77. $(2r)^2 - \pi r^2 = (4 - \pi)r^2$

Section 10.4

1. Both are the area of the base times the height.

3. The radius of the can that minimized its surface area is between 0.5 and 0.6 of a foot.

5. a. 148 cm^2 **b.** 120 cm^3

7. a. 80.48 in.^{2} **b.** 75.36 in.^{3}

9. a. 408.2 ft^2 **b.** 628 ft^3

11. a. 5,024 cm^2 **b.** 33,493.33 cm^3

13. 75 ft^3 **15.** 180 ft.^{3} **17.** 18.33 m^3 **19.** 1,728

21. 91   **23.** 25   **25.** about 3.7 yd

27. the rectangular cake

29. 2,198; 2,260.8; the radius is being squared, so increasing it contributes greater to the increase.

31. 188.4; 200.96; the radius is being squared, so increasing it contributes greater to the increase.

33. 84 ft^3 **35.** 2,164 mi

37. Its volume is less than the volume of a cylinder with radius r and height h, so it is some fractional part of $\pi r^2 h$, namely, $\frac{1}{3}\pi r^2 h$.

39. The volume is four times as large, because in the formula for the volume of a cone, the radius is squared.

41. Let d be the diameter of the can. The height of the can is $3d$; the circumference of the can is $\pi d \approx 3.14d$, which is larger.

43. radius ≈ 0.68 ft

47. The smaller cubes have more surface area. For example, compare the surface area of one 3-in. cube with the surface area of twenty-seven 1-in. cubes.

49. 6.08 in.

51. $\pi r \sqrt{r^2 + h^2} - \pi\left(\frac{r}{2}\right)\sqrt{\left(\frac{r}{2}\right)^2 + \left(\frac{h}{2}\right)^2} = \frac{3}{4}\pi r\sqrt{r^2 + h^2}$

Section 10.5

1. We realized that moving three columns to the right in the table gave us $10^3 = 1,000$ as many objects.

3. $\dfrac{1.6\ kilometers}{1\ mile}$

5. 1,135 dg   **7.** 4,572 mm   **9.** 15.24 cm

11. 0.02159 dam   **13.** 1.77 dL   **15.** 24,000 dL

17. 2,800 mm   **19.** 350 dL

21. a; a juice glass is about one-eighth of a quart or about one-eighth of a liter.

23. c; an inch is about 2.5 cm, so 5 cm would correspond to a 2-in. nose.

25. b; the dog might be about 2 ft tall, or about $\frac{2}{3}$ of a meter.

27. 59.05 ft   **29.** 105.73 oz   **31.** 554.77 al

33. 1,056.7 qt   **35.** 69.29 in.   **37.** 49.56 tons

39. 7.92 dm   **41.** Don't give him an inch.

43. It is first down and 10 yards to go.

45. **a.** 160 cu m   **b.** 160,000 L   **c.** 160,000 kg

47. 49.72   **49.** 135.93 kL   **51.** $1.25 per pound

53. $8.25   **55.** 60 m   **57.** 12.75 km per liter

59. $86.11   **61.** 65°C   **63.** 140°F   **65.** 68°F

67. 45°C   **69.** 1 hectare = 10,000 sq m   **71.** 90   **73.** 10

75. More decimeters because decimeters are smaller than hectometers.

77. Because dekagrams are much larger than milligrams, we would need fewer dekagrams. Therefore, we would move the decimal point to the left.

Chapter 14

Section 14.1

1. We drew a tree diagram.

3. We know from Chapter 13 that there are $C(52, 5)$ ways to choose 5 cards from 52.

5. The bread could only make one-half of a revolution before hitting the floor. With three lines, there is only a one-third chance that you are in the fastest line.

7. {(1, 6), (2, 5), (3, 4), (4, 3), (5, 2), (6, 1)}

9. {HHH, HHT, HTH, THH}

11. {(r, b), (r, y) (b, r), (y, r)}

13. {(b, b, r), (b, r, b), (r, b, b), (b, b, y), (b, y, b), (y, b, b)}

15. **a.** 16
  b. {(1, 1), (1, 3), (2, 2), (2, 4), (3, 1), (3, 3), (4, 2), (4, 4)}
  c. $\frac{1}{2}$ **d.** $\frac{3}{16}$

17. **a.** 24
  b. {CKMJ, CKJM, CJMK, CJKM, MKCJ, MKJC, MJCK, MJKC, KCJM, KMJC, JCKM, JMKC}
  c. $\frac{1}{2}$ **d.** $\frac{1}{4}$

19. **a.** 20
  b. {(s, c), (s, w), (s, d), (s, h), (c, s), (w, s), (d, s), (h, s)}
  c. $\frac{2}{5}$ **d.** $\frac{3}{5}$

21. a) $\frac{1}{9}$ b) 8 to 1   **23.** a) $\frac{1}{4}$ b) 3 to 1   **25.** 0.000495

27. 0.002   **29. a.** $\frac{5}{9}$ **b.** 5 to 4   **31.** 0.49   **33.** 0.26

35. The probability that the child is a carrier is $\frac{1}{2}$.

		Second Parent	
		s	n
First Parent	s	ss	sn
	s	ss	sn

37. a.

		First-Generation Plant	
		r	r
First-Generation Plant	w	wr	wr
	w	wr	wr

b. All flowers will be pink. $P(\text{pink}) = 1$; all other probabilities are 0.

39. a.

		Second Parent	
		N	c
First Parent	N	NN	Nc
	c	cN	cc

b. $P(\text{disease}) = \frac{1}{4}$

41. 0.43   **43.** $\frac{22}{36} = \frac{11}{18}$ **45.** $\frac{2}{36} = \frac{1}{18}$ **47.** 0.57

49. 0.54   **51.** $\frac{1}{336}$ **53.** $\frac{2}{7}$ **55.** $\frac{5}{12}$

57. a. 3 to 7   **b.** 7 to 3   **59.** 45,057,474 to 1

61. $P(E) = \dfrac{\text{number of times } E \text{ occurs}}{\text{number of times experiment is performed}}$

63. All plants had one yellow and one green gene, and yellow was dominant.

65. An outcome is an element in a sample space; an event is a subset of a sample space.

67. Rolling a total less than 13 when rolling two dice

73. 0.000027

Section 14.2

1. It was easier to compute $P(A')$ and then subtract it from 1 instead of computing $P(A)$ directly.

3. Your chances of winning a big lottery are very small compared to many other real-life events.

5. 0.985   **7.** $\frac{999}{1,000}$ **9.** $\frac{25}{36}$ **11.** $\frac{31}{32}$

13. $\frac{7}{13}$ **15.** $\frac{11}{18}$ **17.** 0.10   **19.** 0.55

21. $\frac{15}{26}$ **23.** 0.923   **25.** 0.54   **27.** 0.08

29. 0.92   **31.** 0.84   **33.** 0.65   **35.** 0.19

37. Because $E \cup E' = S$ and $P(S) = 1$.

39. false   **41.** true

43. If E and F are disjoint, then $P(E \cap F) = 0$.

45. $P(A) + P(B) + P(C) - P(A \cap B) - P(B \cap C)$

47. 0.96   **49.** 0.14

Section 14.3

1. the probability that the total was odd, given that the total was greater than nine

3. We found that $P(G\,|\,F) \neq P(G)$, which meant that knowing that event F occurred had an effect on the probability of G.

5. $\frac{1}{6}$; $\frac{1}{3}$ 7. $\frac{1}{6}$; $\frac{2}{11}$ 9. $\frac{1}{2}$ 11. $\frac{1}{10}$ 13. $\frac{2}{4}$ 15. $\frac{2}{3}$

17. 0   19. $\frac{50}{61}$ 21. $\frac{2}{61}$ 23. 0.947   25. 0.90

27. a) $\frac{1}{221}$ b) $\frac{1}{169}$ 29. a) $\frac{40}{221}$ b) $\frac{30}{169}$ 31. a) $\frac{8}{663}$ b) $\frac{2}{169}$

33. $\frac{7}{17}$ 35. $\frac{11}{1,105}$ 37. $\frac{117}{850}$ 39. $\frac{1}{729}$ 41. 0.74

43. 0.63   45. dependent   47. independent   49. $\frac{1}{3}$

51. $\frac{8}{15}$ 53. 0.1029   55. 0.2646

57. Forty percent of the available spaces in dorm Y are rooms.

59. 0.50

61.

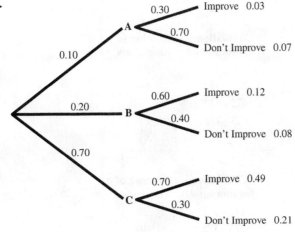

63. 0.64   65. 0.375   67. 0.336   69. 0.736

71. 0.424

73. Multiply both sides of the equation by $P(E)$ to get $P(E \cap F) = P(F\,|\,E) \cdot P(E)$.

75. Answers will vary.   77. Answers will vary.

Section 14.4

1. We multiplied the value of the laptop by the probability of it being stolen.

3. −$0.50; no   5. $1.39; $2.39   7. −$2.50; $2.50

9. −$0.40; $0.60   11. −$2.00; $3.00   13. $328

15. −$0.08   17. −$0.29

19. Student should guess; expected value is $\frac{1}{16}$.

21. two options   23. −$7.50   25. $44   27. $25,000

33. a. $29.80 b. $27.35   35. a. 7 b. 7   37. no

Chapter Review Exercises

1. a. {HHT, HTH, THH}
   b. {(2, 6), (3, 5), (4, 4), (5, 3), (6, 2)}

3. To calculate the empirical of an event E, we divided the number of the times the event occurs by the number of the times the experiment is performed. To calculate theoretical probability we use known mathematical techniques such as counting formulas.

5. a. $\frac{2}{19}$ b. 45 to 55 or 9 to 11

7. $\frac{8}{13}$ 9. Answers will vary   11. a. $\frac{1}{17}$ b. $\frac{4}{663}$

13. 0.385   15. $0.38   17. 0.219

Chapter Test

1. a. {(4, 6), (5, 5), (6, 4), (5, 6), (6, 5), (6, 6)}
   b. {HHHT, HHTH, HTHH, THHH, HHHH}

3. a. $\frac{3}{31}$ b. 17 to 3

5. When calculating $P(B\,|\,A)$, we are calculating the probability of B assuming that event A has occurred. In calculating $P(A\,|\,B)$, we are assuming that B has occurred and then calculating $P(A)$.

7. −$\frac{1}{6}$ 9. 0.0879   11. $\frac{1}{2}$ 13. −$0.40

15. a. $\frac{11}{221}$ b. $\frac{8}{663}$

Chapter 13

SECTION 13.1, PAGE 778

1. Statistics   3. Descriptive   5. Sample   7. Random

9. Cluster   11. Unbiased   13. Stratified sample

15. Cluster sample   17. Systematic sample

19. Convenience sample   21. Random sample

23. a) Answers will vary.   b) Answers will vary.
    c) Answers will vary.

25. President; four out of 44 U.S. presidents have been assassinated (Lincoln, Garfield, McKinley, Kennedy).

SECTION 13.2, PAGE 781

1. The patients may have improved on their own without taking honey.

3. Mama Mia's may have more empty spaces and more cars in the parking lot than Shanghi's due to a larger parking lot or because more people may walk to Mama Mia's than to Shanghi's.

5. More people drive on Saturday evening. Thus, one might expect more accidents.

7. Most driving is done close to home. Thus, one might expect more accidents close to home.

9. We don't know how many of each professor's students were surveyed. Perhaps more of Professor Malone's students than Professor Wagner's students were surveyed. Also, because more students prefer a teacher does not mean that he or she is a better teacher. For example, a particular teacher may be an easier grader and that may be why that teacher is preferred.

11. Just because they are more expensive does not mean that they will last longer.

13. There may be deep sections in the pond, so it may not be safe to go wading.

15. a)    **b)**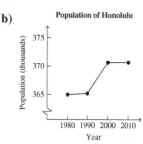

17. a)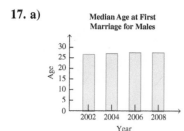

b)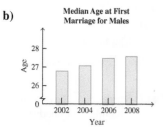

19. a)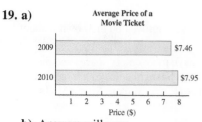

b) Answers will vary.

21. Yes, the sum of its parts is 121%. The sum of the parts of a circle graph should be 100%. When the total percent of responses is more than 100%, a circle graph is not an appropriate graph to display the data. A bar graph is more appropriate in this situation.

23. A decimal point

1. Frequency   **3.** Mark   **5.** Histogram   **7.** Stem
9. a) 20   **b)** 7   **c)** 19   **d)** 16–22   **e)** 51–57

11.

Number of Visits	Number of Students
0	3
1	8
2	3
3	5
4	2
5	7
6	2
7	3
8	4
9	1
10	2

13.

Circulation (ten thousands)	Number of Magazines
173–322	33
323–472	10
473–622	1
623–772	1
773–922	1

15.

Circulation (ten thousands)	Number of Magazines
173–272	28
273–372	10
373–472	5
473–572	1
573–672	0
673–772	1
773–872	1

17.

Population (millions)	Number of Cities
7.0–7.9	6
8.0–8.9	4
9.0–9.9	1
10.0–10.9	3
11.0–11.9	1
12.0–12.9	2
13.0–13.9	3

19.

Population (millions)	Number of Cities
6.5–7.5	3
7.6–8.6	4
8.7–9.7	4
9.8–10.8	3
10.9–11.9	1
12.0–13.0	3
13.1–14.1	2

21.

Percent	Number of States
6.4–8.3	2
8.4–10.3	13
10.4–12.3	14
12.4–14.3	9
14.4–16.3	9
16.4–18.3	2
18.4–20.3	0
20.4–22.3	1

23.

Percent	Number of States
6.4–7.8	1
7.9–9.3	7
9.4–10.8	12
10.9–12.3	9
12.4–13.8	7
13.9–15.3	8
15.4–16.8	4
16.9–18.3	1
18.4–19.8	0
19.9–21.3	1

25. 1|2 represents 12

```
0 | 4  6  7  8
1 | 2  2  3  5  6  7  8  9
2 | 1  2  3  5  7
3 | 3  4
4 | 0
```

27. a)

Salaries (1000s of dollars)	Number of Social Workers
27	1
28	7
29	4
30	3
31	2
32	3
33	3
34	2

b) and c)

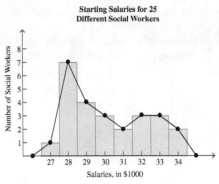

Starting Salaries for 25 Different Social Workers

d) 2|8 represents 28

```
2 | 7  8  8  8  8  8  8  8  9  9  9  9
3 | 0  0  0  1  1  2  2  2  3  3  3  4  4
```

29. a)

Total Gross (millions of dollars)	Number of Tours
80–91	12
92–103	4
104–115	3
116–127	2
128–139	3
140–151	0
152–163	1

b) and c)

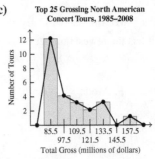

Top 25 Grossing North American Concert Tours, 1985–2008

31. a) 28 **b)** 4 **c)** 2 **d)** 75

e)

Number of Televisions	Number of Homes
0	2
1	4
2	8
3	6
4	4
5	3
6	1

33. a) 7 **b)** 16 **c)** 36

d)

Number of Messages	Number of People	Number of Messages	Number of People
3	2	7	3
4	3	8	8
5	7	9	6
6	4	10	3

e)

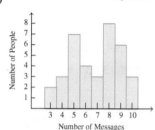

Number of E-Mail Messages Sent

35.

Tution/Fees:	$5026.65
Room:	$5303.48
Board:	$3336.53
Computer costs:	$903.34

37. a) Answers will vary. **b)** Answers will vary.
c) Answers will vary. **d)** Answers will vary.
e) Answers will vary.

39. a) There are 6 F's. **b)** Answers will vary.

40. February, since it has the fewest number of days

SECTION 13.4, PAGE 802

1. Average **3.** Mean **5.** Mode **7.** Quartiles

9. a) $\bar{x}$ **b)** μ

11. 14, 13, 13, 17 **13.** 79.3, 82, none, 76

15. 8, 8, none, 8 **17.** 13.1, 11, 1, 18.5

19. 11.9, 12.5, 13, 11.5

21. a) 198.7 **b)** 197.5 **c)** None **d)** 208.5

23. a) 4.9, 5, 5, 6 **b)** 5.3, 5, 5, 6 **c)** Only the mean
d) The mean and the midrange

25. A 79 mean average on 10 quizzes gives a total of
790 points. An 80 mean average on 10 quizzes requires
a total of 800 points. Thus, Jim missed a B by 10 points,
not 1 point.

27. a) 23.0 pints **b)** 22.5 pints **c)** 18.5 pints **d)** 25.1 pints

29. a) $4.6 billion **b)** $3.3 billion
c) None **d)** $8.4 billion

31. 552

33. One example is 72, 73, 74, 76, 77, 78.

35. a) Yes **b)** No **c)** No **d)** Yes

37. a) 29 or greater **b)** Yes, 99 or greater
c) 20 or greater **d)** 80 or greater

39. One example: 1, 2, 3, 3, 4, 5 changed to 1, 2, 3, 4, 4, 5.

41. No. By changing only one piece of the 6 pieces of data,
you cannot alter both the median and the midrange.

43. The data must be ranked.

45. He is taller than approximately 35 percent of all kindergarten
children.

47. a) $23 **b)** $20 **c)** $34 **49.** Second quartile, median

51. a) $580 **b)** $590 **c)** 25%
d) 25% **e)** 17% **f)** $60,000

53. a)

Ruth	Mantle
0.290	0.300
0.359	0.365
0.301	0.304
0.272	0.275
0.315	0.321

b) Mantle's is greater in every case.
c) Ruth: 0.316; Mantle: 0.311; Ruth's is greater.
d) Answers will vary.
e) Ruth: 0.307; Mantle: 0.313; Mantle's is greater.
f) Answers will vary.
g) Answers will vary.

55. 90 **57. a)** Answers will vary. **b)** Answers will vary.
c) Answers will vary.

58. a) Answers will vary. One example is 2, 3, 5, 7, 7.
b) Answers will vary.

SECTION 13.5, PAGE 812

1. Variability **3.** Standard deviation **5.** Sample

7. 11, $\sqrt{16.5} \approx 4.06$ **9.** 6, $\sqrt{4.67} \approx 2.16$

11. 11, $\sqrt{15.2} \approx 3.90$ **13.** 5, $\sqrt{3} \approx 1.73$

15. $205, $\sqrt{4780.57} \approx 69.14

17. $190, $\sqrt{4725.25} \approx 68.74 **19.** Answers will vary.

21. The first set will have the greater standard deviation because the scores have a greater spread about the mean.

23. The sum of the values in the (Data − Mean)^2 column will
always be greater than or equal to 0.

25. a) $63, $\sqrt{631.6} \approx 25.13 **b)** Answers will vary.
c) Answers remain the same, range: $63, standard devia-
tion $\approx$ $25.13.

27. a) Answers will vary. **b)** Answers will vary.
c) Answers will vary.
d) If each number in a distribution is multiplied by n, the
mean and standard deviation of the new distribution
will be n times that of the original distribution.
e) 20, 10

29. a) The standard deviation increases. There is a greater
spread from the mean as they get older.
b) $\approx$ 133 lb **c)** $\approx$ 21 lb
d) Mean: $\approx$100 lb; normal range: $\approx$ 60 to 140 lb
e) Mean: $\approx$62 in.; normal range: $\approx$ 53 to 68 in. **f)** 5%

31. a)

East		West	
Number of Oil Changes Made	Number of Days	Number of Oil Changes Made	Number of Days
15–20	2	15–20	0
21–26	2	21–26	0
27–32	5	27–32	6
33–38	4	33–38	9
39–44	7	39–44	4
45–50	1	45–50	6
51–56	1	51–56	0
57–62	2	57–62	0
63–68	1	63–68	0

b)

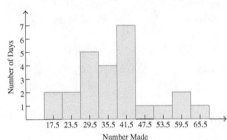

Number of Oil Changes Made Daily at East Store

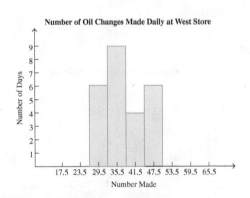

Number of Oil Changes Made Daily at West Store

c) They appear to have about the same mean since they are both centered around 38.

d) The distribution for East is more spread out. Therefore, East has a greater standard deviation.

e) East: 38, West: 38   **f)** East: ≈ 12.64, West: ≈ 5.98

32. Answers will vary.

33. 6, 6, 6, 6, 6

SECTION 13.6, PAGE 828

1. Rectangular   **3.** Right   **5.** Bimodal   **7.** Standard

9. Below   **11. a)** 68%   **b)** 95%   **c)** 99.7%

13. Answers will vary.   **15.** Answers will vary.

17. Normal   **19.** Skewed right   **21.** 0.5000   **23.** 0.8185

25. 0.0630   **27.** 0.0375   **29.** 0.0429   **31.** 0.0166

33. 76.11%   **35.** 89.74%   **37.** 97.13%   **39.** 97.50%

41. 21.96%   **43. a)** Emily, Sarah, Carol   **b)** Jenny, Shenice
   c) Sadaf, Heather, Kim

45. 50%   **47.** 10.56%   **49.** 69.15%   **51.** 24.17%

53. 44.00%   **55.** 29.02%   **57.** 59.87%   **59.** 50.00%

61. 11.51%   **63.** ≈ 23 cars   **65.** 95.47%   **67.** 13,380 boxes

69. 69.15%   **71.** 0.62%   **73.** ≈ 83 families   **75.** 1.79%

77. The standard deviation is too large.

79. a) *B*   **b)** *C*   **c)** *A*

81. The mean is the greatest value. The median is lower than the mean. The mode is the lowest value.

83. Answers will vary.

85. a) Katie: $z = 2.4$; Stella: $z = 1.7$

   b) Katie. Her z-score is higher than Stella's z-score, which means her sales are further above the mean than Stella's sales.

87. a) Answers will vary.   **b)** Answers will vary.
   c) Answers will vary.   **d)** Answers will vary.
   e) Answers will vary.   **f)** Answers will vary.

89. −1.18   **90.** Answers will vary.   **91.** 2

REVIEW EXERCISES, PAGE 848

1. a) A population consists of all items or people of interest.

   b) A sample is a subset of the population.

2. A random sample is one where every item in the population has the same chance of being selected.

3. The candy bars may have lots of calories, or fat, or sodium. Therefore, it may not be healthy to eat them.

4. Sales may not necessarily be a good indicator of profit. Expenses must also be considered.

5. a)   **b)**

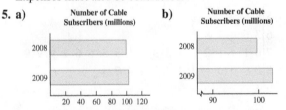

Number of Cable Subscribers (millions)

6. a)

Class	Frequency
35	1
36	3
37	6
38	2
39	3
40	0
41	4
42	1
43	3
44	1
45	1

b) and c)

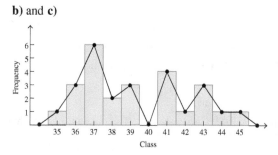

7. a)

High Temperature	Number of Cities
58–62	1
63–67	4
68–72	9
73–77	10
78–82	11
83–87	4
88–92	1

b) and c)

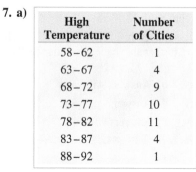

d) 5|8 represents 58

```
5│8
6│3 6 6 7 8 8 9
7│0 1 1 1 2 2 3 3 3 4 5 5 5 6 6 7 9 9 9
8│0 0 0 0 1 2 2 2 3 4 4 7
9│1
```

8. 80 **9.** 81 **10.** None **11.** 80 **12.** 26
13. $\sqrt{80} \approx 8.94$ **14.** 13 **15.** 13 **16.** 7 and 12
17. 13.5 **18.** 19 **19.** $\sqrt{40} \approx 6.32$ **20.** 68.26%
21. 95.44% **22.** 94.52% **23.** 5.48% **24.** 72.57%
25. 34.1% **26.** 34.5% **27.** 29.0% **28.** 2.3%

29. a)

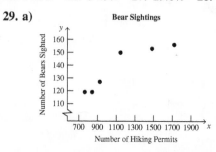

b) Yes; positive **c)** 0.925 **d)** Yes
e) $y = 0.04x + 88.17$ **f)** ≈ 148 bears

30. a)

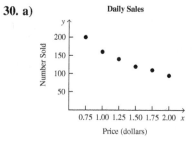

b) Yes; negative **c)** -0.973 **d)** Yes
e) $y = -79.4x + 246.7$ **f)** ≈ 120 sold
31. 180 lb **32.** 185 lb **33.** 25% **34.** 25% **35.** 14%
36. 19,200 lb **37.** 238 lb **38.** 150.6 lb **39.** 3.53
40. 2 **41.** 3 **42.** 7 **43.** 14 **44.** $\sqrt{7.97} \approx 2.82$

45.

Number of Children	Number of Presidents
0–1	8
2–3	16
4–5	10
6–7	6
8–9	1
10–11	1
12–13	0
14–15	1

46. and 47.

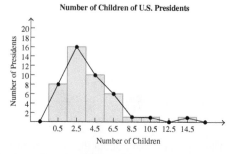

48. No, it is skewed to the right. **49.** Answers will vary.
50. Answers will vary.

1. 42 **2.** 43 **3.** 43 **4.** 39.5 **5.** 25 **6.** $\sqrt{84} \approx 9.17$

7.

Class	Frequency
25–30	7
31–36	5
37–42	1
43–48	7
49–54	5
55–60	3
61–66	2

8.

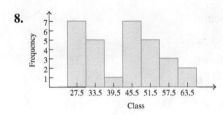

9.

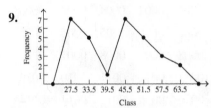

10. $735   **11.** $710   **12.** 75%   **13.** 79%   **14.** $74,000

15. $780   **16.** 87.10%   **17.** 89.44%   **18.** 10.56%

19. 94.52%

20. a)   Hourly Minimum Wage in the U.S.   **b)** Yes   **c)** 0.970   **d)** Yes

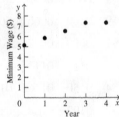

e) $y = 0.56x + 5.29$ **f)** $9.77

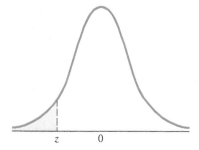

Table entry for z is the area to the left of z.

Table 13.7 Areas of a Standard Normal Distribution

(a) Table of Areas to the Left of z When z is Negative

z	.00	.01	.02	.03	.04	.05	.06	.07	.08	.09
−3.4	.0003	.0003	.0003	.0003	.0003	.0003	.0003	.0003	.0003	.0002
−3.3	.0005	.0005	.0005	.0004	.0004	.0004	.0004	.0004	.0004	.0003
−3.2	.0007	.0007	.0006	.0006	.0006	.0006	.0006	.0005	.0005	.0005
−3.1	.0010	.0009	.0009	.0009	.0008	.0008	.0008	.0008	.0007	.0007
−3.0	.0013	.0013	.0013	.0012	.0012	.0011	.0011	.0011	.0010	.0010
−2.9	.0019	.0018	.0018	.0017	.0016	.0016	.0015	.0015	.0014	.0014
−2.8	.0026	.0025	.0024	.0023	.0023	.0022	.0021	.0021	.0020	.0019
−2.7	.0035	.0034	.0033	.0032	.0031	.0030	.0029	.0028	.0027	.0026
−2.6	.0047	.0045	.0044	.0043	.0041	.0040	.0039	.0038	.0037	.0036
−2.5	.0062	.0060	.0059	.0057	.0055	.0054	.0052	.0051	.0049	.0048
−2.4	.0082	.0080	.0078	.0075	.0073	.0071	.0069	.0068	.0066	.0064
−2.3	.0107	.0104	.0102	.0099	.0096	.0094	.0091	.0089	.0087	.0084
−2.2	.0139	.0136	.0132	.0129	.0125	.0122	.0119	.0116	.0113	.0110
−2.1	.0179	.0174	.0170	.0166	.0162	.0158	.0154	.0150	.0146	.0143
−2.0	.0228	.0222	.0217	.0212	.0207	.0202	.0197	.0192	.0188	.0183
−1.9	.0287	.0281	.0274	.0268	.0262	.0256	.0250	.0244	.0239	.0233
−1.8	.0359	.0351	.0344	.0336	.0329	.0322	.0314	.0307	.0301	.0294
−1.7	.0446	.0436	.0427	.0418	.0409	.0401	.0392	.0384	.0375	.0367
−1.6	.0548	.0537	.0526	.0516	.0505	.0495	.0485	.0475	.0465	.0455
−1.5	.0668	.0655	.0643	.0630	.0618	.0606	.0594	.0582	.0571	.0559
−1.4	.0808	.0793	.0778	.0764	.0749	.0735	.0721	.0708	.0694	.0681
−1.3	.0968	.0951	.0934	.0918	.0901	.0885	.0869	.0853	.0838	.0823
−1.2	.1151	.1131	.1112	.1093	.1075	.1056	.1038	.1020	.1003	.0985
−1.1	.1357	.1335	.1314	.1292	.1271	.1251	.1230	.1210	.1190	(.1170)
−1.0	(.1587)	.1562	.1539	.1515	.1492	.1469	.1446	.1423	.1401	.1379
−0.9	.1841	.1814	.1788	.1762	.1736	.1711	.1685	.1660	.1635	.1611
−0.8	.2119	.2090	.2061	.2033	.2005	.1977	.1949	.1922	.1894	.1867
−0.7	.2420	.2389	.2358	.2327	.2296	.2266	.2236	.2206	.2177	.2148
−0.6	.2743	.2709	.2676	.2643	.2611	.2578	.2546	.2514	.2483	.2451
−0.5	.3085	.3050	.3015	.2981	.2947	.2912	.2877	.2843	.2810	.2776
−0.4	.3446	.3409	.3372	.3336	.3300	.3264	.3228	.3192	.3156	.3121
−0.3	.3821	.3783	.3745	.3707	.3669	.3632	.3594	.3557	.3520	.3483
−0.2	.4207	.4168	.4129	.4090	.4052	.4013	.3974	.3936	.3897	.3859
−0.1	.4602	.4562	.4522	.4483	.4443	.4404	.4364	.4325	.4286	.4247
−0.0	.5000	.4960	.4920	.4880	.4840	.4801	.4761	.4721	.4681	.4641

For z-scores less than −3.49, use 0.000 to approximate the area.

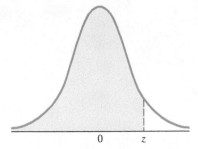

Table entry for z is the area to the left of z.

Table 13.7 Areas of a Standard Normal Distribution *(continued)*

(b) Table of Areas to the Left of z When z is Positive

z	.00	.01	.02	.03	.04	.05	.06	.07	.08	.09
0.0	.5000	.5040	.5080	.5120	.5160	.5199	.5239	.5279	.5319	.5359
0.1	.5398	.5438	.5478	.5517	.5557	.5596	.5636	.5675	.5714	.5753
0.2	.5793	.5832	.5871	.5910	.5948	.5987	.6026	.6064	.6103	.6141
0.3	.6179	.6217	.6255	.6293	.6331	.6368	.6406	.6443	.6480	.6517
0.4	.6554	.6591	.6628	.6664	.6700	.6736	.6772	.6808	.6844	.6879
0.5	.6915	.6950	.6985	.7019	.7054	.7088	.7123	.7157	.7190	.7224
0.6	.7257	.7291	.7324	.7357	.7389	.7422	.7454	.7486	.7517	.7549
0.7	.7580	.7611	.7642	.7673	.7704	.7734	.7764	.7794	.7823	.7852
0.8	.7881	.7910	.7939	.7967	.7995	.8023	.8051	.8078	.8106	.8133
0.9	.8159	.8186	.8212	.8238	.8264	.8289	.8315	.8340	.8365	.8389
1.0	.8413	.8438	.8461	.8485	.8508	.8531	.8554	.8577	.8599	.8621
1.1	.8643	.8665	.8686	.8708	.8729	.8749	.8770	.8790	.8810	(.8830)
1.2	.8849	.8869	.8888	.8907	.8925	.8944	.8962	.8980	.8997	.9015
1.3	.9032	.9049	.9066	.9082	.9099	.9115	.9131	.9147	.9162	.9177
1.4	.9192	.9207	.9222	.9236	.9251	.9265	.9279	.9292	.9306	.9319
1.5	.9332	.9345	.9357	.9370	.9382	.9394	.9406	.9418	.9429	.9441
1.6	.9452	.9463	.9474	.9484	.9495	.9505	.9515	.9525	.9535	.9545
1.7	.9554	.9564	.9573	.9582	.9591	.9599	.9608	.9616	.9625	.9633
1.8	.9641	.9649	.9656	.9664	.9671	.9678	.9686	.9693	.9699	.9706
1.9	.9713	.9719	.9726	.9732	.9738	.9744	.9750	.9756	.9761	.9767
2.0	.9772	.9778	.9783	.9788	.9793	.9798	.9803	.9808	.9812	.9817
2.1	.9821	.9826	.9830	.9834	.9838	.9842	.9846	.9850	.9854	.9857
2.2	.9861	.9864	.9868	.9871	.9875	.9878	.9881	.9884	.9887	.9890
2.3	.9893	.9896	.9898	.9901	.9904	.9906	.9909	.9911	.9913	.9916
2.4	.9918	.9920	.9922	.9925	.9927	.9929	.9931	.9932	.9934	.9936
2.5	.9938	.9940	.9941	.9943	.9945	.9946	.9948	.9949	.9951	.9952
2.6	.9953	.9955	.9956	.9957	.9959	.9960	.9961	.9962	.9963	.9964
2.7	.9965	.9966	.9967	.9968	.9969	.9970	.9971	.9972	.9973	.9974
2.8	.9974	.9975	.9976	.9977	.9977	.9978	.9979	.9979	.9980	.9981
2.9	.9981	.9982	.9982	.9983	.9984	.9984	.9985	.9985	.9986	.9986
3.0	.9987	.9987	.9987	.9988	.9988	.9989	.9989	.9989	.9990	.9990
3.1	.9990	.9991	.9991	.9991	.9992	.9992	.9992	.9992	.9993	.9993
3.2	.9993	.9993	.9994	.9994	.9994	.9994	.9994	.9995	.9995	.9995
3.3	.9995	.9995	.9995	.9996	.9996	.9996	.9996	.9996	.9996	.9997
3.4	.9997	.9997	.9997	.9997	.9997	.9997	.9997	.9997	.9997	.9998

For z-scores greater than 3.49, use 1.000 to approximate the area.